McGRAW-HILL PUBLICATIONS IN THE
BOTANICAL SCIENCES

EDMUND W. SINNOTT, Consulting Editor

Principles of

GENETICS

SELECTED TITLES FROM

McGRAW-HILL PUBLICATIONS IN THE BOTANICAL SCIENCES

EDMUND W. SINNOTT, *Consulting Editor*

Babcock and Clausen—Genetics

Belling—The Use of the Microscope

Boysen Jensen—Growth Hormones in Plants

Braun-Blanquet and Fuller and Conard—Plant Sociology

Curtis—The Translocation of Solutes in Plants

Eames—Morphology of Vascular Plants

Eames and MacDaniels—Plant Anatomy

Fitzpatrick—The Lower Fungi

Gäumann and Dodge—Comparative Morphology of Fungi

Haupt—An Introduction to Botany

Haupt—Laboratory Manual of Elementary Botany

Hill—Economic Botany

Hill, Overholts, and Popp—Botany

Johansen—Plant Microtechnique

Loomis and Shull—Methods in Plant Physiology
Experiments in Plant Physiology

Lutman—Microbiology

Maximov—Plant Physiology

Miller—Plant Physiology

Pool—Flowers and Flowering Plants

Sass—Elements of Botanical Microtechnique

Seifriz—Protoplasm

Sharp—Introduction to Cytology

Sharp—Fundamentals of Cytology

Sinnott—Botany

Sinnott and Dunn—Genetics

Smith—Cryptogamic Botany
Vol. I, Algae and Fungi
Vol. II, Bryophytes and Pteridophytes
Fresh-water Algae of the U. S.

Swingle—Systematic Botany

Weaver—Root Development of Field Crops

Weaver and Bruner—Root Development of Vegetable Crops

Weaver and Clements—Plant Ecology

Wodehouse—Pollen Grains

There are also the related series of McGraw-Hill Publications in the Zoological Sciences, of which A. Franklin Shull is Consulting Editor, and in the Agricultural Sciences, of which Leon J. Cole is Consulting Editor.

Principles of
GENETICS

By EDMUND W. SINNOTT

Professor of Botany, Columbia University

and L. C. DUNN

Professor of Zoology, Columbia University

THIRD EDITION
NINTH IMPRESSION

McGRAW-HILL BOOK COMPANY, Inc.

NEW YORK AND LONDON
1939

THE MAPLE PRESS COMPANY, YORK, PA.

PREFACE

Progress in genetics has been so rapid during the past six years as to require considerable modification of the treatment of many of the topics discussed in the second edition of this book. The chief progress has resulted from improvements in technique, first, in cytological methods, especially in dealing with the giant salivary gland chromosomes of certain insects and in the study of the mechanism of germinal and somatic crossing over; second, in the use of radiations for the study of mutation; third, in the application of the methods of descriptive and experimental morphology, especially of transplantation in animals, to the analysis of genic effects on development; and fourth, in the use of mathematical and statistical methods for the study of populations. All these methods have contributed primarily to developmental or physiological genetics and to evolutionary or population genetics, two fields which are now receiving particular emphasis. The basic principles of genetics have not been radically altered, although the proof of the "position effect" hypothesis bids fair to require a reassessment of previous postulates concerning the gene. This new material has been added in the present edition. It has been possible for the authors to be brief in these regards because reviews of two of the fields chiefly affected (Dobzhansky's "Genetics and the Origin of Species" and Goldschmidt's "Physiological Genetics") have appeared recently and the student will find full discussions and bibliographies in these books. In addition there have been included a new chapter on cytoplasmic inheritance, in order to repair an obvious defect of previous editions; new material on the interpretation of heterosis and of multiple-factor inheritance; new evidence on mutation frequency in natural populations and on allo- and autopolyploidy; and a number of other topics of current interest. The heart of the book, however, continues to be general and well-established principles and the exemplification of these in problems for the student to solve.

To make room for the new topics and the many new illustrations without increasing the length of the book, the authors have redistributed and rewritten much of the material in the latter half of the book. A short and simplified treatment of elementary biometric methods has been given in connection with multiple-factor inheritance, and methods of testing ratios for goodness of fit have been given in connection with the first discussions of segregation and independent assortment. Tables of χ^2 and p have been added.

A chapter on Genes and Chromosomes now contains the chief evidence on gene locations and chromosome changes in Drosophila. The addition of up-to-date maps of genetic, metaphase, and salivary chromosomes together with lists of all the more important loci, drawings of the external features of the fly, and directions for the preparation of food media (in the Appendix) make this chapter useful as a guide to the study of heredity in this widely used laboratory animal.

Inbreeding and heterosis are now treated in a separate chapter, and the origin of hereditary variations in two chapters, one dealing with gene mutations and induced mutations and the other with chromosome changes. The discussion of Genetics and Evolution has been rewritten and shortened. Attention is focused on chromosome changes in nature, on the origin of evolutionary segregation, and on the parts played by mutation rate, population size, isolating factors, and hybrid sterility in evolutionary change. The chapter on Genetics and Development has been reorganized and simplified by the inclusion of fewer (but better) illustrative cases.

The problems are an integral part of the text and follow directly the chapters to which they refer. The many new ones deal with the added material. The lists of literature cited, while not complete, will help the student in verifying the facts given and should introduce him to other topics not treated in the text, a function formerly served by the reference problems, which are omitted in this edition.

The authors are indebted to Dr. A. F. Blakeslee, Dr. C. B. Bridges, Dr. M. Demerec, Professor Th. Dobzhansky, and Dr. B. P. Kaufmann for their courtesy in supplying new illustrations; to the late Professor E. W. East for criticism of Chapters X and XII; to Professor P. W. Whiting for his help with Chapter XI; to Dr. Katherine Brehme, Dr. Nathan Kaliss, Mr. Arthur Steinberg, and Mr. H. L. Weaver for assistance with the manuscript and proofs; and to Professor R. A. Fisher and Messrs. Oliver and Boyd for permission to reproduce the table of χ^2 and p. Mr. Jack Godrich has prepared several new illustrations, and to him and to Mrs. Cecil Killien and Miss Dorothy Davis the authors extend their thanks for help with the manuscript.

THE AUTHORS.

NEW YORK,
  December, 1938.

CONTENTS

FOREWORD

There is a common feeling that a textbook is a full and final exposition of the subject which it treats, and that by virtue of "knowing the book" one acquires all the knowledge of the subject which it is necessary to have. Such beliefs have little to justify them. No text is or can be complete or final; nor, if it were, would an understanding of the subject be gained by committing the whole book to memory. Knowledge is not acquired in this way, but grows in the minds of those who discover for themselves new facts and relationships.

The principles of genetics have developed out of the arduous study of scores of investigators, and understanding of principles can best be gained by the student through a process which is somewhat similar to that employed in their original discovery. This process begins with, and is continually stimulated by, curiosity as to the methods and the mechanism of inheritance; it proceeds by the collection and study of facts, and by a critical discrimination between those which are true and relevant and those which are untrue or irrelevant; and finally it involves a considerable practice of the reasoning faculty by which deductions are made, and applied or tested on many similar cases. It is only in this way that the process of inheritance can be *understood*. The learning of facts alone cannot accomplish this.

As an aid to such a comprehension of the science of genetics, this book includes problems of three types, which form an integral part of the subject matter. These are designed to stimulate curiosity, to provide opportunity for practicing and extending the methods and applying the theories outlined in the text, and to point the way to other related facts not specifically treated in this book. They are not designed as memory tests, although the continual use of facts in solving problems is at once the best method of committing these facts to memory as well as of understanding them.

One of these aids consists of questions for thought and discussion. Answers to these are not to be found in the text itself, but may be reached by a process of reasoning for which only the premises are given. Familiarity with the subject matter of the text will provide the raw material, while the synthesis resulting in a correct answer or intelligent discussion must take place in the student's mind.

Other problems are designed to provide more extended practice in reasoning from principles. Nearly all of this type require some computation and may be most profitably studied as laboratory exercises under the guidance of an instructor. It is desirable to use labor-saving or "short-cut" methods (such as the checkerboard method described on page 70) wherever possible, in order that the mechanical work involved in calculation may not be regarded as the chief benefit to be derived from the problems. Sufficient information for solving all of them is contained in the text or in the supplementary notes in the problems.

The references cited will aid the student in examining the original publications from which our knowledge is derived. Of these Mendel's paper is still the most important and can be read with interest by all students. Citations of current literature are not intended to be complete; they should, however, indicate to the student that the subject as a whole is not contained in the text but is growing by the continual accretion of reports of experiments, all of which do not yield results in entire consonance with the few points of view which it is possible to present in a brief textbook. Some of the references will lead to new material not mentioned in the text, which must be reconciled with the fundamental principles of genetics, while others may serve to make connections between the student's knowledge of genetics and his experience in other directions.

PRINCIPLES OF GENETICS

CHAPTER I

THE SCIENCE OF GENETICS

Between those things which are *alive*—plants, animals, and man—
and those things which are lifeless there exists a great gap, which science
has not yet bridged. All living things are endowed with certain characteristic properties of structure and of behavior which in the aggregate
have been named *life*, but as to what calls forth this remarkable phenomenon out of lifeless matter we are still essentially ignorant.

There is, however, general agreement concerning the chief peculiarities of living things. Life is always associated with a characteristic
substance known as *protoplasm*, which is defined not merely by the
materials of which it is composed but by the complex manner in which
these materials are integrated into a living system. Protoplasm is not
a continuous and homogeneous mass throughout the organism but is
divided into definite though minute functional and structural units, the
cells. Within each cell is a denser body—the *nucleus*—which exerts a
governing influence over the activities of the cell. The cells are organized
into animal and plant bodies each with a definite shape and structure
and with peculiarities of behavior characteristic of the species of which
it is a member. In the various cells of this body, complex chemical and
physical changes take place whereby growth, repair, and reproduction
are effected and the necessary energy for the vital activities of the organism is released. These various characteristics of living things can be
readily observed and described, but thus far there has been less success
in explaining and understanding them. Many of the major problems
of biology, which deal with the fundamental peculiarities of life, are still
to be solved, and it is the province of genetics to elucidate the laws by
which some of the aspects of life may be understood.

The Continuity of Life.—Living organisms are characterized not
merely by the specific peculiarities of form and function which we have
just mentioned; their origin is also remarkable. The conclusions reached
by all thorough study of the life histories of animals and plants clearly
show that every living individual must always arise from some preexisting
living individual and never directly from lifeless matter itself. The work

1

of Spallanzani and of Pasteur gave the death blow to the old belief in
the "spontaneous generation" of living things out of dead material and
proved that even among the most minute organisms the spark of life
can be kindled only by life itself. Every animal and plant is therefore
to be looked upon as the latest member of a long and uninterrupted
succession of living beings, extending back, generation after generation,
to the dawn of life. This is the essential teaching of the theory of evolution. The actual origin of life itself is lost in the mists of antiquity, but
the pageant of the evolutionary history of living things, which unfolds
itself in the fossil record of ancient times, makes it clear beyond any
reasonable doubt that the animals and plants of today are direct lineal
descendants of earlier and more primitive types. Continuity is of the
essence of life.

Reproduction.—Since individual living things grow old and die, however, this continuity must be maintained by the transmission of life from
one individual to a succession of new ones, its offspring. This process is
known as *reproduction* and may take place in various ways.

In the simplest methods, commonly called *asexual* or *vegetative* reproduction, the body of the parent becomes divided into two or more parts,
each of which grows into a new individual. With animals this method
is uncommon except in the simplest types, but among plants the fact
that a small portion of the body, when removed and placed under favorable conditions, will often restore the missing parts and establish itself
as a new individual makes multiplication of this type easy and effective
both in nature and through the various arts of plant propagation.

Far commoner and more important than this asexual or vegetative
method of reproduction, however, is that called *sexual*. An essential
feature here is that the function of forming the new individual is dele-
gated to *single cells*, which are set apart for this purpose. Sexual reproduction consists of the *union of two specialized sexual cells or gametes to
form one cell*, the fertilized egg or *zygote*, from which develops a new
individual. To insure the successful consummation of this process is
the function of a great variety of structures throughout the animal and
the plant kingdoms. In all except the lowest forms the gametes themselves are of two different types: small, usually motile, male gametes and
relatively large, nonmotile female ones. Among animals the male
gametes are known as *sperms* and are produced in a testis, and the female
gametes are known as *eggs* or *ova*, produced in an ovary. At fertilization
a sperm and an egg come together and unite, the nucleus of one fusing
completely with that of the other. The single cell resulting from this
union begins to divide, forming a group of cells which develops into an
embryo and finally into an adult organism. Among lower plants conditions are essentially like those in animals, although the sexual organs are

extremely varied in character. In the higher plants, however, a series of complicated reproductive structures—the flower, fruit, and seed—have

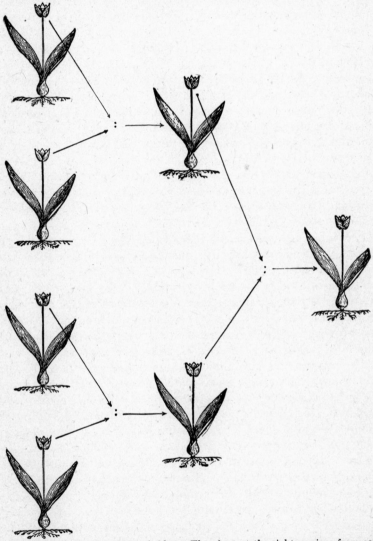

Fig. 1.—The narrow hereditary bridge. The plant at the right receives from each of its parents only one minute sexual cell, a male gamete from one and a female gamete from the other. The parents, in turn, receive from each of the grandparents but one sexual cell. Thus the bridge which connects one generation with the next, and over which the entire inheritance must pass, is an exceedingly narrow one.

been evolved. The male gametes are here produced within the minute *pollen grains,* and the female gametes within the *ovules* or potential seeds. The fertilized egg develops into the embryo of the seed.

In all these cases of sexual reproduction the essential feature is that a parent contributes to each of its offspring only a *single minute cell*—a bit of living substance so small that it is usually far beyond the limit of vision for the unaided eye. This extremely narrow bridge is the only direct physical link between parent and offspring, and across it everything must pass which is transmitted from one generation to the next (Fig. 1).

Heredity.—As a result of this reproductive activity a continuous succession of new individuals arises. One of the most remarkable features of the process is that these new individuals *tend to resemble their ancestors very closely*. The offspring of a corn plant develop into corn plants and never into anything else; and those of horses always into horses. Furthermore, any particular kind or variety of corn or horses produces individuals of just that variety. Even very specific characteristics are often transmitted with great exactness through a long series of generations. In man himself the same phenomenon is no less evident than in the lower organisms. In his own family everyone must have observed some instances in which a trait has been repeatedly passed from parent to child or where it "runs in the family," cropping out here and there in one or a few individuals. This resemblance among individuals related by descent is called *heredity*.

Heredity is such a universal and familiar fact that its significance is often not realized. The physical bridge—the reproductive cells or gametes—which connects one generation with the next is an extremely narrow one. The sperms of animals are exceedingly minute, and the effective parts of the eggs, the nuclei, are no larger. It has been estimated that all the sperm from which the present population of the world (about 1,500,000,000) arose would make no larger bulk than a drop of water, and the nuclei of the same number of eggs would occupy about the same amount of space. In the living substance of the minute sexual elements must in some way be transmitted *all* the characteristics which the new individual inherits from its parents. Any particular adult character, such as size, shape, or color, obviously cannot be found in these cells; but something representing these characters and capable of producing them in the new individual must be there. In the case of man, the color of his eyes, hair, and skin; his susceptibility to various defects and diseases; the size, shape, and proportions of his body; his specific mental traits and capacities, together with many other characteristics, are definitely known to be inherited. In every human sperm, therefore, and in every egg there must be properties which represent all these characteristics and which, in cooperation with each other and with the factors in the environment, determine what kind of man or woman will develop from the fertilized egg. These minute particles of living substance, into which so much is packed and out of which so much emerges, are certainly among the most remarkable bits of matter in existence.

Variation.—Close as these hereditary resemblances are, however, they are almost never *exact* resemblances. A group of offspring from the same parents may differ among themselves, and some or all of them may differ from their parents or more remote members of their family. In a group of brothers and sisters no two are exactly alike, but each has his distinctive peculiarities, and although all the children may show resemblances to their parents, they do so in different degrees. In the lower animals and in plants, where the number of offspring is usually very great, there often seems to be a much closer similarity between individuals, but even here critical study and increased familiarity will in most cases bring differences to light.

These differences are known by the general name of *variations*. Many of them are due to a parceling out of traits among the various offspring according to a definite method of inheritance. Many others, however, are due to differences in heat, light, moisture, food, or other factors in the environment, for it should be remembered that most characteristics are profoundly affected by the surroundings in which the individual develops. Variations are, therefore, of many kinds and are due to many causes, but their presence is one of the most distinctive features of living organisms and indeed has been said to be the only invariable thing in the organic world.

Genetics and Its History.—That branch of the science of biology which is concerned with the phenomena of inheritance and variation and which particularly endeavors to discover the laws governing these similarities and differences between individuals related to one another by descent is called *genetics*. Unlike most of the other sciences genetics is very young, for as a distinct and recognized branch of knowledge its history goes back only about a third of a century. Development has been extremely rapid during that time, and through the activity of a large number of investigators, it is still proceeding apace. The first knowledge of the facts of inheritance, however, began at a much earlier date, and what modern genetics is can perhaps best be understood by going back somewhat into the past.

From the earliest times men have recognized the facts that "like begets like" and that offspring differ somewhat among themselves and from their parents. They have long used this knowledge, more or less unconsciously, perhaps, in choosing for breeding purposes those individuals among their domesticated animals and plants which best suited their requirements. Only rarely were deliberate breeding methods used which depended on an empirical knowledge of the methods of reproduction, such as the artificial pollination of the female date palm, which was practiced in Egypt and Mesopotamia many centuries before the Christian era. The early husbandmen bred their animals and plants without any general knowledge of the reproductive processes, and the legacy of valuable cultivated plants, which is the earmark of permanent civilizations, resulted from taming the wild species and selecting fortuitous variations among them. A scientific understanding of the problems of heredity and variation, however, has begun to be reached only recently, and both its beginning and its progress have depended on improved knowledge of the reproductive process and more particularly of the sexual method.

The Discovery of Sexuality.—The existence of sexual reproduction among animals was early recognized, as was the fact that offspring inherit their characteristics from both parents. The ideas entertained by the ancients as to the exact mechanism of the process, however, were often grotesque, and it was not until biology was placed on a modern basis, following the invention of the microscope and the establishment of the cell theory, that the existence of gametes was determined. The male cells, spermatozoa, were recognized by the early microscopists in the latter half of the seventeenth century, and their function as initiators of development in the egg was demonstrated experimentally early in the eighteenth century, although the nature of both egg and sperm as single cells and of fertilization as the union of their nuclei was not made clear until the latter half of the nineteenth century.

Fig. 2.—Joseph Gottlieb Kölreuter (1733–1806). (*Courtesy of Genetics.*)

In the plant kingdom the very fact of sexuality was long unknown, as was the important part played by pollen in seed development. Camerarius, a physician of Tübingen, concluded as early as 1694 from experiments with plants that their reproduction also followed the sexual method known in animals, with the pollen functioning as the male, the ovule as the female, element. In 1760 the German botanist Kölreuter (Fig. 2) performed the first careful experiments in plant hybridization, crossing two species of tobacco by placing the pollen of one on the stigmas of the other. The offspring resulting from this experiment were intermediate in most respects between the two parent species, thus proving not only that pollen performed an essential function in seed production but that parental characters were transmitted both through the pollen and through the ovules. The growth of the pollen tube, the passage down it of the male gametes, the union of one of them with the egg cell in the ovule, and the subsequent development therefrom of the embryo of the seed were established at a later date when microscopical technique had become more highly perfected. Kölreuter performed a number of other experiments in hybridization, endeavoring to find how characters were transmitted from parent to offspring and later generations. He initiated a new direction in biological inquiry—the experimental study of hybridization—and it was the employment of this method which led most directly to the eventual discovery of the fundamental principles of heredity.

In the late eighteenth and nineteenth centuries two other streams of biological interest became well marked, each dealing with what appeared to be problems of greater theoretical importance than the more modest and limited inquiries of the plant hybridizers. One of these dealt with the gradual evolution of animal and plant species and culminated in the publication of Darwin's "Origin of Species" in 1859. The other had for its object the elucidation of the problems of individual structure and development, the whole outlook on which had been altered first by Caspar Friedrich Wolff's epigenetic theory of development and later by the generalization of the cell theory in 1838 by Schleiden and Schwann and its later application to the study of reproduction.

The work of the plant hybridizers who followed Kölreuter showed that offspring tended to inherit equally from the pollen and from the seed parent; that the hybrids, although generally representing an intermediate or average condition between the parents, did sometimes resemble one parent much more closely than the other (Gärtner); and that the progeny of the hybrids might contain individuals very much like each of the parental types (Goss). Naudin in 1862 concluded that a hybrid is a mixture of the potentialities of both parents and that these may separate and be distributed among the progeny of a hybrid. This so-called "splitting" of hybrids was the nearest approach to the great principle of heredity which was discovered by Mendel, who stands at the apex of this group of experimental botanists.

Mendel and His Work.—Gregor Mendel (Fig. 3), whose experiments in plant hybridization laid the foundation for most of the modern work on heredity and may well be said to have established genetics as a science, was a monk, and later abbot, in the Augustinian monastery at Brünn, Austria (now Brno, Czechoslovakia). In the cloister gardens he made crosses between varieties of the garden pea which differed in height, flower color, seed color, and other respects. The discoveries which resulted from these experiments were due, not only to Mendel's unusual keenness in observation and clarity in reasoning, but to several notable improvements in his method over those of his predecessors. He made repeated artificial hybridizations between plants which differed in various characteristics, but instead of studying inheritance in the whole complex individual as a unit, he singled out separate characteristics and observed them by themselves. He kept accurate pedigree records, which enabled him to know the ancestors of every individual plant. Perhaps more important still, in all cases where contrasting traits appeared in a group of offspring (both red-flowered and white-flowered plants, for example) he *counted* the number of individuals of each type and thus obtained a

Fig. 3.—Gregor Johann Mendel (1822–1884).   (*From A. F. Shull.*)

statistical statement of his results. In short, he applied exact *experimental methods* to the problems of heredity.

The results which Mendel obtained from these hybridization experiments were chiefly important in showing that inheritance was not a hit-or-miss affair but was subject to certain definite rules or laws; and that, consequently, if one knew enough about the ancestry and constitution of two parent plants, he could predict with a considerable degree of accuracy, not only what their offspring would look like, but the relative frequency with which the contrasting characters, brought in from various ancestral lines, would appear among them. Mendel discovered that the individual behaves in inheritance as though it were an aggregation of independent and separable characteristics, each of which is a distinct "unit" and may exist with any combination of other characteristics in a given individual. He also found that when two contrasting characters are brought together by a cross, the hybrid offspring are alike and often resemble one of the parents in this particular character much more closely than they do the other. Still more important, if two hybrids are bred together, both grandparental characteristics appear among the offspring and are sorted out in a definite fashion, a certain proportion of the individuals resembling one grandparent and another resembling the other. The particular combination of characteristics which distinguishes an individual may thus be broken up among its descendants, the various traits being sorted out among the offspring independently of one another, so that all sorts of new combinations may make their appearance, each in a definite and predictable fraction of the whole. Mendel thus formulated the first *laws* of inheritance and established the basis on which the later development of genetics has taken place.

Investigations since Mendel.—Important as Mendel's work has proved to be, it was not recognized as such by the scientists of his day. The results of his experiments with peas were collected in a single paper and published in 1866 in the proceedings of the Naturforschender Verein of Brünn, where they remained neglected for over thirty years. Meanwhile the great controversy over the theory of evolution had begun, following the publication of Darwin's "Origin of Species" in 1859, and the attention of biologists was centered upon argument and speculation rather than upon a careful experimental study of plants and animals themselves. Rather fantastic theories, based on little or no experimental evidence, were put forward, one of them by Darwin himself, to explain how parental traits were transmitted to offspring. The facts of heredity and variation were recognized, and indeed the theory of Natural Selection was based upon them, but there was no establishment of anything like general laws of inheritance. In this period, however, the German zoologist Weismann, who was an able supporter of Darwin, called attention to the fact that some traits of an individual are due to the inherent characteristics of its living substance and that others are produced by the surroundings in which it has developed. Weismann believed that the latter type, which are now called "acquired" characters, are never inherited, and he performed a series of experiments to demonstrate the fact. This problem of the "inheritance of acquired characters" has since received a great deal of attention, and most of the evidence obtained supports Weismann's contention.

Weismann also correctly identified the material basis of heredity with the nuclei of the gametes and showed that, in many animals at least, the tissues from which the reproductive cells are formed were specialized for this purpose very early in development and were to some extent insulated from the tissues of the rest of the body and not susceptible to changes which brought about variations in the body. This dichotomy in animal development Weismann summarized in his famous distinction between the *germ plasm* as the continuing, potentially immortal succession of reproductive cells and the *somatoplasm*, or the temporary, mortal envelope—the body—which the gametes produced anew in each generation. Germ plasm gave rise to both new germ plasm and somatoplasm, but the soma never gave rise to germ plasm. This distinction had great influence in focusing attention on the nuclear material of the gametes as the seat both of heredity and of heritable variations; but since the distinction between germ plasm and somatoplasm does not seem to exist in plants, in which the processes of heredity and variation are similar to those in animals, it cannot be considered as of fundamental or universal importance.

In the last years of the nineteenth century Francis Galton, a cousin of Darwin, became interested in heredity, particularly in its reference to man. He was the first to apply methods of statistical analysis to the phenomena of variation and heredity and thus established that branch of biological science which is now called *biometry*. Galton devised methods for measuring the degree of resemblance between parents and offspring and endeavored to determine the particular contribution which was made to an individual by each of its ancestors.

At the very end of the nineteenth century interest in the problems of inheritance, which had been steadily growing, was brought to a head by the dramatic discovery and recognition of Mendel's work. It so happened that three botanists, de Vries in Holland, Correns in Germany, and von Tschermak in Austria, who were themselves making experimental studies of heredity in plants, within the same year (1900) independently unearthed Mendel's paper and proclaimed its importance to the world. Bateson in England had already recognized the discontinuous nature of hereditary variations and had obtained results from breeding experiments with poultry which led him to appreciate and quickly to confirm Mendel's chief principle and to show that it applied to animals as well as plants. Many investigators in America and Europe soon began to study the applicability of Mendel's laws to all sorts of plants and animals and made the youthful science of genetics one of the most active fields of biological research.

It will be impossible here to mention more than a few of the investigators who have made important contributions to genetics during the past forty years or to outline the many advances in interpreting, amplifying, and modifying Mendel's principles to conform to the great array of new facts which have been brought to light. The importance of *mutations*, those sudden and unexplained changes in type which sometimes occur in plants and animals, was emphasized by de Vries, whose intensive study of this aspect of genetics led him to propose the Mutation

Theory of evolution, based on a study of large, discontinuous variations as opposed to the many small but continuous ones chiefly emphasized by Darwin. The variations occurring in plants, which from their methods of reproduction (self-fertilization and asexual propagation) provide material for the study of inheritance uncomplicated by hybridization or crossing, were investigated by the Danish botanist Johannsen. He advanced the Pure-line hypothesis, which assumes that all individuals descended from a common ancestor by such methods of reproduction have an identical inherited constitution, or *genotype*, and will continue to breed true regardless of environmental differences, forming lines genetically pure for all their characters. Characters involving size or quantity, which for the most part do not show sharp and simple Mendelian assortment and which in their inheritance were long thought to be exceptions to Mendel's laws, have been definitely brought into line with the Mendelian explanation by the Multiple-factor hypothesis, independently proposed by East and Nilsson-Ehle.

The study of genetics stimulated the study of the material basis of heredity in the cell, and in particular of those remarkable bodies in the nucleus, the *chromosomes*. Cytology, under the leadership of O. Hertwig, Van Beneden, Boveri, and Wilson, made rapid strides in the late nineteenth and early twentieth centuries, and the laws governing the behavior of the chromosomes at cell division and especially during the maturation of the gametes were discovered. The proof by Boveri that each pair of chromosomes has an individuality of its own led both him and Sutton to the theory that Mendel's units are located in the chromosomes, a fruitful hypothesis which was later proved by other workers. The knowledge thus gained, supplementing the results from breeding experiments, has thrown much light on the actual mechanism of inheritance. As a result, biologists are beginning to understand such problems as the factors which determine sex; the peculiar manner in which certain traits tend to stay together or show *linked* inheritance, in apparent violation of Mendel's Law of Independent Assortment; and most recently they have been able to specify the actual location of the factors of inheritance in the chromosomes. To T. H. Morgan and his associates and students is due the credit for opening up this new field of genetic research; and the small vinegar fly, *Drosophila melanogaster* (Fig. 4), upon which most of their work has been based, has now assumed as great an importance in genetics as the famous peas studied by Mendel. In the last few years an experimental attack on the problem of how new hereditary variations (mutations) arise has been begun. Mutations have been artificially induced by the application of radiant energy, and this promises to lead to a new understanding of this fundamental question of evolution.

The Value of Genetics.—Genetics is one of the youngest of the sciences, and the various ways in which it may prove its usefulness are only beginning to be recognized; but so many fields of human thought and activity involve an application of the principles of inheritance that the science which is concerned with these principles seems destined to be of great service in helping to solve some of the important theoretical and practical problems which confront us.

In Agriculture.—The most obvious use to which a knowledge of the principles of genetics may be put is in the field where they first began to be studied—the practical breeding of our domestic animals and plants. The domestication and improvement of valuable animals and plants have been followed by an increase in knowledge of their nutrition, growth, and diseases and a progressive improvement in methods of care, feeding,

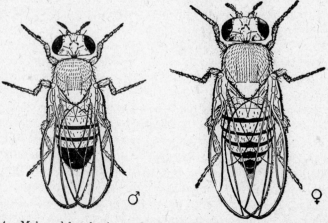

Fig. 4.—Male and female vinegar fly, *Drosophila melanogaster.* (*After Morgan.*)

and cultivation. Most of these advances have been in the manipulation of the environment and have proved to be of temporary value, calling for renewed efforts in every year or generation. The limit of advance in this direction is being approached, and we are now recognizing that further progress must be gained chiefly through improvements in the inborn qualities of the animals and plants themselves. Such gains will have the advantage of being permanent, since we know that they may be transmitted to future generations. Already practical breeders, working without the newer knowledge of inheritance, have produced and improved a remarkable array of useful varieties on which our present agriculture is founded, but there is need for further improvement, particularly with respect to such traits as disease resistance and high productivity, which have become more important under modern conditions. Genetics, as such, has already made several practical contributions to breeding and has aided in the development of several valuable varieties of agricultural animals and plants. It has also been of value in explaining the reasons for the success or failure of many old established practices and in subjecting ancient beliefs about breeding to a critical examination by which errors have been corrected and in some cases unexpected improvements suggested. By its explanation, in terms of the Mendelian mechanism, of the effects of inbreeding and of the vigor which often follows crossing of different races or lines, it has made possible the development of systems of breeding which bid fair to place this fundamental economic industry on a rational and scientific basis. By demonstrating the methods by which new mutations may be induced, it has greatly increased the number and variety of hereditary variations which are the raw materials with which the breeder works. The ultimate value of genetics to agriculture will probably be found to consist quite as much in the new methods which it introduces and in the general point of view toward plants and animals which it stimulates on the part of the breeder as in specific improvements or additions to his supply of breeds and varieties.

In Human Society.—The advancing knowledge of inheritance is also beginning to prove of value in a field which has seldom been invaded by biology—the improvement of the human race itself. It has become evident that the characteristics of men are subject to the same laws of inheritance which govern the traits of animals and plants. The applied science of *eugenics* is seeking to learn more about these traits and, on the basis of this knowledge, to devise a program for the improvement of the heritable qualities of mankind. This obviously cannot be accomplished by a direct application of the breeding methods which have been developed with animals and plants; but through the awakening of an intelligent interest in the problem, much progress may be made, both in a gradual elimination of defective stocks and in the increase of more desirable human material. Genetics has already weakened the prevalent belief that human traits result chiefly from the action of external or environmental agencies and has promoted a more general understanding of the fact that forces innate in man are no less important in controlling and directing his fate than are those which originate in his surroundings.

In Scientific Theory.—Important as genetics has been and promises to be in practical matters, its potential contributions to biological theory are even greater. An understanding of the method of evolution in the animal and plant kingdoms must be based on a knowledge of the way in which traits are transmitted from parents to offspring, and genetic investigation has already been of marked service in leading to a conception of evolution based on experimental evidence rather than on random observation and speculation. An unexpected outcome of genetic research has also been a much more definite knowledge of the structure of living protoplasm itself. Breeding investigations have enabled us not only to identify the chromosomes of the nucleus as the seat of genetic factors but even in some cases to map the exact position of these factors in the chromosomes.

In Education and Culture.—A study of genetics is useful, not only for the reasons which we have enumerated, but for its own intrinsic interest and value as well. Perhaps the chief gain to be derived from the pursuit of any science lies in a stimulation of interest and curiosity as to natural phenomena, practice in inductive reasoning from observed fact to theory, and training in the formation of critical judgments. Genetics is a particularly favorable subject for the exercise of all these faculties because of the peculiar interest which always attaches to the origin and differentiation of living things and of man himself; and because the growing complexity of the facts and theories of inheritance requires, for their mastery, a considerable degree of reasoning power and mental alertness. Genetics, moreover, because of its very youth is developing rapidly, and its results and conclusions, changing in many important respects from year to year, require for their understanding frequent employment of those powers of logical reasoning and critical discrimination which constitute the basis for a scientific attitude toward facts.

REFERENCES

Boveri, T. 1904. Ergebnisse über die Konstitution der chromatischen Substanz des Zellkerns. Jena.

Galton, F. 1883. Inquiries into the human faculty. New York.

Iltis, H. Life of Mendel. 1932. Translated by E. and C. Paul. New York.

Lock, R. F. 1906. Recent progress in variation, evolution, and heredity. London and New York.

Mendel, G. J. 1865. Versuche über Pflanzen-Hybriden. Verh. Naturforschenden Verein Brünn **4.**

————. Experiments on plant hybridization. (Translated by Bateson and later issued as a pamphlet by the Harvard University Press. The same translation appears as an appendix in W. E. Castle: Genetics and eugenics, 1st and 2d ed. Cambridge, Mass., 1916 and 1920; and in W. Bateson: Mendel's principles of heredity. New Haven. 1913.)

Morgan, T. H. 1932. The rise of genetics. Proc. VI Int. Congress Genetics **1.**

Nordenskiöld, E. 1929. The history of biology. (Translated by L. B. Eyre.) New York.

Roberts, F. 1929. Plant hybridization before Mendel. Princeton.

PROBLEMS

1. If life can come only from preexisting life and if "spontaneous generation" is impossible, how do you think life originated?

2. Organic life always ends in death. What effect does this fact have on the evolutionary history of animals and plants?

3. Is asexual reproduction commoner in animals or in plants?   Explain.

4. What advantages and what disadvantages in evolution will a genetically mixed population be likely to have as compared with one that is relatively pure genetically?

5. Why do you think it was that, although plants and animals had been bred for thousands of years, the fundamental laws of inheritance were not discovered until very recently?

6. In the history of a science what method of investigation generally precedes that of experiment?   Illustrate this evolution in method from the history of some science.

7. What is the essential characteristic of the "experimental" method of investigation?

8. Animal breeding has, until recently, made greater progress than plant breeding.   Why?

9. Why have pedigrees been kept much more carefully for our domestic animals than for our cultivated plants?

10. In what way may knowledge of genetics be of value in explaining organic evolution?

11. What improvements in the human race can you think of which might be made possible by an increased knowledge and application of the principles of genetics?

CHAPTER II

HEREDITY AND VARIATION

The chief aim of genetics is to discover, to classify, and to explain the facts of heredity and variation. Heredity is the tendency of animals and plants to resemble their ancestors and relatives, whereas variation is the tendency to depart or differ in any particular from the others of their kind. Both tendencies are familiar to all observers of man, animals, or plants. Heredity is illustrated by the remarkable resemblances which are often seen between father and son, variation by the many imperfections in this resemblance resulting in distinct differences in their physical and mental traits. These two great tendencies, the one toward resemblance or sameness, the other toward variety or differentness, exist together in all forms of life. They are fundamental peculiarities of protoplasm, which is at once stable and tenacious of its form and adaptable and responsive in its reactions. Both are essential to the progress and success of the individual and of the species, just as the conservative and the radical are necessary to the advance of civilization. The one holds gains already made; the other provides the innovations which result in change and continued development. Variation, it might be said, creates new kinds of living things; heredity preserves them.

Heredity.—When one remembers that one generation of complex adult individuals is connected with the next only through single reproductive cells, the universal resemblance of parents and offspring, which we have called heredity, becomes an indication of a deep-seated similarity governed by a fundamental law or set of causes. A phenomenon so general demands an explanation, and in seeking for it we must first examine the central fact more carefully and specify in what degree and in what ways the offspring resemble the parents.

In the first place, it is clear that there is no exception to the similarities between parent and offspring in *general* features. We have no difficulty in recognizing the "humanness" of every child that is born nor in identifying the descendants of a maize plant as members of that species. The success of naturalists in classifying the animals and plants of the world in an orderly system in which each individual has its assigned place, and the practical rule which has guided them, namely, that individuals which look most alike are probably most closely related, both bear witness to the general truth of hereditary resemblance.

16

Moreover, resemblance extends to many of the more special structural and functional features of organisms which are shared by members of the same species, variety, or local race. Thus we can identify the progeny of pure-bred fox terriers not only as mammals, carnivores, and canines, but as members of a single variety of dog marked by features of size, color, behavior, and other traits which they share with their parents and relatives. This resemblance may extend to those relatively minor characters by which we infer the relationship between brother and sister or father and son—the color of eyes or form of hair and similar evidences of the inheritance of single features. The extreme case of this kind of resemblance between relatives is found in the so-called *identical* twins in man (Fig. 5). These are twins which even parents sometimes find it difficult to distinguish. They are always of the same sex and are very similar in all of their physical and mental characteristics. Here, extreme similarity is undoubtedly due to extreme closeness of relationship, for it is known that such twins arise from a single egg. They probably begin, in fact, as a single individual, which at an early division gives rise to two embryos.

FIG. 5.—Identical twins. These two boys have exactly the same heredity since both developed from a single fertilized egg cell. (*From Journal of Heredity.*)

The heredity of the two members of such a pair is thus identical. That their resemblance is chiefly due to this fact is shown by observations on members of a pair of identical twins which have been separated at birth and reared in different environments. Under different conditions they retain their similarity in most of their physical and mental characteristics. This may extend to such details as the contraction of similar illnesses at similar ages and to the manifestation of similar abilities in school work.

From these few instances, it is apparent that heredity is a conditioning factor in the development of similarities in related organisms. The traits affected may be of many diverse kinds, appearing at all stages of the life cycle. Gross structural features such as size, shape, and color are, of course, the most obvious, but it is perhaps more significant that the heredity received from the parents determines, in plants, the kinds of proteins and carbohydrates and even the special characteristics of the starch grains which are formed, while in animals it fixes the chemical peculiarities of the blood and the tissues, particularly as exhibited in their reaction to foreign proteins. Heredity likewise influences the physiological reactions of the organism. It decides whether an individual or a race of plants will be parasitized by a fungus of one variety or of another; whether an insect is to survive successfully at a higher or at a lower temperature; whether or not a child is to distinguish all of the colors of the spectrum or only certain of them, that is, to be color-blind; whether a plant is to convert some of the soluble sugars which it manufactures into red or blue or brown pigments or into no pigment at all. These diverse peculiarities influenced by heredity in turn influence others in the organism and affect its relation to its surroundings and its chances of survival in nature. Certain caterpillars of one species of butterfly absorb into their body fluids the several components of chlorophyll, the green coloring matter of leaves, so that they appear green like the leaves on which they feed. Others of the same species with a slightly different heredity can absorb only specific parts of chlorophyll and assume a blue-green color. Those of the former sort are less likely to be discovered by their natural enemies the birds than are the latter, since they are less conspicuous on green foliage.

What is Inherited.—In all of these cases, and in every case of hereditary resemblance, the individuals which look alike have received something in the reproductive cells from which they arose which directs the development of their general and their particular traits of all kinds into specific channels. A little consideration will show that what is inherited is in each case a tendency to react in a specific way to the specific environment in which the individual finds itself. This is obvious in the case of hereditary susceptibility to disease. If a plant inherits a constitution which fits it to be the ideal home for one variety of fungus parasite, then the presence of this parasite in the plant's environment is a necessary condition for the appearance of this peculiarity of the plant. This dependence of all hereditary traits on environmental factors is not so obvious in the structural characters among animals and plants which live in a fairly stable and constant environment, but even here it can be shown to be the case as well. When a variety of maize, known as sun-red (Fig. 6), is grown in the field, red color appears in the leaves, in the outer husks of the ear, and in other parts exposed to the sun. When these parts are shielded from the sunlight, however, no red color develops. The sun-red trait is inherited but requires the presence of sunlight to develop. In rabbits there is a true-breeding variety known as Himalayan (Fig. 7) in which the pink eyes and the pattern of black ears, feet, and tail and white body are transmitted faithfully to the descendants. If fur is plucked from the white parts and the animal is placed in the cold while the fur is growing in again, the new fur comes in not white but black.   On the other hand, if fur is plucked from the black parts and the part is kept warm (by a bandage, for example), the new hair comes in not black but white.   It appears at first that the black-and-white pattern is itself inherited, but the experiment shows that what is really inherited is the ability of certain parts to form pigment or not to form it, depending on the particular temperature which obtains in that part at a specific time.   The pattern is thus a function both of heredity and of environment, and this is true of all "hereditary" characters.

Fig. 6.—Sun-red corn. The ear at the bottom had been protected from light and the one in the middle exposed to light at its tip, which turned red. In the ear at the top the word "LIGH(T)" was cut out of the husks and the area thus exposed turned red. (*From Blakeslee, in Journal of Heredity.*)

Fig. 7.—The effect of temperature on hair color in rabbits.   The white hair on a small area of the backs of these Himalayan rabbits was pulled out and the animals then placed in a cold room. The hair which later grew in was *black*. Hair regenerated in a warm temperature is usually white. (*From Laura Kaufman, in Biologia Generalis.*)

These cases illustrate the universality, the diversity of effect, and the dual nature of the characters of the organism which are influenced by heredity, but they lead us no nearer to an understanding of the process of inheritance.   In order to learn how resemblances are transmitted, a specific trait, such as eye color in man, must be observed in several generations of individuals developing in a common environment.   The trait thus studied need not necessarily differ in any important respect from those distinctive of species, race, or family, but its inheritance is typical of the laws which probably govern the inheritance of these more complex traits.   Eye color in man may happen to be a character which distinguishes one individual from another, but it may be one item in a racial complex as well.   Thus a racial group of northern Europe is, in general, blue-eyed; while the southern European type is prevailingly brown- or dark-eyed.   The particular interest for genetics lies in the presence of blue or brown eyes in single related individuals.

"Factors" and "Characters."—Investigation shows that marriages of blue-eyed persons with brown-eyed ones from a prevailingly brown-eyed family produce exclusively brown- or dark-eyed children. When these children marry other brown-eyed children of similar ancestry (that is, having one blue-eyed and one brown-eyed parent), *their* children are found to resemble the brown-eyed grandparent in a large proportion (about three-fourths) of the cases, while the remainder, about one-fourth, are blue-eyed. Thus each grandparental type reappears in a definite proportion of the grandchildren. The regularity with which such a result is obtained and the distinctness with which traits like blue and brown eyes are assorted to different individuals among the progeny have led to a definite conception of the mechanism of heredity which will be more fully described in the next chapter. It should be pointed out here, however, that blue eyes appear to pass as a *unit* to one group of progeny, while brown eyes pass as a *unit* to another group, and since the only mode of hereditary transmission is through the reproductive cells or gametes of the parents, it may be assumed that the gametes of the parents differ in respect to something which represents or determines the development of eye color in the progeny. This something which appears to pass through the reproductive cells and to influence a particular character in the offspring is known as a *factor*, or *gene*. The *character* difference "brown or blue eyes," therefore, is ascribed to a *factor* difference in the reproductive cells which give rise to the child; and thence to the gametes of the parents and more distant ancestors.

Here, as in the case of sun-red corn and the Himalayan rabbit, the character itself is, properly speaking, not inherited at all; all that can be transmitted is a *factor* which influences the growth of the individual in a specific way. Here also the role of the environment is less marked, since hereditarily brown-eyed persons seem to develop this character in the various environments under which life is possible, but it is none the less certain that the components which go to form the brown color, in common with all the other necessary materials for life except those contained in the sperm and egg cell, must have entered the organism from the external world, and if these were withheld, the factor could not have led to its specific result.

The reproductive cells or gametes appear to contain factors representing all of the inherited characters of the animal or plant, and the organism from this point of view is a complex mosaic of a vast number of inherited units which in every generation pass through the single reproductive cells of each parent and find expression in the various traits of the offspring (Fig. 8). The factor hypothesis, which has been amply verified by data from all forms of life, has led to the discovery of the laws governing the behavior of these units in heredity.

Complexities of the Factor Hypothesis.—In the inheritance of blue and dark eyes in man a single factor appeared to be responsible for the difference. It must not be concluded from this that any character of the organism is completely determined by a single factor. Complete analysis generally shows that many factors, which may not always be entirely separable in their inheritance, are involved in the production of characters which appear to be quite simple and that the expression of these factors in development is influenced by many agencies both within the organism and in its environment. The gray or grizzled pattern of many wild rodents, such as mice and rats, appears to be a simple trait, yet its development depends on the interaction of at least a dozen different factors affecting the various colors involved and their distribution in the fur. Many characters, such as horns in some breeds of sheep, are chiefly affected by a single factor, but their expression is greatly

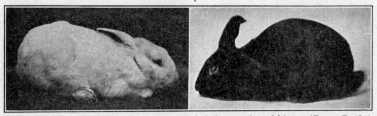

Fig. 8.—Black and white, a unit character difference in rabbits.   (*From Castle.*)

influenced by the sex of the individual; while in other cases, for example in the inheritance of color blindness in man, the inherited factor itself is constantly associated with the factors which determine the sex of the individual. Other internal agencies such as hormones or the secretions of the ductless glands in vertebrates are known to affect the expression of the genetic factors and often to serve as one channel by which the factors affect development.

These examples indicate that heredity is operative everywhere and that throughout the organic world there is a constant tendency for offspring to resemble their parents. They also show that heredity is not a simple process but that different characters, even in the same individual, are inherited in different ways. To classify this host of diverse and often seemingly contradictory facts and to discover the general laws which underlie them is the province of the student of heredity, and although a promising beginning has been made at this task, many of the phenomena of inheritance are still unexplained and unpredictable.

Variation.—The obverse to the picture of hereditary resemblance which we have examined is the equally striking fact of *differences* between individuals, races, or species (Figs. 9 and 10). Since variations appear as departures from exact hereditary resemblance, it is plain that we must consider inheritance from this point of view as well. Variations, like resemblances, are not all simple and self-evident in nature but are remarkably diverse in cause and character. Among them we are able to discover several distinct types, which while similar in appearance are quite different in their underlying causes. Some differences between related organisms are clearly due to the direct action of different environments; others are due to the sorting out of hereditary variations into

Fig. 9.—Extreme size variations in horses. A Percheron draft horse and a Shetland pony colt. (*Courtesy of Iowa State College.*)

different combinations in the generations following crosses of individuals of unlike heredity; while a third type is due to sudden changes in the physical mechanism of heredity.

Variations Due to Environment.—Differences between the members of a pair of human identical twins which have been reared apart in very different environments obviously cannot be ascribed to differences in hereditary constitution, since this is identical in both members of the pair. Such differences as may, eventually, distinguish the two members —as to whether they are tanned or pale, well fed or undernourished, scarred from accident or operation, or different (as they are sometimes found to be) in emotional nature and reaction—may all be well explained as caused by the different environments under which they have lived. Although in this case the differences may be slight and their relationship

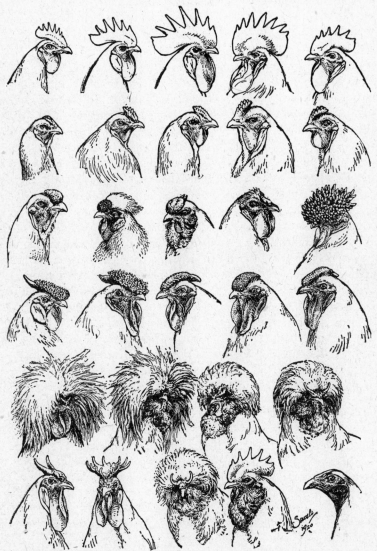

Fig. 10.—Variation in the head appendages of male fowls. Each form is typical of a pure breed or variety of domestic fowls. (*From Robinson.*)

to the environment obvious, in most instances it is difficult to distinguish by inspection alone between the marked variations brought about by the action of the environment and those due to other causes. If we divide into two parts a lowland plant with luxurious growth, thin wide leaves, and tall flower stalks and transplant half of it to a high mountain side, where conditions of temperature, light, moisture, and nutrition are all different, we find after a time that the mountain plant, although having the same heredity as the lowland one, has so altered its form and structure as to be radically different. If we did not know the history of these two plants and the effects which environmental agencies have on plant growth, we might even assign them to different varieties.

Pure Lines and Selection.—The distinction between variations due to the action of the environment and those due to differences in genetic constitution was made very clear by the experiments of the Danish botanist Johannsen in the early years of this century. He worked chiefly with beans, and since these plants are normally self-fertilized, he was able to establish a number of what he called *pure lines*, each consisting of the descendants of a single self-fertilized individual and each presumably pure genetically. These lines differed considerably in seed weight, their averages ranging from about 35 to about 65 centigrams, and these differences were evidently genetic ones. Within each of these lines there was much variation in seed weight, but this seemed to be due only to environmental influences, for when the lightest and the heaviest seed from a single plant or from several plants in a single pure line were selected and planted, the average seed weight from the resulting plants was essentially the same (Table I). Thus selection among variations which were caused by the environment was ineffectual in changing the genetic constitution of the stock. Where genetic differences exist, as between different pure lines or in a population where Mendelian segregation is occurring, selection, of course, is an important factor in producing change; but once genetic purity has been attained, all differences

TABLE I.—THE RESULTS OF SELECTING THE LARGEST AND THE SMALLEST SEEDS IN TWO LINES OF BEANS DESCENDED FROM A SINGLE PLANT (*Data from Johannsen*)

Generation	Average weight of selected parent seeds		Average weight of progeny seeds	
	Lighter seeds	Heavier seeds	From lighter parent	From heavier parent
1	60	70	63	65
2	55	80	75	71
3	50	87	55	57
4	43	73	64	64
5	46	84	74	73
6	56	81	69	68

except newly occurring mutations are environmental ones and apparently are not inherited. These results of Johannsen have since been duplicated with many other plants, and with animals.

Specific Modifications.—The effects of the environment on animals and plants may cause profound and widespread modifications in development. It is easy to observe the striking and general differences in height, number of leaves, and yield of fruit or seed which distinguish plants grown in poor soil from others of the same variety which have grown in rich soil. The effect of nutrition may be sharp and specific as in sweet potatoes, which when grown in soil rich in potassium are round and fleshy but when deprived of this element produce long and spindling roots.

In the same way, the quality and quantity of food determine to a considerable degree the size and productivity of animals. The precise ration fed to a steer, a cow, or a laying hen makes a great deal of difference in the number of pounds of beef, quarts of milk, or dozens of eggs which are produced. So powerful is the effect of the environment on characters of this sort (which are obviously very important ones economically) that most of our agricultural practices are concerned with such a manipulation of the environment—whether of fertilizers, water, temperature, food, or other factors—that the most desirable variations shall be induced.

The separate factors of nutrition may have very specific effects, as, for example, the appearance of rickets or of the striking changes brought about by scurvy or by beriberi, where some single vitamin is deficient in the diet. The practice of medicine, too, is chiefly concerned with modifying the animal organism through its environment.

Some remarkable variations are brought about in both animals and plants by changes in the amount or kind of light to which they are exposed. In the absence of light, green plants can make very little growth because of their inability to carry on the essential process of photosynthesis. Two plants from the same lot of seed, one grown in the dark, the other in the light, come to differ very strikingly in almost all of their characters. The plant grown in the dark is paler, taller, and more spindling than the one reared in the light. Such a plant is not able to mature and does not flower or set seed. Alteration in the relative amount of light, especially in the length of daily exposure to light, also brings about important differences in plants, particularly with reference to the relation between their vegetative and reproductive activities. Garner and Allard found that a relatively short daily period of illumination retards the growth of some species and that these will grow vigorously and reach reproductive maturity only if the days are relatively long (Fig. 11, lower). There are other species, however, in which the effect of short days is to hasten flowering and fruiting, activities which may be indefinitely deferred if the plant is exposed to long daily illumination (Fig. 11, upper). Light may also have a direct effect on certain characters, as in the variety of corn previously described in which

Fig. 11.—Variations caused by differences in the daily period of illumination. The plants at the left have been exposed during growth to a relatively short daily illumination; those at the right to a relatively long one. Above, plants of Cosmos, a "short day" plant, in which flowering is hastened by shortened days. Below, red clover, a "long day" plant, in which a shortened day greatly retards flowering. (*From Garner and Allard.*)

certain parts of the plant turn red when exposed to sunlight, while unexposed parts remain green. Such examples illustrate well that the characters of plants depend on a complex chain of reactions, some of which can take place only in the presence of a given amount or kind of light.

Animals as well as plants show many modifications (changes in sex glands, moulting and changes in plumage color in birds) due to the length of day to which they are exposed.

In addition to these few examples, variations in other external factors such as temperature, water, altitude, and barometric pressure lead to pronounced modification of form in organisms. Less obvious but perhaps more important physiological modifications are brought about by factors originating outside animals and plants but producing their effects by subtle internal changes. Consider the effect, for example, of introducing into the blood stream of an animal substances to which his blood reacts in a specific way so that a more or less lasting immunity to a specific disease is produced; or the ingestion of glandular material from another animal which changes him from a cretinous dwarf to an individual of normal size.

The obvious conclusion to be drawn from all such examples is that many of the variations exhibited by animals and plants have a direct relation to the conditions under which they live. It becomes, therefore, a question of great theoretical and practical importance to determine whether these variations of which the causative factors are known are or may become *hereditary*.

The Inheritance of Acquired Characters.—At first glance it might seem that the inheritance of such environmental variations would offer the most obvious explanation of the origin of new heritable traits. It has frequently been assumed that small or dwarf races of animals and plants are descended from ancestors which for many generations were subjected to an inadequate food supply, adverse climate, and other conditions which are known to limit growth in size. Specific variations such as hornlessness or taillessness might also be thought to have arisen from the practice of dehorning or of docking the tail continued over many generations. During the last century such hypotheses have been subjected to many tests by experiment, and although the verdict of many of these experiments is inconclusive, it is possible to derive some definite answers from the data.

Historical.—Lamarck (Fig. 12), a French biologist (1744–1829), was the first modern thinker to recognize the problem clearly and to offer an explanation of the origin of variations and of the method of evolution. He supposed that variations were induced in the individual by such external and internal agencies as the direct action of the environment or the use and disuse of a part, or that they arose in response to an urgent need on the part of the organism. The characters so called into being he regarded as truly heritable, and the environment which had directly or indirectly caused variations to appear was in his theory the directing agent in evolution. To Lamarck *all* variations were acquired and *all* variations were heritable. Darwin, who established the theory of organic evolution, made little inquiry into the causes of variation, although like Lamarck he thought that some, at least, originated through the direct action of the environment. He regarded most of the hereditary changes in the organism as spontaneous variations of unknown nature, and these provided the differences in adaptability from which the environment selected the best or fittest to survive. Darwin foreshadowed the modern view of the question by recognizing that not all variations were due to a

FIG. 12.—Jean Baptiste Lamarck (1744–1829). (*From A. F. Shull, after Locy.*)

single set of causes and that not all were equally heritable. Weismann, following Darwin, established this important distinction and showed that many variations caused by the environment or artificially induced, such as mutilations or injuries, were not inherited, while variations of another kind were inherited. The latter, the cause of which he did not know, he called congenital or germinal, as distinguished from acquired or environmental variations.

In support of his contention that characters acquired by the organism were not inherited, Weismann developed the *germ plasm* theory, which considers the reproductive tissue (the germ cells) as separate and distinct from the other tissues of the body (the *somatoplasm*). The environment, Weismann believed, was able to cause many variations in the somatoplasm, but such changes could not be transferred to the germ plasm (which was the sole seat of hereditary characters) and, therefore, could not become inherited. Some experimental evidence for the noninheritance of such acquired characters as mutilations and some evidences of the structural and physiological independence of body and germ cells in higher animals were obtained by Weismann and have been added to and corroborated by later investigators.

Although the conception of a distinct germ plasm is useful and aids in explaining many facts and in planning experiments with higher animals, it is undoubtedly of limited application. It does not apply at all in the lower animals, where no practical distinction between soma and germ can be made, or in plants, where many or all parts of the plant body may give rise to germ cells or to new individuals without the intervention of a sexual process. Even in the higher animals it is possible that the gametes may arise from tissue which is not fundamentally different from that which produces other parts of the body and that the gonads are not completely insulated from those forces which effect changes in the body tissues.

The Problem and Its Present Status.—The chief question involved in the so-called "inheritance of acquired characters" is the apparently simple one as to whether such variations as have been cited above, which are produced by the action of environmental factors, use, or habit on the tissues of adult or developing organisms, are ever inherited. These variations represent the responses of the animal or plant to external stimuli, and this responsiveness or sensitiveness is known to be a general property of all living substance. The point at issue is whether the particular response made by an ancestor (as, for example, the greater growth reaction of plants to good soil or of animals to food, heat, or light) has any determining effect on the responses to be made by its descendants. Does the fact that the parent has responded in a way which leads to a visible variation predetermine the response of the offspring, or make it any easier for the offspring to develop this same character in the absence of the same stimulus? If it does, it will mean that the characters acquired by the adult organism may be transferred and impressed on the germ cells and affect all future generations.

Without citing the detailed evidence (which the interested student may consult in the references listed at the end of this chapter), it may be stated by way of summary that acquired characters, as defined above, are probably never inherited. The negative evidence is very considerable, showing that mutilations, the effects of poisons, alcohol, and similar agencies, variations due to amounts or kinds of food or to temperature or light, and effects of acclimatization or domestication are not transmitted *as such* to descendants. The few experiments leading to the opposite conclusion are of doubtful validity and do not in any case amount to proof. It is safe to say, therefore, that the heritable characters with which genetics deals have not arisen in this way. In a later chapter we shall see that new *genes* or *factors* may arise and new arrangements in the material basis of heredity, that is, in the chromosomes, may take place by sudden chemical and physical changes in the chromatin of the nucleus and that these may occur more frequently in the presence of greater intensities of certain kinds of energy, for example, from X rays, radium, and heat, than are ordinarily present in the environment. The response here is made by the cells antecedent to the gametes, not by the body of the parent, and there is no evidence of that correspondence between the stimulus and the kind of character produced which the "inheritance of acquired characters" seems to require. The increased frequency of new heritable changes under increased environmental stimuli is thus quite different in principle and in implication from the inheritance of bodily "acquirements."

Variations Due to Hybridization and Recombination.—Many variations are not due primarily to the environment but to a reappearance or recombination of hereditary traits among the descendants of individuals of mixed or impure genetic constitution. The appearance of one blue-eyed child among the otherwise brown-eyed progeny of two brown-eyed parents represents such a variation. It is an indication of a *difference* which was already present in the ancestry of the parents and which came to light when two factors for blue eyes met in the chance combination of an egg and a sperm each carrying blue.

The reappearance of ancestral traits may sometimes be delayed for so long that the variation when it appears may seem to be entirely new. Cases of this sort have been known in the breeding of pure-bred cattle. In the United States only black and white Holstein-Friesian cattle are eligible for registry in the herd books of the breed, and only this type is bred. Occasionally a red and white calf appears from a pedigree in which there have been only black and white ancestors for seven or eight generations. Were it not known that the Holsteins are descended from Dutch herds in which both red and black animals were frequent and that red is due to a hereditary factor which is masked or hidden by black, a red calf might be thought to be a new variation. Its occurrence is known, however, to be merely a reappearance of an ancestral trait.

Where the individuals which are crossed differ in only a single character, but little variation occurs among the offspring. Where a cross brings together individuals unlike in several characteristics, however, variation is markedly greater, for the number of possible combinations of traits will increase. In new individuals, traits from one ancestor may be combined with different traits from another. The characters themselves

Fig. 13.—Variability in maize seeds. Left: Ear of maize from hybrid or crossbred ancestry, showing variations in color, size, shape, and chemical constitution of the seeds. Right: Types of seeds from different varieties of maize. (*Courtesy of the Journal of Heredity.*)

are not new, but the *combinations* may be, and it is this which produces much of the variation among progeny from the same parents (Fig. 13). If two pairs of characters are involved, for example, there will be four possible combinations among the descendants; if three, there will be eight; if four, sixteen; and so on.

Size or quantitative characters, insofar as they are inheritable, also show this increased variability following a cross. If a genetically large animal is crossed with a genetically small one, for example, the first-generation offspring are often intermediate in height, and uniform, but *their* descendants are generally highly variable, ranging all the way from large to small. There is reason to believe that this increase in variability is also due to a recombination of genetic factors, although here the factors all affect the same character, that is, size.

This increase in variability which always follows hybridization between unlike individuals has resulted in the appearance of many new character combinations in animals and plants and has made it possible for breeders, by practicing selection among these, to develop new and valuable types. It also accounts for the well-known fact that hybrids or mongrels, whatever their own excellent qualities, do not breed true and hence are valueless for breeding purposes where uniformity of type is desired.

On the whole, most of the hereditary variations found in animals and plants are due to the sorting out and recombining of separate factors which take place automatically and continually in the method of cross-breeding, which is the rule in most of the higher plants and animals.

Variations Due to Mutation.—Variations due to the environment can be controlled by a proper manipulation of the environment itself, and variations due to the sorting out and rearrangement of factors can also be controlled through a knowledge of the laws which govern the behavior of these factors. There is a third type, however, which it is as yet impossible to predict and over which there is no control.

If one observes carefully a large group of animals or plants over a number of generations, an occasional individual will be found which differs from the rest of the population and transmits its differences to its descendants, but the origin of these cannot be ascribed to changes in the environment or to the past history or characters of the race. Such a suddenly appearing new variation is known as a *mutation*.

In the history of plant and animal breeding occur many instances of such sudden variations. In the latter part of the eighteenth century, for example, there appeared in the flock of Seth Wright, a New England farmer, a male lamb with remarkably short, bowed legs. Wright reared this lamb and bred from it, thereby originating the Ancon breed of sheep, so short-legged that they could not jump over an ordinary stone wall.

This breed became extinct about sixty years ago, but some fifty years later another short-legged lamb appeared suddenly in the flock of a Norwegian farmer, representing probably a new appearance of the same mutation. From this a new strain of short-legged sheep has been bred (Fig. 14).

In the same way hornless mutant individuals have appeared in almost all breeds of horned cattle, and hornless races of these breeds have been developed from them. Pacing horses, double-toed cats, "mule-footed"

Fig. 14.—Ancon or short-legged sheep, a variation which arose by mutation. (*From Storrs Agricultural Experiment Station.*)

swine, albino rats, and many other new, distinct, and true-breeding types have appeared as mutations among animals.

In the little vinegar fly, Drosophila, which has been bred so extensively and under such close observation in biological laboratories for over thirty years, several hundred mutations have occurred, each resulting in a specific change in some character of the fly.

The same type of variation has appeared in plants. The Shirley poppy, the dwarf "Cupid" sweet pea, and the dwarf, cut-leaved, double-flowered, and white-flowered races of many plants have each descended from a single plant of this type which appeared under cultivation. The new or *mutant* character has arisen suddenly, has bred true from the beginning, and has thus given rise to a new and distinct race.

Most of these mutations in plants arose from seed, but in some instances the mutant character was found to be confined to a single branch. Such a branch, when artificially propagated, remains true to its new type. Many horticultural varieties, especially those with variegated foliage, have arisen from such mutations or "bud sports."

Early students of mutation emphasized the wide divergence of mutant forms from the normal type, but it is now recognized that mutational differences may be large or small and that it is not their magnitude but their clear distinction from the parent form and their ability to reproduce the new type which distinguish them from other kinds of variation. In many cases, indeed, it is very difficult to tell whether one is dealing with a mutation or with a complicated case of the sorting out of genetic factors.

Variations may therefore be divided into three main groups: (1) those which are due to differences in the environment; (2) those which are due to reappearance and recombination of genetic factors; and (3) those which are due to mutation, the origin of which we do not understand.

REFERENCES

See titles at end of Chap. I; also:

BATESON, W. 1894. Materials for the study of variation. London.
CONKLIN, E. G. 1915. Heredity and environment in the development of men. Princeton.
DUNN, L. C. 1932. Heredity and variation. New York.
EAST, E. M. 1929. Heredity and human affairs. New York.
JENNINGS, H. S. 1930. The biological basis of human nature. New York.
LAMARCK, J. B. 1873. Philosophie zoologique. Paris.
LANGE, J. 1931. Crime and destiny. New York.
MATSUURA, H. H. 1929. A bibliographical monograph on plant genetics. Tokyo.
NEWMAN, H. H. 1921. Readings in evolution, genetics, and eugenics. Chicago.
   (See especially Chap. 23, Are acquired characteristics hereditary?)
————. Biology of twins. Chicago.
PEARSON, K. (editor). 1912. Treasury of human inheritance. London.
PUNNETT, R. C. 1927. Mendelism. 7th ed. Cambridge (England).
SHULL, A. F. 1938. Heredity. 3d ed. New York.

PROBLEMS

12. What has been the effect of human variability on the development of human societies?

13. Do you think that variations due to inborn genetic differences or to the environment and training are the more important in determining differences between persons?

14. What family do you know of which has included a large number of eminent people? How do you explain the occurrence of such families?

15. In what way could our knowledge of the inheritance of eye color in man be used to decide a case of disputed paternity?

16. How are individual variations utilized in the identification of persons?

17. Some races of teasel have spirally twisted stalks if grown in rich soil but normal straight ones if grown in poor soil. How does a normal plant from such a race differ genetically from a normal plant of a race which never shows twisting?

18. Measles and chicken pox killed thousands of natives of the South Sea Islands at the first coming of the white men, but these diseases are rarely fatal to Europeans. Explain.

19. The Napoleonic wars are said to have reduced somewhat the average stature of the French people. To what might such a result be due?

20. The chestnut bark fungus, introduced some years ago into the United States, has exterminated all the native American chestnut trees over a wide area. In China, its native home, the species of chestnut are almost immune to its attack. How do you explain this difference between American and Chinese chestnut trees?

21. The hair color of an individual may be brown in youth, black at maturity, and white in old age. What color would you call his hair in a study of inheritance of hair color in his family? In investigating the inheritance of hair color, what precaution, therefore, should be exercised?

22. If the peculiarities of large groups of organisms have arisen first in one or a few individuals from which the group has descended, why is it that living members of the two groups today—a sheep and a goat, for example, or an apple tree and a pear tree—cannot be successfully crossed?

23. Why is a study of identical twins of particular importance in helping to determine the relative influences of heredity and environment in man?

24. Why is it more difficult to study the inheritance of such characters as size and yield than of color?

25. How could you determine whether a given case of variation is due to environmental or genetic influences?

26. What mechanism, either physical or chemical, can you imagine whereby a *factor* in a gamete might determine the appearance of a *character* in the individual produced by that gamete?

27. If acquired characters are not inherited, how do you think it has come about that plants and animals are so well adapted to the conditions under which they live?

28. How could you explain the possession by animals of highly developed instincts which the individual itself has had no opportunity of acquiring, assuming (1) that acquired characters are inherited; (2) that they are not?

29. What advantages and what disadvantages to human society would result from the inheritance of acquired characters?

30. If members of a white-skinned race are exposed to bright sunlight, their skin is darkened or "tanned." Races native to regions of bright sunlight, like negroes in the tropics, are genetically dark-skinned. How would Lamarck explain the dark skin of such races? How would Darwin?

31. Which do you think are more important in producing evolutionary change, those variations which are due to segregation and recombination of factors or those which are due to mutation? Explain.

32. In what class of variations would you place two-headed animals, giants, dwarfs, and similar "freaks"?

33. How can you tell whether a new trait is a mutation or the result of complex segregation following a cross?

34. What explanation have you for the present great variability of the human race? Why would you expect the population of the United States to be more variable than that of most European countries?

35. A relation is sometimes traced between the Inquisition, which was particularly active in Spain, and the decline of Spain as a great power which took place not long afterward. What genetic basis do you think there may be for this?

CHAPTER III

MENDEL'S LAWS OF INHERITANCE. I

The facts discussed in the previous chapter make it very evident that the problem of inheritance, far from being a simple and clearly defined one, involves a whole series of problems touching many fields. Different characters are inherited in very different ways, and variations may be due to all sorts of causes. Knowledge derived from a study of one species is often useless in the case of another. When the great assemblage of diverse and often seemingly unintelligible facts which students of inheritance are amassing is considered, it is not surprising that earlier biologists were long unable to reduce them to an orderly and understandable basis.

No branch of knowledge, however, is entitled to be called a science until its various facts can be arranged and classified under certain definite principles or *laws*, a knowledge of which makes it possible to understand these facts, at least in part, and to predict or control them. The conception of scientific law is so important and often so poorly understood that it may be profitable to digress a little here and to consider briefly what a law of science is and how it may be discovered and applied.

The Laws of Science.—The external world is continually presenting to the senses a multitude of diverse objects, the character and relationships of which cannot be discerned by observation. Many of these phenomena appear at first sight to be irregular and unpredictable and to have no definite relationship to one another. It is soon noted, however, that running through this apparent confusion there are indications of regularity and order and that some events follow others so invariably that one may confidently depend upon their always doing so. The observer thus learns to distinguish the relationships known as *cause* and *effect*. The constant association between the position of the moon and the height of the tides, and between the length of a pendulum and the rate of its oscillation, are examples of such evident uniformities. This conception of *orderliness* in nature grows upon the student as he acquires more facts and studies them more critically, and he soon realizes how useful a recognition of this orderliness may be in foreseeing events and in directing their course.

That the universe is indeed fundamentally orderly and that more complete knowledge will make it possible in time to perceive this order in all things is the faith of every scientist. To the constant relationships in nature which he is learning to recognize in ever-growing numbers he has given the name of *laws;* and the chief purpose of scientific investigation is to extend existing knowledge of these laws over a wider and wider field until all facts which now seem confused and irregular shall take their places in an orderly system.

The formulation of a scientific law is by no means an easy matter, however, and has often required an exercise of supreme genius. An attempt to establish such a law involves several distinct and well-recognized steps. First, as much information or data as possible concerning the phenomena under investigation must be gathered. This may be done by direct observation under natural conditions; but a more fruitful procedure, and one employed wherever possible, involves a control of conditions by the observer himself so that a definite *test* may be performed. This method is known as an *experiment,* and since it makes it possible for us to single out a particular group of phenomena and test their behavior at will under conditions which are known and can be regulated, it provides more exact information than can be gained in any other way, an advantage which has made the experimental method one of the most useful tools of modern science. The information thus gained, which is often somewhat unintelligible at first sight, must then be arranged and classified. This step, and the observations which precede it, will in nearly all cases involve the fundamental methods of *counting* and *measuring*, which distinguish the scientific approach to facts. If the classification is wisely made, the discerning eye may perhaps begin to see certain simple relationships which underlie the facts, and eventually a tentative explanation or *hypothesis* may be framed to account for these observed relationships. The hypothesis is then thoroughly tested by further observation and experiment, and if it continues to explain satisfactorily all the facts which are brought forward, it leaves the realm of conjecture and becomes accepted as an established scientific law. A law is thus a brief statement or explanation of some uniform and constant relationship which has been found to hold through a large series of natural events.

Mendel and His Methods.—Mendel's discovery of these first laws of inheritance led through precisely the steps of observation and experiment, classification, tentative explanation or hypothesis, testing, and final deduction which have been outlined above. The most important facts in the life and work of this Austrian monk whose name has become woven so closely into the fabric of genetic science have already been presented. In the garden of his monastery at Brünn, Mendel began in 1857 to observe carefully the resemblances and differences among various races of garden peas. It is perhaps noteworthy that he was not a professional biologist but that these experiments were his chief avocation, stimulated by a natural curiosity which he had the leisure to indulge.

Mendel was prepared for his work by a fine enthusiasm and a thoroughly scientific spirit.   He was also familiar with the results of earlier investigators on the subject which most interested him, the effect of crossing or hybridization on plants.   His success was due not only to these qualities of mind but also to a wise choice of materials and methods of investigation.

Counting of Different Types of Offspring.—Mendel endeavored to avoid the complexities which had troubled earlier students of heredity by simplifying the problem as far as possible.   Many workers had noticed

Fig. 15.—One of the pairs of character differences studied by Mendel in peas.   At left, flowers and pods axillary, borne along the stem; at right, flowers and pods terminal and stem somewhat flattened.   (*From O. E. White.*)

that when plants of different varieties were crossed, great variability appeared among the progeny of the hybrids, as had always been apparent from the results of breeding mongrel animals.   No one, however, had been able to simplify these confused and puzzling observations until Mendel brought to their solution a new and effective method.   This consisted in actually *counting the numbers of each type of progeny* which resulted from a given cross, in grouping them into definite and easily recognized classes, and in observing the relative sizes of these classes.   He thus for the first time began to reduce the phenomena of inheritance to a *measurable* basis and employed the exact quantitative methods used so successfully in many other sciences. Herein lay one of Mendel's chief contributions to genetic discipline.

Study of Single Traits.—Where earlier investigators had made general observations upon the animal or plant as a whole, studying at once the great variety of traits and structures transmitted to each by inheritance, Mendel instead still further simplified the problem by confining his attention to a single character at a time (Fig. 15). In studying flower color, for example, he chose for his hybridization experiments plants which were contrasted in this one character alone, crossing a red-flowered plant with a white-flowered one and paying no attention for the time being to whether these plants were tall or dwarf, yellow-seeded or green. When the behavior of each single trait was established, he then studied two traits together, such as flower color and vine height, and thus extended his analysis still further. By attacking the problem bit by bit he at last succeeded in discovering order and regularity where his predecessors had been able to see only confusion.

Pedigree Records.—In tracing these characteristics from generation to generation a careful technique and a thorough system of recording observations became necessary, since it was of the utmost importance to know exactly which plants were the parents of each individual or the offspring of a given cross. This involved the task of keeping full and precise pedigree records of all plants studied, including the identification of each by a number or symbol, an exact statement of its parentage, and a complete description of its various traits insofar as they concerned the problems under investigation.

These innovations of Mendel—counting the different types of offspring, studying single characteristics independently of the whole individual, and keeping accurate pedigree records of the members of successive generations—are simple enough in themselves, but such a thorough application of the experimental method to breeding problems had never been made by any other investigator. The important discoveries which Mendel made were largely due to these new methods, and they have since been the basis of all careful genetic research.

Material and Technique.—Mendel also chose his material wisely and adapted his technique to conform to the objects which he had in mind. The garden pea is a naturally self-fertilized species. Its flowers are so constructed that the reproductive parts are covered by the petals and not directly exposed to insects or the wind. Pollen normally falls on the adjacent stigma and thus effects fertilization of the ovules of the same flower. Only in rare cases do insects penetrate the flowers, so that there is ordinarily no cross-pollination between plant and plant except as it may be artificially effected by the experimenter. Mendel could, therefore, open a flower bud and remove the stamens before any pollen had been shed (thus preventing self-pollination) and later place on the stigma of this flower, pollen from the plant which he wished to use as the other parent in a cross. It was, of course, necessary to guard this artificially fertilized flower against contamination by pollen of unknown origin which might be brought thither by wind, insects, hands, or instruments. If he wished to determine the kind of progeny which would appear in the second hybrid generation following a cross, he therefore had only to allow the flowers of these plants to fertilize themselves naturally. The pea had the further advantage of being available in a large number of well-marked varieties which bred true and were all fertile when crossed with one another. In some of these, as in the varieties offered by seedsmen today, the plants were tall and regularly attained a height of 6 feet or more, whereas others were low and dwarf. Some varieties had yellow seed and others green; some had round seeds and others wrinkled ones; some had colored flowers and others white; and there were a number of other readily distinguishable differences. In several particulars, therefore, the pea was more satisfactory material with which to work than most other plants would have been.

Mendel's procedure was to cross two plants differing in one of these contrasted character pairs, to plant the seed thus obtained, and to observe the appearance of the first hybrid, or "F_1," generation.[1] He then crossed two hybrid plants together (or allowed them to effect self-fertilization) and raised as large a number as possible of second generation, or F_2, offspring. These were found to display more or less variation in the character studied, and he accordingly classified them, counting the number of plants possessing each of the contrasted traits. Mendel not only crossed plants differing in one trait but later made hybridizations involving two character differences and observed their behavior in the first and second hybrid generations.

From a study of such comparatively simple data were formulated hypotheses which have since been so widely verified by experiments with many other plants and animals that they are now clearly established as Mendel's Laws of Inheritance. These include the two major principles of Segregation and Independent Assortment, together with a number of less fundamental generalizations.

Dominance.—One of the first facts brought out by Mendel's experiments was that the two members of a given pair of contrasting characters, when brought together in a cross, differ markedly in their ability to express themselves in the resulting hybrid offspring. When he crossed a pure-breeding red-flowered plant with a pure-breeding white-flowered one, for example, the progeny were found to resemble exactly the red-flowered

---

[1] The parental generation is technically known as the P_1, the first generation following a cross as the F_1 (first filial generation), the second as the F_2, and so on.

parent (Fig. 16). No white-flowered plants and no intermediates appeared. He knew that whiteness had not really been eliminated, for in the subsequent generation white-flowered plants cropped out again; but in the hybrid itself whiteness seemed to be suppressed or to recede from view and redness to dominate. Mendel therefore called such a trait as redness of flowers a *dominant* one and such a trait as whiteness a *recessive* one. All of the seven characters in peas reported by Mendel behaved in this way, one of each pair of contrasting traits appearing to be dominant and the other recessive. Thus the round form of seed was

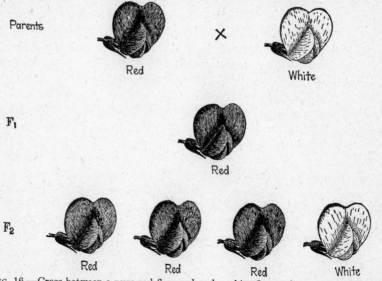

Fig. 16.—Cross between a pure red-flowered and a white-flowered pea plant, showing the dominance of red flower color in F_1. If an F_1 plant is self-fertilized the resulting F_2 generation is three-fourths red-flowered and one-fourth white.

found to be dominant over the wrinkled; the yellow color of the cotyledons over the green; the inflated form of pod over the constricted; the green color of the unripe pods over the yellow; the axillary position of the flowers and pods over the terminal; and the tall vine habit over the dwarf.

In all these cases the dominance of one character over the other was essentially complete. Mendel emphasized this fact, and later investigators have found many characters which show similarly complete or practically complete dominance. In very many other cases, however—and their number grows as the knowledge of inheritance in plants and animals becomes greater—dominance is absent, and the hybrid individuals resemble neither parent exactly but are more or less intermediate between the two. In the snapdragon, for example, a crimson plant crossed with a white one gives first-generation hybrids which are all *pink* in flower color (Fig. 17).   In the same way a black Andalusian fowl bred with a splashed white one produces offspring which are "blue" in the color of their plumage (Fig. 18); and in Shorthorn cattle the cross of red coat by white gives offspring which are "roan," their coats consisting of a mixture of red and white hairs.   In other instances the hybrid offspring may resemble one parent much more closely than they do the other but may not resemble it exactly, so that dominance is incomplete.   There may thus be all stages between complete dominance and the absence of

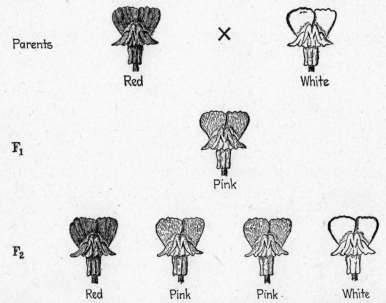

FIG. 17.—Cross between a red-flowered and white-flowered snapdragon showing absence of dominance in F_1.   If an F_1 plant is self-fertilized the resulting F_2 generation is one-fourth red, one-half pink, and one-fourth white.

dominance; and these various conditions may all be found among the different traits of a single individual.

That the seven characters thoroughly studied by Mendel happened to show the phenomenon of complete dominance undoubtedly aided him in perceiving the more essential features of inheritance, but we do not now attach the same importance to dominance as did Mendel himself.   A recognition of it, however, is important in several respects.   Earlier breeders had naturally taken it for granted that the *appearance* of an individual was a sure indication of its genetic constitution and the way in which it would breed.   Mendel's work has shown that this is not necessarily true but that dominance, partial or complete, may enable a hybrid or mongrel to masquerade as a pure-bred individual.   This fact is not

Fig. 18.—The inheritance of blue in Andalusian fowls. When black is crossed with splashed white all the F₁ birds are *blue*. These, if bred together, produce ¼ black, which breed true; ½ blue, which breed like the F₁, blue; and ¼ white, which breed true.

only of theoretical interest but is of great importance in the practical breeding of animals and plants.

Unit Characters and Factors.—As before noted, Mendel carried his experiments beyond the first hybrid generation and grew a second one by crossing together (or by self-fertilizing) plants of this F_1. Sometimes a third and a fourth generation were also successively studied. The most notable feature of the F_2 raised from the cross of red-flowered with white-flowered plants was that, instead of being uniformly red like the F_1, this generation included both red and white individuals (Fig. 16). These plants resembled exactly the red and white grandparents, and no other kinds of plants appeared. In succeeding generations these same two types of flower color maintained their individuality and independence. A similar result was obtained in the second generation bred from the hybrids between other pairs of contrasted characters (Table II). These facts all vindicated the soundness of Mendel's method in studying inheritance character by character, for they showed that the traits which differentiated these various types of peas from one another were essentially independent things which did not lose their identity in the hybrid but were passed on unchanged to the second and later generations. This independence was still further emphasized by the results of experiments (to be described later) in which individuals differing in more than one trait were crossed. Such a conception of the individual as an aggregation of more or less independent and separable "unit characters," each of which is distinct and may exist with any combination of others, was an entirely new one.

TABLE II.—SUMMARY OF F_2 RESULTS OF MENDEL'S EXPERIMENTS WITH PEAS

Character	Dominants	Recessives	Total
	No.　　%	No　　%	
Form of seed................	5,474 (74.74)	1,850 (25.26)	7,324
Color of cotyledons...........	6,022 (75.06)	2,001 (24.94)	8,023
Color of seed coats...........	705 (75.90)	224 (24.10)	929
Form of pod.................	882 (74.68)	299 (25.32)	1,181
Color of pod................	428 (73.79)	152 (26.21)	580
Position of flowers...........	651 (75.87)	207 (24.13)	858
Length of stem..............	787 (73.96)	277 (26.04)	1,064
	14,949 (74.90)	5,010 (25.10)	19,959

Mendel soon observed that for each of these various traits there was to be found a contrasting one, such as red flower color with white, yellow seed coat with green, tall vine with dwarf, and so on. These pairs of contrasting unit characters which he brought together in his hybrids Mendel called "differentiating characters." The occurrence of such a paired condition in practically all characteristics of plants and animals is abundantly supported by all the available evidence. Such pairs of characters were later termed *allelic* pairs, each of the two members being the *allele* of the other.

In Mendel's own paper and in much of the early work of his successors, no sharp distinction was drawn between the actual and visible trait or character and that "something" which exists in the gametes and which ultimately causes the development of this character in the individual resulting from their union. The actual character which is seen, such as red flower color, for example, obviously cannot be present in the gametes, but something representing it and capable of producing it must be there. This is called the *factor* or *gene* for the character in question. An important result of later Mendelian investigation is a recognition that the same factor may, under different environmental conditions, give rise to characters which are also markedly different. The continuing and stable thing, therefore, is the factor itself rather than the character, and the unity which Mendel observed lies rather in this underlying factor than in the visible, and perhaps variable, character which it produces.

The Principle of Segregation.—The behavior of these units in the second and later generations from a cross led to the discovery by Mendel of one of the most fundamental principles which govern the transmission of characteristics from generation to generation. It has been seen that when he crossed a pure-breeding red-flowered plant with a white-flowered one, the offspring were all red-flowered; and that when one of these red-flowered offspring was self-fertilized (or when two of them were crossed), the resulting second-generation plants consisted of both red-flowered and white-flowered individuals. The two contrasted characters (alleles) had been brought together in the F_1 hybrid (where one dominated the other), but in the second generation they had become sharply separated from one another again and were distributed to different individuals. This separation and redistribution of unit characters in the offspring of hybrid individuals is known as *segregation* and has been found to be a constant feature of all inheritance.

The segregation of characters is by no means a random and irregular process but tends to result in the production of a definite proportion between the numbers of individuals of one type and those of the other, a fact made clear for the first time through Mendel's method of counting the numbers of each. In the experiment in question, for example, he raised 929 plants in the F_2 generation and found that in 705 of them the flower color was red, while in 224 it was white, thus displaying a ratio of approximately three-fourths of the dominants to one-fourth of the recessives (Fig. 16). This ratio, which may be expressed as ¾:¼, 75:25 per cent, or 3:1, was found to hold true in the F_2 generation from crosses involving all of the other character pairs studied, the larger group

FIG. 19.—The 3:1 ratio in an F_2 generation. Seedlings from a cross of two green plants each carrying a recessive albino factor, showing segregation into three-fourths green and one-fourth albino plants. (*From Connor and Karper, in Journal of Heredity.*)

always being that with the dominant character and the smaller one that with the recessive. The actual counts which Mendel obtained in these various crosses are set forth in Table II. Later work on peas by other investigators has completely confirmed Mendel's results. In the cross

TABLE III.—SUMMARY OF F_2 RESULTS IN INHERITANCE OF SEED COLOR IN PEAS (*After Johannsen*)

Investigator	Yellow seeds		Green seeds		Total
	No.	%	No.	%	
Mendel, 1865.............	6,022	(75.05)	2,001	(24.95)	8,023
Correns, 1900.............	1,394	(75.47)	453	(24.53)	1,847
Tschermak, 1900..........	3,580	(75.05)	1,190	(24.95)	4,770
Hurst, 1904...............	1,310	(74.64)	445	(25.36)	1,755
Bateson, 1905.............	11,902	(75.30)	3,903	(24.70)	15,806
Lock, 1905................	1,438	(73.67)	514	(26.33)	1,952
Darbishire, 1909..........	109,060	(75.09)	36,186	(24.91)	145,246
Totals.................	134,707	(75.09)	44,692	(24.91)	179,399

involving yellow seeds and green seeds, F_2 generations totaling 179,399 individuals have been recorded (Table III), of which 134,707, or 75.09 per cent, were yellow-seeded and 44,692, or 24.91 per cent, green-seeded. Other examples of this characteristic Mendelian ratio are shown in Figs. 19 and 20.

It will be shown a little later that this ratio depends on a random union between different gametes, and it should be emphasized that these results of actual breeding do not display simple and exact ratios any

P_1

F_1

F_2

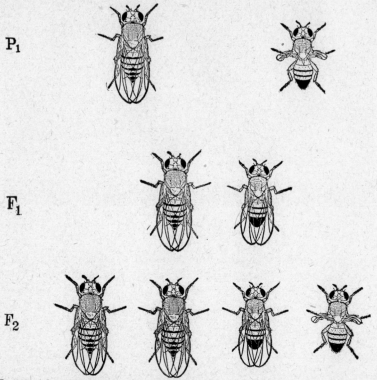

Fig. 20.—Cross between long-winged (wild-type) vinegar fly and vestigial-winged fly, producing long-winged offspring in the F_1, which if bred to each other give in the next generation (F_2) ¾ long to ¼ vestigial. (*From Morgan.*)

more than the tossing of coins or the throwing of dice always give exact and predictable results, and for the same reason. It must not be expected, for example, that with every three red-flowered plants there shall always be associated one with white flowers any more than that in tossing coins heads will invariably alternate with tails. This ratio—and the same is true of the other Mendelian ratios—merely indicates what may be expected on the basis of probability. Experience, agreeing with theoretical expectation, has shown that the larger the number of individuals raised the closer the F_2 ratio approaches $\frac{3}{4}:\frac{1}{4}$, a fact strikingly emphasized in the table just cited (Table III).

Mendel was not content to leave the matter here, however, but studied the progeny of these second-generation hybrids. In the cross

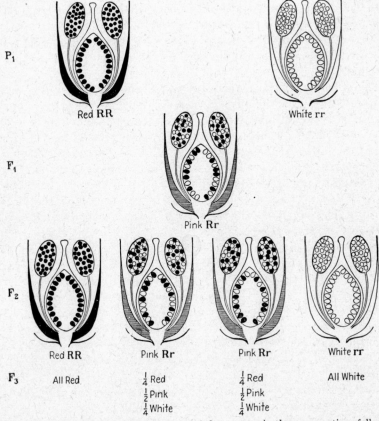

Fig. 21.—Diagram showing the character of the gametes in three generations following a cross between a red-flowered and white-flowered plant. The gametes are represented by pollen grains and ovules, the black ones carrying the factor for red and the white ones that for white. In the (pink) F_1 dominance of red is not complete (corolla shaded), but of the F_1 gametes half carry red and half white, and *none are pink*. In the F_2 one-fourth of the plants are red-flowered, and all their gametes carry the factor for red; one-half are *pink-flowered*, with half their gametes carrying red and half white; and one-fourth white-flowered, their gametes all carrying white. The character of the offspring of these F_2 types, when self-fertilized, is shown in the F_3 generation.

involving flower color, he found that the white-flowered F_2 plants bred perfectly true to white flower color through all subsequent generations. The red-flowered plants, however, although looking alike, did not all behave in the same way. About one-third of them bred true to red, but two-thirds produced both red and white offspring in the ratio of about

$\frac{3}{4}:\frac{1}{4}$, thus resembling exactly the F_1 hybrids. The history of three generations following a cross which involves a single character difference is set forth in Fig. 21.

In the F_2, therefore, approximately one-fourth of the individuals were found to be true-breeding dominant plants, one-half hybrid dominants like the F_1, and one-fourth true-breeding recessives. The fundamental ratio, based on the genetic constitution and breeding behavior of the F_2 individuals, is, therefore, $\frac{1}{4}:\frac{1}{2}:\frac{1}{4}$ and more accurately represents the actual facts than the ratio of $\frac{3}{4}:\frac{1}{4}$, which is based on appearance alone.

The difference between these two ratios, the actual and the visible, is due to the effect of dominance, whereby the pure reds and the hybrid reds resemble each other, thus reducing the three actual classes to only two visibly different ones. In character pairs which do not exhibit dominance, however, the $\frac{1}{4}:\frac{1}{2}:\frac{1}{4}$ ratio may be observed directly, as in the inheritance of red and white flower color in snapdragons (Fig. 17), and these examples give a clearer insight into the phenomena of segregation than do those where dominance is complete. In the inheritance of coat color in Andalusian fowls, likewise, it is found that when black is crossed with splashed white the crossbred (F_1) birds are neither black nor white but a mixture of the two called "blue" (Fig. 18). When two such blue fowls are bred together, they produce on the average about 25 per cent black, 50 per cent blue, and 25 per cent white progeny, a ratio of $\frac{1}{4}:\frac{1}{2}:\frac{1}{4}$. Here there are three visibly different classes, corresponding exactly to the three which are genetically different. It is evident, moreover, that such a trait as blue plumage color in poultry is not a true Mendelian character at all, in the sense that it is inherited independently and will segregate, but that it is merely the expression of the two contrasted factors when both are present.

In their simplest form, then, the facts as to segregation may be stated as follows: When individuals differing in a single trait are crossed, each trait behaves as a unit, passes intact through individuals of the first generation, where it may or may not be visibly expressed, and emerges unchanged in the second generation. Here one-fourth of the individuals tend to resemble, in appearance and breeding behavior, one of the original pure types; one-fourth tend to resemble the other; and one-half to resemble the first-generation hybrids.

Explanation of Segregation.—The explanation which Mendel proposed for the occurrence of segregation and its characteristic ratios involved a radically new conception of the manner in which heritable traits are transmitted from generation to generation. As previously stated, the only physical link between parent and offspring is the sexual cell or gamete, which contains factors for every heritable trait which the offspring displays. In the illustration previously employed, then, it may be assumed that all the gametes of the parent red-flowered pea plant carry a factor for redness of flowers (in addition, of course, to many others), since such a plant, when self-fertilized, produces only red-flowered offspring. In the same way, all the gametes of the white-flowered plant carry a factor for whiteness. When a cross is made between a red-flowered and a white-flowered plant, two gametes, one carrying red and the other white, unite to produce a plant which is hybrid for this particular character. This hybrid plant obviously must contain in every one of its cells factors for

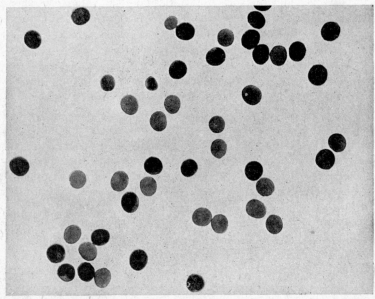

Fig. 22.—Microphotograph of pollen from an anther of a maize plant heterozygous for the starchy-waxy factor pair showing segregation for this factor. The pollen has been treated with iodine making the "starchy" grains appear dark in contrast to the "waxy" ones, which are light. (*From Demerec.*)

both redness and whiteness. It so happens that in this case only redness becomes visibly expressed in the plant, in contrast to those instances where dominance is absent and where both the contrasting factors influence the appearance of the hybrid individual. Now the essential feature of Mendel's explanation of segregation lies in his assumption as to the manner in which this hybrid red-and-white-carrying individual produces gametes. The fact that, where two such hybrids are crossed (or where one is self-fertilized), some of the offspring are true-breeding reds which never produce white-flowered plants among their offspring naturally implies that each of the gametes which united to produce such true-breeding progeny carried a factor for red but none for white. Similarly, the occurrence of pure-breeding white-flowered plants implies the union of two white-carrying gametes which lack factors for red. From these considerations, Mendel drew the inference that when such a hybrid individual, containing factors for both red and white, itself produces gametes, these gametes are not all alike but are of *two different kinds, half of them carrying only the factor for redness and half of them carrying only the factor for whiteness.* The correctness of this inference may sometimes be proved by direct observation, as in the case of certain plants where the pollen grains produced by a heterozygous individual fall clearly into two equal groups, the members of which differ in size, shape, or chemical constitution (Fig. 22).

This inference has two implications: first, that every gamete is *pure,* containing only one member of a given factor pair and thus never showing the hybrid character of the individual producing it; and, second, that in the formation of gametes there is a reduction in the amount of genetic material carried, each gamete containing only *half* of the factorial equipment which is present in an ordinary body cell. The essential feature of the mechanism of segregation, therefore, lies in the circumstance that a factor carried by the gametes of one parent and its contrasting factor carried by the gametes of the other parent come together and coexist for a generation in the cells of the resulting hybrid offspring *without blending or losing their identity;* and that, when such a hybrid individual produces its own sexual cells, in turn, these two factors become completely and cleanly separated again or *segregated* from one another, each of the new gametes being entirely pure and containing either the one factor or the other but *never both.*

The characteristic $\frac{1}{4}:\frac{1}{2}:\frac{1}{4}$ ratio displayed by the offspring of the hybrid individuals is readily explained if one makes, as did Mendel, one further assumption, namely, that in fertilization there is no affinity between gametes carrying the same factors but that the different types *unite at random,* any pollen grain (or sperm) fertilizing any ovule (or egg), and all possible combinations of factors being thereby produced through the operation of chance alone. Since a hybrid produces two kinds of male gametes and two kinds of female ones, as regards any given factor pair, there will evidently be four possible combinations in fertilization: one involving two factors for one of the members of the pair, another involving two factors for the other member, and two in which unlike factors are united.

The Genotype and Its Representation.—The mechanism of segregation and the appearance of the characteristic ratios which accompany it are perhaps best understood if the common Mendelian method of notation is employed and the factorial make-up of individuals and of their gametes is represented by simple letters or formulas. It should be emphasized that every individual is in a genetic sense a *double* structure, since it arises from the union of two gametes and thus draws half of its inheritance from one parent and half from the other. If in the cross which has been used as an example C represents the factor for colored (red) flowers and c the factor for white,[1] the pure-breeding colored-flowered parent, which received the factor C from both of its parents, may,

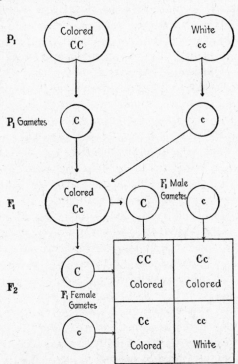

FIG. 23.—Chart showing the behavior of the factors in the cross illustrated in Fig. 16 (colored and white flowers in peas) and giving the genotypes and phenotypes of parents and F_1, the gametes which they produce, and the random union of F_1 gametes to form the three genotypic and two phenotypic classes of F_2 zygotes shown in the checkerboard.

therefore, be represented by the formula CC; and the pure-breeding white-flowered parent by cc (Fig. 23). This formula applies to every *body cell* of the plant. Of course, it should be borne in mind that here only one of the large number of factor pairs which are actually present is being represented. Now in the cell divisions which just precede the formation of the gametes, cytological research has strikingly confirmed Mendel's assumption that there is a reduction by half in the amount of

[1] The dominant (or more dominant) factor of a pair may be designated by a large letter and the other factor by the corresponding small letter, thus indicating immediately which factors comprise a pair (of alleles).

hereditary material,[1] and it is therefore justifiable to assume that every sexual cell produced is no longer a double structure (like the body cells) but carries just *half* of each of the factor pairs which occur in the parent plant. The gametes of the colored-flowered parent in the illustration would, therefore, be represented by C, and those of the white-flowered parent by c. When these two plants are crossed and an egg, C, is fertilized by a male gamete, c (or vice versa), the genetic formula of the resulting hybrid plant is obviously Cc. Since color is completely dominant here, this plant appears colored flowered, but in its factorial make-up (technically known as its *genotype*, as distinguished from its appearance or *phenotype*) there is present a recessive factor for white. If there were no dominance and the hybrids were intermediate in appearance—pink, perhaps—it would, of course, still be represented by the same genotype. When the two members of a given factor pair are alike (as in the parent plants between which this cross was made), the individual is said to be *homozygous* for the factor in question; when the two members are different (as in this hybrid), it is said to be *heterozygous*. The essence of the phenomenon of segregation lies in the fact that, when this heterozygous individual produces gametes, *these* are not hybrid or heterozygous at all, but half of them are C and half c. Thus the hybrid character of a plant cannot be carried by its gametes, which must be entirely one thing or entirely the other, and are thus *pure*. The factors C and c, brought in from the original red and white parents, have coexisted in the hybrid without influencing each other in the least and have now parted company or become segregated.

In the offspring of these hybrid F_1 plants (derived through either cross- or self-fertilization) appear the characteristic $3/4 : 1/4$ or $1/4 : 1/2 : 1/4$ ratios described, and their occurrence is readily explained if it is assumed that fertilization is a purely random process. The gametes of each hybrid parent, after the reduction and segregation which accompany their origin, are of two sorts, approximately half of them carrying the factor C and the other half the factor c, so that if pollen of a hybrid is placed on the stigma of a hybrid and the fertilization which follows is a free and random union, there are four possible combinations which may result in the offspring produced. C male gametes may fertilize C eggs, forming CC plants; C male gametes may fertilize c eggs, forming Cc plants; c male gametes may fertilize C eggs, also forming Cc plants; or c male gametes may fertilize c eggs, forming cc plants. Each of these combinations, on the basis of pure chance, is just as apt to occur as any other, and each should thus give

---

[1] The chromosomes of the nucleus are in all probability the actual bodies in which the genetic factors are carried, and it has been shown that in the reduction division just preceding the production of gametes the number of chromosomes in the nucleus is halved (p. 164).

rise to approximately one-fourth of the progeny.   The genotypes of the
original parents and of the F_1 and F_2 generations for flower color in peas,
which shows dominance, and for flower color in snapdragons, which does
not, are set forth graphically in Figs. 23 and 24.

Segregation and the Theory of Probability.—Evidence that chance
alone is concerned in determining the various combinations between

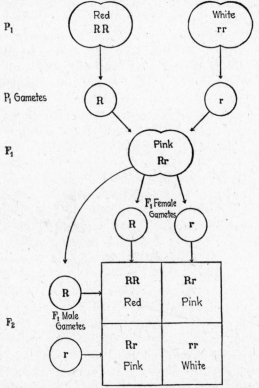

Fig. 24.—Chart showing the behavior of the factors in the cross illustrated in Fig. 17
(red and white flowers in snapdragons) giving the genotypes and phenotypes of parents
and F_1, the gametes which they produce, and the random union of F_1 gametes to form
the three genotypic and three phenotypic classes of F_2 zygotes shown in the checkerboard.

different types of gametes is provided by the similarity between results
obtained in the F_2 ratios and those which should theoretically appear
on the basis of probability.   For example, if a coin is tossed, there is one
chance out of two that it will fall heads and an equal chance that it will
fall tails; or, to express it another way, the tosses will fall about half heads
and half tails.   If *two* coins are tossed *at the same time*, the chance of any
particular combination of such independent events—such as heads with
heads, heads with tails, or tails with tails—may readily be computed by
multiplying the chances of each of the two separate events.   Since for

each coin the chances are one out of two ($\frac{1}{2}$) that heads will be thrown, the chances for heads on both coins at the same throw are one out of four ($\frac{1}{2} \times \frac{1}{2}$). Similarly, the chance for heads on one and tails on the other, for tails on one and heads on the other, or for tails on both is in each case one out of four. On the basis of pure chance, therefore, we may expect in a series of double throws that $\frac{1}{4}$ of the throws will give two heads, $\frac{1}{2}$ the combination of heads and tails, and $\frac{1}{4}$ two tails. This is the ratio obtained in the F_2.

A closer analogy is perhaps provided by thoroughly mixing large but equal numbers of red and white beans and drawing therefrom pairs of beans at random. The chances of making a draw of two red beans simultaneously is thus one out of four; of a red bean and a white one, one out of two; and of two white beans, one out of four. If the mixture represents the gametes of an individual heterozygous for C, the red beans gametes carrying C, and the white ones those carrying c; and if the random drawing of two beans represents the random union of two gametes, the chances of obtaining the various combinations of C and c gametes in the F_2 may be readily computed and are found to be one out of four for CC (homozygous colored), one out of two for Cc (heterozygous colored), and one out of four for cc (white), the result actually obtained.

The Mendelian explanation of this method of inheritance can be put to many tests. What, for instance, should be the result if an F_1 hybrid plant were to be crossed with the recessive white-flowered type? On Mendel's assumption it would be expected that half of the gametes of the hybrid would carry red and the other half white, while all the gametes of the white-flowered plant would carry white. Thus if pollen from the hybrid is placed on the stigma of the white-flowered plant, there is one chance out of two that a "red" male gamete will fertilize a "white" egg (to produce heterozygous red offspring) and one out of two that a "white" male gamete will do so. The expected progeny would thus be red and white plants in equal numbers. Thousands of tests have shown that this result indeed takes place and that a mating between a heterozygous dominant and a recessive may be expected to give offspring of which about half are red and half are white.

Tests of this sort unite in confirming the explanation which Mendel gave for the behavior of unit factors in crosses, and the principle of Segregation is one of the two major contributions made by him to genetic theory. The conception which it gives of the manner in which heritable traits are transmitted from generation to generation has also led in recent years to some remarkable discoveries as to the actual mechanism of inheritance itself, the details of which will be discussed in a later chapter.

Measure of "Goodness of Fit" of a Ratio.—Obviously, the ratios produced by segregating populations in breeding experiments will rarely be exactly the ones that are theoretically expected, and it is important to know whether a given deviation from expectation is due merely to chance or whether some other factor is operating which has caused a really significant departure. To determine this it is useful to calculate *the probable frequency with which a deviation as great as, or greater than, the observed one will appear if another similar trial is made or another similar sample taken.* The higher this frequency is, of course, the less likely is it that the deviation is a significant one, and the more likely is it that the population is really an instance of the particular ratio chosen.

This probability may be found by comparing the size of the deviation from the expected ratio with the size of what is known as the *standard error* of this ratio (*S.E.*$_r$). The standard error of a ratio may be calculated from the following formula:

$$S.E._r = \sqrt{\frac{pq}{n}}$$

where p is one of the theoretical percentages, q the other (necessarily equaling $1 - p$), and n the total number of individuals. We shall discuss the standard error and its significance in a later chapter (p. 147).

Let it be assumed, for example, that in a given F_2 population, where segregation in a ratio of $\frac{3}{4}:\frac{1}{4}$ is expected, there are actually found 390 individuals showing the dominant trait and 110 the recessive. This is a ratio of .78 to .22, and deviates from the expected ratio of .75 to .25 by .03. The standard error for this theoretical proportion will thus be

$$\sqrt{\frac{.75 \cdot .25}{500}} \text{ or } .0194$$

The deviation is therefore 1.55 times as great as its standard error (.03/.0194 = 1.55).

The deviation may also be compared with its standard error in terms of actual numbers by use of the formula

$$S.E._r = \sqrt{\frac{C_1 C_2}{n}}$$

where C_1 is the expected number in one class and C_2 in the other. In the above example these are 375 and 125, so that

$$S.E._r = \sqrt{\frac{375 \cdot 125}{500}} = 9.68$$

The actual deviation is, of course, 15 (390 − 375); as before, it is 1.55 times its standard error (15/9.68 = 1.55).

How frequently a deviation of this relative size may be expected as a result of chance alone can be calculated from a table like that on page 150

(Table XVI), which is based on the character of what is called the *normal* probability curve, and which will be explained more fully in connection with the table itself. The first column of the table gives the relative size of the deviation in terms of its standard error (or standard deviation) and is merely the deviation divided by its error. The third column shows the calculated percentage frequency with which a deviation of this size, or larger, may be expected to occur again under similar circumstances as a result of chance alone. Thus a deviation of 1.6 times its error may be expected in 10.96 per cent of similar cases, and one of 1.55 times its error (the example here given) somewhat more often than this, actually in about 12 per cent of the cases. Such a relationship may also be expressed as one chance out of eight, or the odds against its occurrence may be given as seven to one.

In general, if the deviation of a ratio from expectation is so great that it is more than twice the standard error of this ratio, it is commonly regarded as significant, since in only about 4.5 per cent of similar cases will as great a deviation occur by chance. A segregating population that deviates from a given expected ratio by less than twice its standard error is therefore probably an instance of the ratio in question. The deviation in the example here cited is thus probably not significant, since one as great would be expected 12 per cent of the time; and the population is therefore probably segregating in the ratio of 75:25 per cent, as was expected. The size of a deviation from expectation in proportion to its error may thus be used as a measure of the "goodness of fit" of any observed ratio to any given theoretical expectation. This general subject is discussed again in Chapters IV and VI.

REFERENCES

Reports to the Evolution Committee of the Royal Society. London. 1908. (Contains papers by Bateson, Punnett, Saunders, and others on some of the first confirmations and extensions of Mendel's principles in other animals and plants.)

Castle, W. E. 1930. Genetics and eugenics. 4th ed. Cambridge (Mass.). (See especially lists of Mendelian characters in animals.)

Cuénot, L. 1902. La loi de Mendel et l'hérédité de la pigmentation chez les souris. Arch. Zool. Exper. Gén. (3). 10; (4). 1. 2. 3. 6. 9.

Lang, A. 1914. Die experimentelle Vererbungslehre in der Zoologie seit 1900. Vol. I. Jena. (A review of Mendelian heredity in the higher animals up to 1914.) (See other references at end of Chap. I.)

PROBLEMS

36. What is the chief practical importance of discovering laws of inheritance?

37. Give other examples, similar to those mentioned in the text, of a constant association between two series of phenomena which indicates a "cause-and-effect" relationship between them.

38. Give an example of a group of natural phenomena, the laws governing the behavior of which have not yet been discovered.

39. Give an example of another biological principle which has been found to apply equally well to animals and plants.

40. What advantage has the method of experiment over that of observation alone as a means of studying natural phenomena?

41. Why have the biological sciences been slower to adopt the experimental method of investigation than have the physical sciences?

42. What advantage and what disadvantage have plants over animals as material for the study of heredity?

43. Explain how it can be that individuals which look very much alike breed very differently.

44. Hybrid animals and plants notoriously fail to breed true. Explain.

45. Why is the F_1 between two homozygous parents as uniform as the parents themselves?

46. In human families traits are often observed to "skip" a generation or two. How do you explain this?

47. Which do you think would be easier to handle in breeding, a trait which shows complete dominance or one which does not? Why?

48. What evidence is there that genetic factors occur in the body cells as well as in the gametes?

49. Does Mendelian segregation take place in asexual reproduction? Explain.

50. Why is the principle of Segregation of more fundamental importance than the principle of Dominance?

Note.—In summer squashes white fruit color is dominant over yellow.

51. If a squash plant homozygous for white is crossed with one homozygous for yellow, what will be the appearance of the F_1? of the F_2? of the offspring of a cross of the F_1 back to its white parent? of the offspring of a cross of the F_1 back to its yellow parent?

52. Let the factor for white fruit be represented by W and that for yellow by w. What kind of gametes as to fruit color will be produced by plants of the genotypes WW, Ww, and ww?

53. What gametes will be produced by the plants involved in the following crosses, in which the genotypes of the parents are given, and what will be the fruit color of the offspring from each cross: $Ww \times ww$; $WW \times Ww$; $ww \times WW$; $Ww \times Ww$?

54. A white-fruited squash plant when crossed with a yellow-fruited one produces offspring about half of which are white and half yellow. What are the genotypes of the parents?

55. If the white-fruited parent in the preceding question is self-fertilized, what will be the fruit color of its offspring?

56. If this same white-fruited parent is crossed with one of its white-fruited offspring mentioned in Problem 54 what chance is there of obtaining from this cross a yellow-fruited plant?

57. Two white-fruited squash plants when crossed produce about three-fourths white and one-fourth yellow offspring. What are the genotypes of these two parents? What will each produce if crossed with a yellow-fruited plant?

58. A cross between a white-fruited and a yellow-fruited squash plant produces all white plants. If two of these F_1 white plants are crossed together, what will be the appearance of *their* offspring?

Note.—In guinea pigs, rough or rosetted coat (R) is dominant over smooth (r).

59. If a homozygous rough-coated animal is crossed with a smooth one, what will be the appearance of the F_1? of the F_2? of the offspring of a cross of the F_1 back to its rough parent? to its smooth parent?

60. A certain rough-coated guinea pig bred to a smooth one gives eight rough and seven smooth offspring. What are the genotypes of parents and offspring?

61. If one of the rough F_1 animals in the preceding question is mated to its rough parent, what offspring may be expected?

62. Two rough-coated guinea pigs when bred together produce 18 rough and 4 smooth offspring. What proportion of these rough offspring may be expected to be homozygous for this character?

Note.—The polled or hornless condition in cattle (P) is dominant over the horned (p).

63. A certain polled bull is bred to three cows. With cow A, which is horned, a polled calf is produced; with cow B, also horned, a horned calf is produced; with cow C, which is polled, a horned calf is produced. What are the genotypes of these four animals and what further offspring would you expect from these three matings?

Note.—In man, brown eyes (B) are dominant over blue (b).

64. A brown-eyed man marries a blue-eyed woman and they have eight children, all brown-eyed. What are the genotypes of all the individuals in the family?

65. A blue-eyed man both of whose parents were brown-eyed marries a brown-eyed woman whose father was brown-eyed and whose mother was blue-eyed. They have one child, who is blue-eyed. What are the genotypes of all the individuals mentioned?

66. What are the chances that the first child from a marriage of two heterozygous brown-eyed parents will be blue-eyed? If the first child is brown-eyed, what are the chances that the second child will be blue-eyed?

Note.—In four-o'clock flowers, red flower color (R) is incompletely dominant over white (r), the heterozygous plants being pink-flowered.

67. In the following crosses, in which the genotypes of the parents are given, what are the gametes produced by each parent and what will be the flower color of the offspring from each cross: $Rr \times RR$; $rr \times Rr$; $RR \times rr$; $Rr \times Rr$?

68. If a red-flowered four-o'clock plant is crossed with a white-flowered one, what will be the flower color of the F_1? of the F_2? of the offspring of a cross of the F_1 with its red parent? with its white parent?

69. If you wanted to produce four-o'clock seed *all* of which would yield pink-flowered plants when sown, how would you do it?

Note.—In Andalusian fowls the heterozygous condition of the factors for black plumage (B) and white (b) is blue.

70. If has long been known that blue Andalusian fowls do not breed true to the blue color of their plumage. How do you explain this?

71. What offspring will a blue Andalusian fowl have if bred to birds of the following plumage colors: (1) black; (2) blue; (3) white?

Note.—In poultry, rose comb is dominant over single comb.

72. A farmer believes that some of his rose-combed Wyandotte fowls may carry a factor for single comb. Can you suggest a method for finding out which fowls are heterozygous?

73. Two black female mice are crossed with a brown male. In several litters female 1 produced 9 blacks and 7 browns; female 2 produced 17 blacks. What deductions can you make concerning inheritance of black and brown coat color in mice? What are the genotypes of the parents in this case?

74. A purple-flowered Jimson weed when self-fertilized gives 30 purple-flowered and 9 white-flowered offspring. What can you conclude from this as to the inheritance of flower color in this species? What proportion of the purple-flowered offspring may be expected to breed true to purple?

75. Assume that in a particular species of plants colored flowers are dominant over white ones and that (as in beans) the flowers are *self-fertilized* in nature. Assume that one heterozygous colored-flowered plant, Cc, becomes established on an island where no other individuals of this species exist and that its offspring thrive and multiply there *in great numbers*. Assume also that it is an annual plant and that thus there is no chance for members of one generation to cross with those of another. What will the *fifth* generation of descendants look like as to flower color?

76. Make just the same assumptions as in Problem 75, *except* that the plant in question (like sunflowers and many other plants and animals) is *self-sterile* and must be crossed with another plant to set fertile seed; that two heterozygous plants, Cc and Cc, are the original invaders; and that the individuals of each generation breed freely together. What will the fifth generation of *these* plants look like as to flower color?

77. A given F_2 population consists of 404 A and 129 a individuals. Calculate the deviation of this segregation from a 3:1 ratio, the standard error of this ratio, and the ratio d/SE_r. Is this deviation significant? Does a single-factor segregation satisfactorily explain the result?

78. For each of the three following F_2 populations, determine whether or not it is to be regarded as an instance of a 3:1 ratio.

A	a
870	330
40	20
306	94

Note.—In the following six human pedigrees the individuals which are solid black possess the trait mentioned. Squares represent males and circles females. Determine for each pedigree the *method of inheritance* of the trait in question (whether dominant or recessive); and, as far as possible, determine for that trait the *genotype of each individual* in the pedigree.

79.

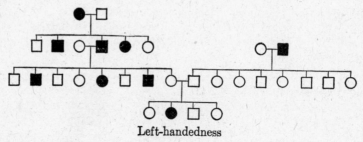

Left-handedness

80.

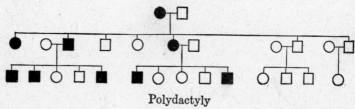

Polydactyly

81.

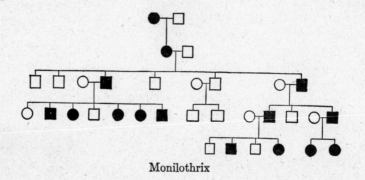

Monilothrix

82.

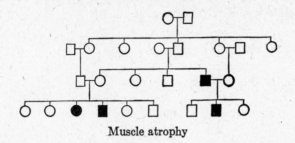

Muscle atrophy

83.

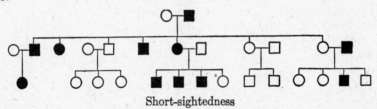

Short-sightedness

84.

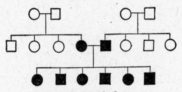

Feeble-mindedness

Note.—In the following four pedigrees, calculate the probability that the trait in question will appear in the offspring of the various matings indicated. Assume that these individuals have had no children and that the only indication as to their genotype is the occurrence of the trait in the pedigree. Assume further (unless there is evidence to the contrary) that individuals who have married into these families and who do not show the trait in question do not carry recessive factors for it.

85.

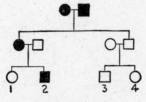

Trait dominant

1 × 3
2 × 4

86.

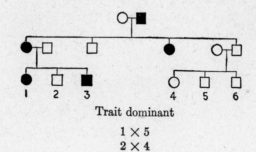

Trait dominant

1 × 5
2 × 4

87.

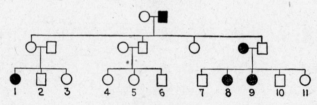

Trait recessive

1 × 6
2 × 4
1 × 7
3 × 10
6 × 11

88.

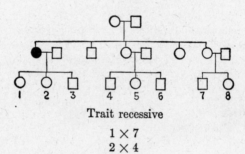

Trait recessive

1 × 7
2 × 4
6 × 8

CHAPTER IV

MENDEL'S LAWS OF INHERITANCE. II

It has been seen that Mendel's genius in studying the inheritance of single characters by themselves led him to a discovery of the principle of segregation, the essential features of which have been discussed in the preceding chapter. This principle is concerned with the hereditary transmission of but one of the many factor pairs which constitute the individual. In most breeding problems, however, it is necessary to be able to follow, not only a single character, but a whole series of them at once and to understand how they behave with relation to each other in their passage from generation to generation.

The Principle of Independent Assortment.—Mendel studied seven pairs of characters in peas, involving seed color, seed surface, flower color, vine height, color of unripe pods, pod shape, and position of flowers. A study of the results of experiments in which plants differing in two or more of these characters were crossed led to his discovery of the second major principle of Mendelian inheritance, namely, "the relation of each pair of different characters in hybrid union is independent of the other differences in the two original parental stocks."

Mendel was led to a recognition of this principle by the results of a cross made between a pea plant having round and yellow seeds and one having wrinkled and green ones.[1] In this case he found, of course, that the F_1 hybrids were all round-seeded and yellow-seeded, since these two characters are both dominant. When two of these F_1 hybrids were crossed, however (or when one of them was self-fertilized), and an F_2 generation raised therefrom, he found that in this generation there appeared not only the two original combinations of characters—round with yellow and wrinkled with green—but two *new* combinations, *round with green* and *wrinkled with yellow*. These four kinds of plants, moreover, were not equal in numbers but appeared in a rather definite ratio, the successful interpretation of which was Mendel's second great contribution to genetic theory. He raised 556 second-generation plants, and the counts which he obtained were as follows:

315 round and yellow.
108 round and green.

[1] Such a cross as this, which involves *two* character differences, is technically known as a *dihybrid* cross.

101 wrinkled and yellow.
32 wrinkled and green.

Considering either of these character pairs *alone*, it is found that approximately three-fourths of the plants show the dominant trait and

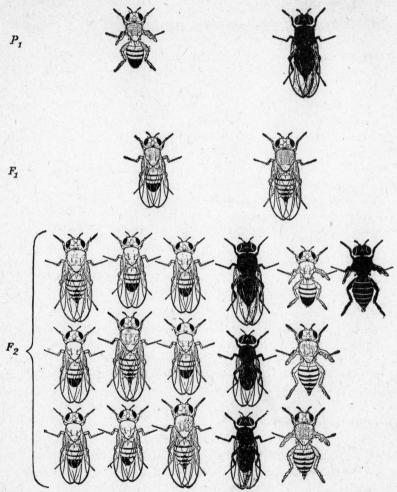

P_1

F_1

F_2

FIG. 25.—The independent inheritance of two pairs of characters in Drosophila. A pure long-winged fly with ebony body mated with a vestigial-winged, gray-bodied one produces all long-winged, gray-bodied flies in F_1. These when inbred produce an F_2 generation consisting of ⁹⁄₁₆ long, gray; ³⁄₁₆ long, ebony; ³⁄₁₆ vestigial, gray; and ¹⁄₁₆ vestigial, ebony. (*From Morgan, Sturtevant, Muller and Bridges, courtesy of Henry Holt & Company.*)

one-fourth show the recessive, as a knowledge of the principle of segregation would lead one to expect. Thus, of the total 556 plants 423, or 76.08 per cent, are round-seeded; 133, or 23.92 per cent, are wrinkled-seeded; 416, or 74.82 per cent, are yellow-seeded; and 140, or 25.18 per cent, are green-seeded.   When both character pairs are considered *together*, however, it is found that the segregation into three-fourths and

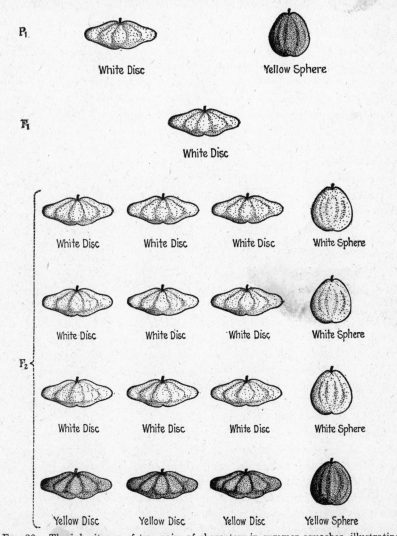

Fig. 26.—The inheritance of two pairs of characters in summer squashes, illustrating Mendel's law of independent assortment.   White is dominant over yellow and "disk" shape over "sphere."   In F_2 there result $\frac{9}{16}$ white, disk; $\frac{3}{16}$ white, sphere; $\frac{3}{16}$ yellow, disk; and $\frac{1}{16}$ yellow, sphere plants.

one-fourth which occurs in each pair when considered alone is *entirely independent* of the similar segregation which takes place in the other pair. Thus, of the three-fourths of the entire group of plants which are round-seeded, approximately three-fourths, in turn, are yellow-seeded and one-fourth are green; and of the other fraction (one-fourth) which are wrinkled-seeded, three-fourths,.again, are yellow-seeded and one-fourth green. This leads to the result that *three-fourths of three-fourths* of the entire number of plants in the F_2 generation, or nine-sixteenths of the entire number of plants, show both dominant characters (round and yellow); *one-fourth of three-fourths*, or three-sixteenths, show one dominant and one recessive (round and green); *three-fourths of one-fourth*, or again three-sixteenths, show the other combinations of dominant and recessive (wrinkled and yellow); and only *one-fourth of one-fourth*, or one-sixteenth, show both recessive characters (wrinkled and green). The counts which Mendel actually obtained in his experiment (315:108:101:32) came very close to these proportions,[1] and he therefore inferred that the second generation from a cross involving two character-pair shows four kinds of individuals, approximately in the ratio of $\frac{9}{16}:\frac{3}{16}:\frac{3}{16}:\frac{1}{16}$, or 9:3:3:1. His results with other characters in peas and similar crosses, which have been made many times by others with various animals and plants, leave no doubt that this ratio is the true one for such dihybrid crosses involving independent characters which show dominance. Similar cases of dihybrid inheritance in Drosophila and squashes are shown in Figs. 25 and 26.

This *independent assortment* of two character pairs is made still more manifest by the fact that the particular combination in which the characters are brought into a cross makes no difference at all in the manner in which they are assorted and recombined in the F_2. In the example cited both dominant characters were brought in by one parent and both recessives by the other, but exactly the same results are obtained in the F_2 if, instead of crossing round and yellow with wrinkled and green, round and green is crossed with wrinkled and yellow. The F_1 is round, yellow; and the F_2 is again $\frac{9}{16}$ round, yellow; $\frac{3}{16}$ round, green; $\frac{3}{16}$ wrinkled, yellow; and $\frac{1}{16}$ wrinkled, green.

Explanation of Independent Assortment.—Perhaps it will be easier to understand what is involved in the principle of independent assortment if the factors are again represented by letters and the genotypes of the various individuals and the gametes which they form are studied in this way. Let the factor for round seeds be represented by R and that for wrinkled seeds by r; and the factor for yellow seeds by Y and for green seeds by y. Mendel's original round, yellow parent plant would thus be represented by the formula $RR\ YY$, and his wrinkled, green plant by $rr\ yy$. It has already been noted that the gametes carry just *half* of the factorial constitution of the parent individual, so that

---

[1] The actual may be compared with the perfect ratio by multiplying the total number of plants, in this case 556, by $\frac{9}{16}$, $\frac{3}{16}$, $\frac{3}{16}$, and $\frac{1}{16}$. The perfect ratio in this case is 312.75:104.25:104.25:34.75.

in this case one parent would produce gametes all of which carried RY; and the other, gametes all of which carried ry; and the resulting F_1 hybrid offspring arising from a union of two of these gametes would consequently have the genotype $Rr\ Yy$. Now the crux of the problem, as in that of segregation, lies in the kinds of gametes produced by this F_1 individual. When the character of seed surface alone is considered, it is found that the $F_1\ Rr$ individual produces gametes half of which carry R and half r. It is clear, however, that every gamete must necessarily contain within itself not only a factor for seed surface but one for seed color as well and, indeed, factors affecting every other character of the plant. Half of these same gametes must, therefore, contain the factor Y and half the factor y; but in any given gamete it seems to be *purely a matter of chance* as to whether the factor for round seeds is associated with that for yellow seeds or with that for green seeds. The particular combination of factors which enters the F_1 plant from each parent (round with yellow and wrinkled with green in this case) has no effect whatever upon the way in which they are associated in the gametes formed by this F_1 plant. *Their assortment is independent.* Of that half of the gametes which carry the factor for round seeds, a half in turn (or a quarter of the whole) carry yellow and a half carry green; and of that half which carry the factor for wrinkled seeds, a half also carry yellow and a half green. The F_1 hybrid may, therefore, be expected to produce four kinds of gametes in approximately equal numbers: $R\ Y$, $R\ y$, $r\ Y$, and $r\ y$.

Now if two such F_1 plants, each of them producing four kinds of gametes, are crossed, there will obviously be 16 possible combinations among their gametes, for there will be four kinds of pollen grains and four kinds of egg cells. The union of these gametes in fertilization is here, too, apparently entirely a random one, any type of pollen grain being as likely to effect fertilization as any other; and any type of egg cell being as likely to be fertilized as any other, no selective preference being exhibited between them. The 16 possible combinations which appear among the F_2 offspring will, therefore, tend to be equally numerous. The parents, F_1, and F_2 of the cross which has been used as an example are represented diagrammatically in Fig. 27 as to both their genotypes and their appearance, the 16 squares in F_2 representing the 16 possible combinations of gametes. A count of these squares makes clear how the 9:3:3:1 ratio arises, for 9 out of these 16 individuals are in appearance round and yellow, 3 are round and green, 3 are wrinkled and yellow, and only 1 is wrinkled and green.

The simplest way to determine the expected combinations produced by random union among gametes is to arrange the gametes from the two sexes on two sides of a checkerboard, as in Fig. 27. In the row of squares

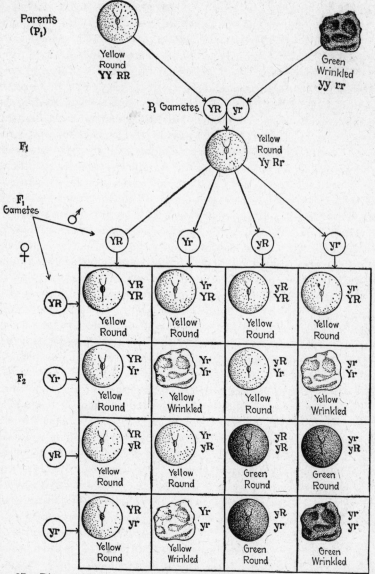

Fig. 27.—Diagram showing the independent assortment in peas of two pairs of characters in which dominance is complete. In a cross between a plant homozygous for yellow and round seeds and a green, wrinkled-seeded one, the appearance, genotype, and gametes of parents and F_1 are shown. The results of random union between the four types of gametes formed by the F_1 heterozygote are presented in the F_2 checkerboard.

from each gamete are written the factors contributed by that gamete. Each square at the intersection of two rows represents the zygote formed by the union of one male and one female gamete, and the genotype and phenotype of each expected type of offspring (16 in this case) may be read directly from the squares.

This principle may perhaps be made a little clearer by a simple comparison. Assume that of all the men in a given country half are brown-eyed and half are blue-eyed, and that half are right-handed and half left-handed. Assume further that there is no connection whatever between these two characters, so that of the brown-eyed men approximately half are right-handed and half left-handed, and of the blue-eyed ones, the same. There will thus be four kinds of male individuals in about equal numbers: the brown-eyed and right-handed, the brown-eyed and left-handed, the blue-eyed and right-handed, and the blue-eyed and left-handed. Finally, assume that the women are divided in just the same way and that in determining what matings shall take place between men and women, eye color and right- and left-handedness play no part whatever, a brown-eyed individual being just as likely to mate with a blue-eyed as with a brown-eyed one, and a right-handed individual with a left-handed as with a right-handed one. The existence of four types of men and four types of women in about equal numbers will thus result in 16 kinds of matings, each as likely to take place as any other, a condition precisely parallel to that which occurs in the union of the four types of gametes of an F_1 dihybrid to form the F_2 generation.

Difference between Genotype and Appearance.—It is obvious, however, that in the F_2 generation the 16 types will not all be *visibly* different, since some of the combinations will look alike, as dominance causes heterozygous individuals to look like homozygous dominant ones. As far as actual appearance goes, therefore, there will be only *four* kinds of individuals instead of 16, and some of these groups will be much more numerous than others.

The way in which new combinations of characters are brought about through hybridization is therefore evident, but it should be remembered that the appearance of many of these F_2 individuals does not give an accurate idea of their genetic constitution, for they may be heterozygous in one or both factors and will therefore not breed true. There are, for example, four kinds of round-seeded and yellow-seeded individuals: those with the genotype *RR YY*, which are homozygous for both round and yellow and will breed true if inbred; those with the genotype *RR Yy*, which are homozygous for round but heterozygous for yellow and will therefore breed true to round but not to yellow; those with the genotype *Rr YY*, which are heterozygous for round and homozygous for yellow and will breed true to yellow but not to round; and those with the genotype *Rr Yy*, which are heterozygous for both and will breed true to neither character but will produce offspring exactly like those of the F₁. A study of the squares in Fig. 27 shows that these four types are not found in equal numbers but in the proportion of 1:2:2:4, respectively. Mendel tested this assumption experimentally and inbred all of his 315 F₂ plants

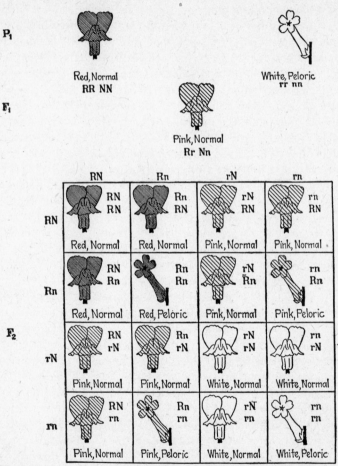

Fig. 28.—Diagram showing the independent inheritance in snapdragons of two pairs of characters, in one of which dominance is complete and in the other of which it is lacking. In a cross between a plant homozygous for red flowers of normal shape and one with white and abnormal (peloric) flowers, the appearance and genotype of parents, F₁, and F₂ are shown.

which bore round and yellow seeds. He obtained offspring from 310 of them, of which 38 produced plants all bearing round and yellow seeds; 65 produced plants all bearing round seeds but some yellow and some green; 60 produced plants all bearing yellow seeds but some round and some wrinkled; and 138 produced plants of all four types.

Of course, it should be borne in mind that the characteristic 9:3:3:1 ratio is to be found only when both characters show complete dominance. If dominance is partial or absent, the heterozygous individuals are different in appearance from the pure ones, and more than four F_2 groups will thus be visibly distinguishable. The results of a dihybrid cross in which one character pair shows complete dominance and the other does not are shown in Fig. 28. The presence or absence of dominance, however, has no bearing whatever on the fundamental fact of the independence of assortment of the factors in the gametes.

The Trihybrid.—When individuals differing in *three* independent characters are crossed, the situation is naturally more complex, but the principle of independent assortment still holds good. If a homozygous round-seeded, yellow-seeded, and colored-flowered pea plant is crossed with a wrinkled-seeded, green-seeded, and white-flowered one, the F_1 hybrids are all, of course, round-seeded, yellow-seeded, and colored-flowered. The F_2, however, will be much more complex than a dihybrid F_2. Since the assortment of these three sets of factors in the gametes is independent, there will evidently be *eight* kinds of gametes: one-half of one-half of one-half, or one-eighth, carrying the factors for round, yellow, and colored; one-eighth those for round, yellow, and white; one-eighth those for round, green, and colored; one-eighth those for round, green, and white; one-eighth those for wrinkled, yellow, and colored; one-eighth those for wrinkled, yellow, and white; one-eighth those for wrinkled, green, and colored; and one-eighth those for wrinkled, green, and white.

In the F_2 generation produced by random union among these eight kinds of gametes there will evidently be 64 equally possible and theoretically equally frequent combinations. As in the dihybrid F_2, many of these will be similar and many others will look just alike but will have different genotypes. These 64 F_2 types, with their appearance and their genotypic constitution, may be presented in a checkerboard which represents the results of a trihybrid cross. A study of such a group shows that there are only eight *visibly different* forms: $27/64$ (or $3/4$ of $3/4$ of $3/4$) have all three dominant characters; three groups each with $9/64$ (or $3/4$ of $3/4$ of $1/4$) show two of the dominants and one of the recessives; three groups each with $3/64$ (or $3/4$ of $1/4$ of $1/4$) show one dominant and two recessives; and only $1/64$ (or $1/4$ of $1/4$ of $1/4$) show all three recessive characters. The ratio of 27:9:9:9:3:3:3:1 is, therefore, typical for such a trihybrid, where all the characters show complete dominance.

As in the monohybrid and dihybrid crosses, many of these F_2 individuals which look alike are quite different genotypically, and will produce very different offspring when inbred (Table IV). Of the $27/64$ which appear round, yellow, and colored, for example, there are eight kinds of plants, each of which will breed differently from the rest. Of course, where one or more of the characters studied show incomplete dominance, so that heterozygous individuals may be distinguished at sight from homozygous ones, the number of visibly different classes will be larger than eight, and the ratio between them will be correspondingly altered.

In the same way, individuals differing in four characters may be brought together in a cross, and in such a case the F_2 is even more complicated than that of a trihybrid, 16 kinds of gametes being produced by the F_1 and 256 possible combinations resulting in the F_2. Crosses of this complexity are rarely worked out in detail and the ratios determined,

TABLE IV.—THE THEORETICAL NUMBER OF INDIVIDUALS, WITH THEIR GENOTYPES AND BREEDING BEHAVIOR, EXPECTED IN F_2 FROM A TRIHYBRID CROSS OF A ROUND, YELLOW-SEEDED, COLORED-FLOWERED VARIETY OF PEAS WITH A WRINKLED, GREEN-SEEDED, WHITE-FLOWERED ONE

Number of individuals	Genotype class	Phenotype class	Ratio of phenotypes	Breeding behavior
1	RR YY CC			Breeds true.
2	Rr YY CC			Segregates round-wrinkled, 3:1.
2	RR Yy CC			Segregates yellow-green, 3:1.
2	RR YY Cc	Round		Segregates colored-white, 3:1.
4	Rr Yy CC	Yellow	27	Segregates round-wrinkled, yellow-green 9:3:3:1.
		Colored		
4	Rr YY Cc			Segregates round-wrinkled, colored-white, 9:3:3:1.
4	RR Yy Cc			Segregates yellow-green, colored-white, 9:3:3:1.
8	Rr Yy Cc			Segregates round-wrinkled, yellow-green, colored-white, 27:9:9:9:3:3:3:1.
1	RR YY cc			Breeds true.
2	RR Yy cc	Round		Segregates yellow-green, 3:1.
2	Rr YY cc	Yellow	9	Segregates round-wrinkled, 3:1.
4	Rr Yy cc	White		Segregates round-wrinkled, yellow-green, 9:3:3:1.
1	RR yy CC			Breeds true.
2	RR yy Cc	Round		Segregates colored-white, 3:1.
2	Rr yy CC	Green	9	Segregates round-wrinkled, 3:1.
4	Rr yy Cc	Colored		Segregates round-wrinkled, colored-white, 9:3:3:1.
1	rr YY CC			Breeds true.
2	rr Yy CC	Wrinkled		Segregates yellow-green, 3:1.
2	rr YY Cc	Yellow	9	Segregates colored-white, 3:1.
4	rr Yy Cc	Colored		Segregates yellow-green, colored-white 9:3:3:1.
1	rr yy CC	Wrinkled		Breeds true.
2	rr yy Cc	Green	3	Segregates colored-white, 3:1.
		Colored		
1	rr YY cc	Wrinkled		Breeds true.
2	rr Yy cc	Yellow	3	Segregates yellow-green, 3:1.
		White		
1	RR yy cc	Round		Breeds true.
2	Rr yy cc	Green	3	Segregates round-wrinkled, 3:1.
		White		
1	rr yy cc	Wrinkled		Breeds true.
		Green	1	
		White		
64				

on account of the very large number of F_2 individuals which must be raised. In actual practice, however, individuals differing in more than four characters are often crossed, and although a large and representative F_2 may not be grown, it is often useful to understand how frequently a particular combination of traits might be expected to appear in such an F_2 and thus to be able to estimate the probability of its occurrence in a given number of F_2 individuals which might be raised.

A study of these complex crosses brings out several points which should be kept in mind. First, as the number of characters involved in a given cross increases, the number of possible character combinations in the F_2 increases greatly, every added character pair multiplying the number of possible combinations by four, the number of genotypically different combinations by three, and the number of visibly different combinations (when dominance is complete) by two, as indicated by the accompanying table (V). Second, as the number of characters involved increases, the chance of recovering one of the original parent types in the F_2 grows rapidly less. When a single factor pair is involved, one in 4 of the F_2 will resemble one of the original parents in appearance and genotype; when two factors are involved, 1 in 16; when three, 1 in 64; when four, 1 in 256; and so on. The generalized formula for determining the number of visibly different classes, of different kinds of gametes, of genotypically different combinations, and of possible combinations of F_1 gametes in crosses involving a known number of factor pairs is shown in the last line of Table V.

TABLE V.—THE RELATION BETWEEN THE NUMBER OF FACTOR PAIRS INVOLVED IN A CROSS AND THE NUMBER OF PHENOTYPIC AND GENOTYPIC CLASSES IN F_2

Number of factor pairs involved in the cross	Number of visibly different F_2 classes of individuals if dominance is complete	Number of different kinds of gametes formed by the F_1 hybrid	Number of genotypically different combinations	Number of possible combinations of F_1 gametes
1	2	2	3	4
2	4	4	9	16
3	8	8	27	64
4	16	16	81	256
n	2^n	2^n	3^n	4^n

A study of the assortment and recombination of factors which go on in the F_2 when more than one factor pair is involved makes it clear how readily new character combinations are formed and emphasizes the importance of hybridization as a cause of increased variation, a fact which has already been noted in the discussion of variation. A thorough

TABLE VI.—VALUES OF P (TOP LINE) FOR VARIOUS VALUES OF CHI SQUARE (VERTICAL COLUMNS) AND FOR VARIOUS DEGREES OF FREEDOM (N')

The degrees of freedom are one less than the number of classes

(From R. A. Fisher, "Statistical Methods for Research Workers," by permission of author and publishers, Messrs. Oliver and Boyd.)

N'	P = 0.99	0.98	0.95	0.90	0.80	0.70	0.50	0.30	0.20	0.10	0.05	0.02	0.01
1	0.00016	0.00063	0.0039	0.016	0.064	0.148	0.455	1.074	1.642	2.706	3.841	5.412	6.635
2	0.0201	0.0404	0.103	0.211	0.446	0.713	1.386	2.408	3.219	4.605	5.991	7.824	9.210
3	0.115	0.185	0.352	0.584	1.005	1.424	2.366	3.665	4.642	6.251	7.815	9.837	11.341
4	0.297	0.429	0.711	1.064	1.649	2.195	3.357	4.878	5.989	7.779	9.488	11.668	13.277
5	0.554	0.752	1.145	1.610	2.343	3.000	4.351	6.064	7.289	9.236	11.070	13.388	15.086
6	0.872	1.134	1.635	2.204	3.070	3.828	5.348	7.231	8.558	10.645	12.592	15.033	16.812
7	1.239	1.564	2.167	2.833	3.822	4.671	6.346	8.383	9.803	12.017	14.067	16.622	18.475
8	1.646	2.032	2.733	3.490	4.594	5.527	7.344	9.524	11.030	13.362	15.507	18.168	20.090
9	2.088	2.532	3.325	4.168	5.380	6.393	8.343	10.656	12.242	14.684	16.919	19.679	21.666
10	2.558	3.059	3.940	4.865	6.179	7.267	9.342	11.781	13.442	15.987	18.307	21.161	23.209

understanding of the principles which are concerned in this process renders it easy to control and to predict the appearance of new types of animals and plants and is one of the chief contributions which the science of genetics has made to the art of practical breeding.

The "Chi-square" Method for Testing Goodness of Fit.—Where a segregating population falls into three or more classes, it is impossible to determine how closely it fits a given theoretical expectation by using the method, described in the previous chapter, of comparing the deviation with its standard error, for there may be several deviations. Instead, biometricians have measured goodness of fit by calculating χ^2 (chi square), and from this determining the probability that a deviation as great or greater will occur by chance. χ^2 is obtained by squaring the deviation of each class from the theoretical expectation for that class, dividing this by the theoretical expectation for that class, and adding together the results from all classes. By means of a table originally calculated by Elderton and presented in a more simplified form by Fisher (Table VI), it is possible to obtain for a given value of χ^2 and a given number of classes, the value of P, which measures the probability that a deviation as great or greater will occur by chance; or in other words the percentage of cases in which such a deviation may be expected by chance.

If, for example, in a given F_2 population where segregation in the proportions of $\frac{9}{16}$ AB, $\frac{3}{16}$ Ab, $\frac{3}{16}$ aB, and $\frac{1}{16}$ ab is expected, there actually occur 456 AB, 155 Ab, 141 aB, and 48 ab, the theoretical expectation would evidently be 450 AB, 150 Ab, 150 aB, and 50 ab. The derivation of χ^2 for this population and ratio is as follows:

	AB	Ab	aB	ab
Actual numbers............................	456	155	141	48
Theoretical expectation on 9:3:3:1 (e).......	450	150	150	50
Deviation from expectation (d)..............	6	5	9	2
d^2..	36	25	81	4
d^2/e......................................	.080	.166	.540	.080

Total (sum of d^2/e) = .866 = χ^2

Consultation of Table VI shows that in a population of four classes a value for χ^2 of .866 means that P will have a value of between .80 and .90, or in other words that in from 80 to 90 per cent of similar cases as great or a greater deviation from a 9:3:3:1 ratio would be found, and that the present population therefore fits that ratio very well. If χ^2 had exceeded 7.81, we should expect as poor a fit in only 5 per cent of similar cases, and when the probability is as low as this, we ordinarily regard the fit as too poor to be explained by chance alone and suspect some other factor to be responsible.

It will be noted that in Table VI the value of N', designating the "degree of freedom," is always one less than the number of segregating classes. This is due to the fact that in calculations of this sort, where a series of classes are involved, the size of the final class cannot be a matter of chance, since it must include everything that is left over. Its size is thus already fixed, and it is not "free" to vary as the others are. In cases like the present one (and most genetic problems) the number of classes is always one more than the degrees of freedom, but in other biometrical problems there may be a greater difference, and the table is therefore more generally useful if the degrees of freedom rather than the class numbers are stated.

The χ^2 method can, of course, be used to measure goodness of fit where there are only two classes, instead of the method of the standard error of the ratio as previously described. It may be employed in all sorts of modified ratios and is of much value in determining which ratio a given segregating population fits best; for this is the one which will give the smallest value of χ^2, and thus the largest value for P, when the ratio of the actual population is compared with it.

Later Modifications of Mendel's Laws.—The dramatic rediscovery of Mendel's work in 1900 and the recognition of its great importance for an understanding of heredity led immediately to an eager study of other animals and plants by many investigators in an endeavor to determine how wide was the application of these generalizations. The number of students of genetics has since increased steadily from year to year, and this field of investigation is now one of the most active in all biology. Hundreds of species have been studied and thousands of breeding experiments performed. As a result there is now a great mass of facts with regard to the manner of inheritance of all sorts of traits in plants and animals and in man himself, and we are now in a far better position to formulate laws of inheritance than was Mendel. Perhaps the most striking result of all this activity has been to establish the essential soundness of Mendel's major conclusions. Many modifications and amplifications in matters of detail have been made, however, and at least one new major principle has been discovered. These matters will be discussed in later chapters but should be briefly mentioned here.

Variability of Factor Expression.—It has been noted that Mendel did not distinguish clearly between the visible *character* and the fundamental *factor* which produced it. Many cases have been observed, however, in which individuals of exactly the same factorial constitution may differ greatly in their appearance if they have developed under different environments. Examples of such variations due solely to the environment were present in a previous chapter. The principles of Mendel, therefore, are applied today to the factors which form the genetic constitution of the individual rather than to the characters or traits which are their visible expressions.

All the characters which Mendel studied showed complete dominance, but many instances have since been found in which dominance is only partial or is absent, factors in a heterozygous condition expressing themselves differently from homozygous recessives or dominants.

Still more important are the many instances now known in which various factors interact upon one another in such a way that the characters produced are markedly affected. The classic example of this is the comb form of poultry. If the factor for "rose" comb and that for "pea" comb are united in a cross, the resulting offspring have combs which are neither rose nor pea but an entirely different type, "walnut." In the same way the kernel color of corn may be affected by a whole series of factors, each of which has some influence upon the others. Whether these mutual effects are due to fairly simple chemical phenomena or are more complex in their causes is not known.

Geneticists today have abandoned the earlier idea that a single factor determines but a single character of the individual, for in many instances a factor which is known from breeding tests to be a single unit is found to affect many different characters. Furthermore, although the essential unity and separateness of genetic factors in *inheritance* have been fully established, the conception that in *development* each produces its effects more or less independently of all the rest has given place to the idea that each factor, although a specific and differentiating unit, operates against the background of the entire genetic complex of the individual.

The Linkage of Factors.—Perhaps the most important modification of mendelism and one which should rank with Segregation and Independent Assortment as a third major law of inheritance is the principle of *Linkage* between factors. As previously mentioned, Mendel noted the independence which different factor pairs displayed in inheritance. As long as only a few characters in a given species were studied, this principle was found to be universally valid, but early in the course of Mendelian investigations cases began to be reported where two or more characters, introduced into a cross together, tended to stay together or to remain "linked" in their passage from generation to generation, rather than to show that independence of assortment assumed by Mendel. These were at first regarded as exceptional instances, and various hypotheses were put forward to account for their occurrence. It was not until the researches of Morgan and his associates on Drosophila began that a logical explanation for the whole matter was obtained. They noted that in this species there are four groups of factor pairs within each of which the factors tended to stay together or remain "linked" in inheritance. Characters belonging to different groups showed typical Mendelian independence of assortment. It was then observed that in the nuclei of the cells of Drosophila there are four pairs of *chromosomes*, and the idea was developed that the chromosomes are the actual physical seat of the genetic factors. The number of these bodies determines the number of groups of factors, and all factors within a given chromosome tend to be linked in inheritance. Furthermore, Morgan and his coworkers were able to ascertain with approximate accuracy the point on the chromosome which a given factor occupies and in this way have made a significant contribution to a knowledge of the structure of chromosomes and of living substance in general. The evidence on which these conclusions are based is somewhat involved and will be discussed in detail later. It is being gathered from many animals and plants besides Drosophila and has now firmly established what was at first a brilliant hypothesis as one of the important principles of inheritance.

References will be found at the ends of Chaps. III and VI.

PROBLEMS

Note.—In the summer squash, white fruit (W) is dominant over yellow (w); and "disk" fruit shape (D) is dominant over "sphere" shape (d).

89. In a cross between a squash plant homozygous for yellow fruit color and disk fruit shape and one homozygous for white fruit color and sphere fruit shape, what will be the appearance, as to color and shape of fruit, of the F_1? of the F_2? of the offspring of a cross of the F_1 with the yellow, disk parent? with the white, sphere parent?

90. What are the gametes formed by the following squash plants, the genotypes of which for fruit color and shape are given; and what will be the appearance of the offspring from each cross?

$WW\ dd \times ww\ DD$ $Ww\ Dd \times Ww\ dd$
$Ww\ DD \times ww\ dd$ $Ww\ Dd \times ww\ dd$
$Ww\ Dd \times Ww\ DD$ $Ww\ Dd \times Ww\ Dd$

Note.—In the following six questions, all of which deal with fruit color and shape in summer squash, the appearance of parents and offspring is stated. Determine in each case the genotypes of the parents.

91. White, disk crossed with yellow, sphere gives one-half white, disk and one-half white, sphere.

92. White, sphere crossed with white, sphere gives three-fourths white, sphere and one-fourth yellow, sphere.

93. White, disk crossed with yellow, sphere gives one-fourth white, disk; one-fourth white, sphere; one-fourth yellow, disk; and one-fourth yellow sphere.

94. White, disk crossed with white, sphere gives three-eighths white, disk; three-eighths white, sphere; one-eighth yellow, disk; and one-eighth yellow, sphere.

95. Yellow, disk crossed with white, sphere gives all white, disks.

96. White, disk crossed with white, disk gives 28 white, disk plants; 9 white, sphere plants; 10 yellow, disk plants; and 3 yellow, sphere plants.

97. A cross between a plant with white, disk fruits and one with yellow, sphere fruits gives 25 plants with white, disk fruits; 26 with white, sphere; 24 with yellow, disk; and 25 with yellow, sphere. If the white, disk parent is self-fertilized, what proportion of its offspring will have yellow, sphere fruits?

Note.—In guinea pigs, rough coat (R) is dominant over smooth coat (r); and black coat (B) is dominant over white (b).

98. Cross a homozygous rough, black animal with a smooth, white one. What will be the appearance of the F_1? of the F_2? of the offspring of a cross of the F_1 back with the rough, black parent? with the smooth, white one?

99. In the F_2 generation in the preceding question, what proportion of the rough, black individuals may be expected to be homozygous for both characters?

100. A rough, black guinea pig bred with a rough, white one gives 28 rough, black; 31 rough, white; 11 smooth, black; and 9 smooth, white. What are the genotypes of the parents?

101. Two rough, black guinea pigs when bred together have two offspring, one of them rough, white and the other smooth, black. If these same parents were to be bred together further, what offspring would you expect from them?

Note.—In Jimson weeds, purple flower color (P) is dominant over white (p); and spiny pods (S) over smooth (s).

102. A purple, smooth Jimson weed plant crossed with a white, spiny one gives 320 purple, spiny and 312 purple, smooth. If these two types of offspring are bred together, what will *their* offspring be like, both as to appearance and as to genotypes?

103. Make the two following crosses in Jimson weeds; (1) homozygous purple, spiny with white, smooth; and (2) homozygous purple, smooth with white, smooth. Cross the F_1 of cross 1 with the F_1 of cross 2. What will be the appearance of their offspring?

Note.—In poultry, feathered legs (F) are dominant over clean legs (f); and pea comb (P) over single comb (p).

104. Two cocks A and B are bred to two hens C and D. All four birds are feathered-legged and pea-combed. Cock A with both hens produces offspring which are all feathered and pea. Cock B with hen C produces both feathered and clean but all pea-combed; but with hen D produces all feathered but part pea-combed and part single. What are the genotypes of these four birds?

105. The offspring of a feathered-legged, pea-combed cock bred to a clean-legged, pea-combed hen are all feathered-legged. Most of them are pea-combed, but some singles appear among them. What are the genotypes of the parents? What would be the offspring expected from a cross of this hen with one of her feathered-legged, single-combed male offspring?

106. In swine, white coat is dominant over black and the "mule-footed" condition over that with normal feet. A white, mule-footed boar, A, always produces white, mule-footed offspring, no matter to what sow he is bred. Another boar B, however, also white and mule-footed, when bred to black sows produces about half white and half black offspring; and when bred to normal-footed sows, about half mule-footed and half normal offspring. Explain this difference between these two animals by comparing their genotypes for these two traits.

Note.—In man assume that brown eyes (B) are dominant over blue (b); and right-handedness (R) over left-handedness (r).

107. A right-handed, blue-eyed man whose father was left-handed marries a left-handed, brown-eyed woman from a family in which all the members have been brown-eyed for several generations. What offspring may be expected from this marriage as to the two traits mentioned?

108. A brown-eyed, right-handed man marries a blue-eyed, right-handed woman. Their first child is blue-eyed and left-handed. If other children are born to this couple, what will probably be their appearance as to these two traits?

109. A right-handed, blue-eyed man marries a right-handed, brown-eyed woman. They have two children, one left-handed and brown-eyed and the other right-handed and blue-eyed. By a later marriage with another woman who is also right-handed and brown-eyed, this man has nine children, all of whom are right-handed and brown-eyed. What are the genotypes of this man and his two wives?

Note.—In cattle the polled condition (P) is dominant over the horned (p); and in Shorthorns the heterozygous condition of red coat (R) and white coat (r) is roan.

110. If a homozygous polled, white animal is bred to a horned, red one, what will be the appearance of the F_1? of the F_2? of the offspring of a cross of the F_1 with the polled, white parent? with the horned, red parent?

111. A polled, roan bull bred to a horned, white cow produces a horned, roan daughter. If this daughter is bred to her father, what offspring may be expected as to horns and coat color?

Note.—In snapdragons red flower color (R) is incompletely dominant over white (r), the heterozygous condition being *pink;* and normal broad leaves (B) are incompletely dominant over narrow, grasslike ones (b), the heterozygous condition being intermediate in leaf breadth.

112. If a red-flowered, broad-leaved plant is crossed with a white-flowered, narrow-leaved one, what will be the appearance of the F_1 and the F_2?

Note.—In garden peas, tall vine (T) is dominant over dwarf (t); green pods (G) over yellow (g); and round seed (R) over wrinkled seed (r).

113. If a homozygous dwarf, green, wrinkled pea plant is crossed with a homozygous tall, yellow, round one, what will be the appearance of the F_1? What gametes does the F_1 form? What is the appearance of the F_2? What is the appearance of the offspring of a cross of the F_1 with its dwarf, green, wrinkled parent? with its tall, yellow, round parent?

114. What will be the appearance of the offspring of the following crosses, in which the genotypes of the parents are given?

$$TT\,Gg\,Rr \times tt\,Gg\,rr \qquad\qquad tt\,gg\,Rr \times Tt\,Gg\,rr$$
$$Tt\,GG\,Rr \times Tt\,Gg\,Rr \qquad\qquad Tt\,Gg\,rr \times tt\,Gg\,Rr$$

Note.—In the following four questions, all of which concern garden peas, find the genotypes of the parents as to vine height, pod color, and seed shape:

115. A tall, yellow, round plant crossed with a dwarf, green, round one produces offspring three-eighths of which are tall, green, and round; three-eighths dwarf, green, and round; one-eighth tall, green, and wrinkled; and one-eighth dwarf, green, and wrinkled.

116. A tall, green, wrinkled plant crossed with a dwarf, green, round one produces offspring three-fourths of which are tall, green, and round and one-fourth of which are tall, yellow, and round.

117. A tall, green, round plant crossed with a tall, yellow, round one produces 26 tall, green, round offspring; 10 tall, green, wrinkled; 9 dwarf, green, round; and 3 dwarf, green, wrinkled.

118. A tall, yellow, round plant crossed with a dwarf, green, round one produces 58 tall, green, round offspring; 61 tall, yellow, round ones; 62 dwarf, green, round ones; 59 dwarf, yellow, round ones; 19 tall, green, wrinkled ones; 20 tall, yellow, wrinkled ones; 21 dwarf, green, wrinkled ones; and 20 dwarf, yellow, wrinkled ones.

119. In tomatoes, red fruit is dominant over yellow, two-loculed fruit over many-loculed, and tall vine over dwarf. A breeder has pure races of red, two-loculed, dwarf plants and of yellow, many-loculed, tall ones. He wants a race of red, many-loculed, tall plants. If he crosses his two races and raises an F_1 and an F_2, what proportion of this F_2 will be, in appearance, the type he desires? What proportion of these will be homozygous for all three characters? How can he determine which are the homozygous plants?

120. In poultry, the white plumage of Leghorns is dominant over colored plumage, feathered shanks over clean, and pea comb over single. If a homozygous white, feathered, pea bird is crossed with a colored, clean, single one, what proportion of the white, feathered, pea birds in the F_2 from this cross will prove to be homozygous if mated to colored, clean, single birds?

121. In snapdragons normal flowers are dominant over peloric ones and tallness over dwarfness. Red flower color is incompletely dominant over white, the heterozygous condition being pink. If a homozygous red, tall, normal-flowered plant is crossed with a homozygous, white, dwarf, peloric-flowered one, what proportion of the F_2 will resemble the F_1 in appearance?

122. If one individual is homozygous for four dominant factors and another for their four recessive alleles, and if these two individuals are crossed, what proportion of the F_2 from this cross will resemble each parent, respectively, in appearance?

123. By finding the values of χ^2 and P, determine how closely each of the four following F_2 populations fits a 9:3:3:1 ratio. Which are to be regarded as examples of this ratio and which are not?

AB	Ab	aB	ab
51	11	16	2
860	315	340	117
75	35	41	9
1,770	610	618	202

124. Determine the goodness of fit of the following F_2 population to a 3:1 ratio, using both the standard error and the χ^2 methods. Which do you think is the more satisfactory method to use in such a case and why?

$$A \qquad a$$
$$1,182 \qquad 418$$

CHAPTER V

THE EXPRESSION AND INTERACTION OF FACTORS

Mendel's great contribution to genetics was the idea that the organism develops under the influence of an aggregation of separable units which segregate and recombine in the gametes according to certain definite laws. The laws which Mendel himself framed, however, and which have been discussed in the preceding chapter, were based on the study of a few simple cases of inheritance, and in presenting them the matter and the method of inheritance have been reduced to the simplest possible terms. Later research soon discovered that the phenomena of heredity and variation were by no means so simple as these particular examples and that the principles which Mendel established, while fundamental to all inheritance, are not alone sufficient to explain all the detailed facts.

The conception of the individual as a group of unit factors, each producing a single invariable character and each entirely independent of the others, is far too simple, for experience has shown that the same factor often produces a variety of effects on many characters under different external or internal conditions. Each "character" is more complex than Mendel imagined it; and many factors, although *inherited* as independent units, are far from independent in their *expression*, but often interact upon one another in producing the actual bodily traits. Some of the ways in which the genes influence the characters of the organism will be discussed in more detail in Chapter XVI, which deals with genetics and development. Here we shall list some of the complexities which result from the interaction of factors, particularly as these affect the visible results of segregation and independent assortment.

Dominance.—One influence in determining to what degree a given factor shall express itself seems to inhere in its relation to the other member of the allelic pair of which it forms a part. In cases of apparently complete dominance one factor seems to have as great an effect as two, while in cases of incomplete dominance the two members of the pair seem to have equal effects and produce a blended or intermediate condition, as in the Andalusian fowl and many similar cases. However, no sharp distinction between complete or incomplete dominance is possible, since careful examination often discloses some effect of the apparently recessive condition. The dominance of round over wrinkled in peas seems to be complete, yet microscopic examination shows that the starch grains of

85

the hybrid are intermediate in several respects between those of the parent types. Many cases are known in which factors have a dominant effect on one set of characters but a recessive effect on others. In some cases each member of a pair of factors produces its own effect independently, and the heterozygote is thus neither a blend nor an intermediate but a mosaic.

The accumulated evidence of genetics shows that there are all degrees of dominance and that there is no general rule or law. It is obvious now that dominance is not a simple matter but that it is affected by various external influences and by the age, sex, and other internal conditions of the individual as well as by other genetic factors.

Influence of External Conditions.—In the Jimson weed (Datura) purple stem color is completely dominant over green, if the heterozygous plants are grown out of doors in the summer. In the greenhouse in winter the heterozygotes are distinguishable from the homozygous purple plants by the paler color. The hybrids between a red- and an ivory-flowered snapdragon may be red if grown in bright light and at a low temperature; ivory, if kept in a shaded, warm place; or intermediate in color, under intermediate conditions.

Influence of Internal Conditions.—Some factors appear to be dominant in one sex but recessive in the other. In some breeds of sheep, males with a single gene for the hornless condition (heterozygotes) are horned, while females of the same genetic constitution are hornless. The horned condition behaves as dominant in males and recessive in females. Baldness in man is said to be inherited in a similar fashion.

Occasionally a factor may appear to have a recessive effect in young heterozygotes but a dominant one at some later stage. The difference between left (sinistral) and right (dextral) coiling in snails appears to depend chiefly on a single pair of genes. The heterozygote may be either dextral or sinistral depending on the character of the mother for this trait, since the direction of coiling is maternally determined. Such heterozygotes, however, produce only *dextral* offspring, thus proving that the dextral condition is dominant although the dominant effect has here been delayed for a whole generation.

Of greater importance and more general occurrence are the effects of other genetic factors upon dominance. Thus the factor for forked bristles in Drosophila ordinarily behaves as a recessive but in the presence of one other independent factor may act as a partial dominant. The short-tailed mutation behaves as a dominant in most strains of the European house mouse but as nearly a complete recessive when introduced into the Asiatic house mouse. So many cases of this sort have been described that it may be said that the degree of dominance depends generally on the whole genetic constitution of the animal and on the conditions of its development and is not a property of single factor pairs. Dominance appears thus to be a question of development and will be so discussed later.

Factor Interaction.—It is a general rule that single factors do not produce their effects alone but in cooperation with the other factors of the organism. There are many clear cases in which factors belonging to *different* pairs, although inherited independently, act together in producing a given character, which thus appears to depend not on one factor but on an interaction between two or more of these.

Combs in Fowls.—The first case of this kind was discovered a number of years ago by Bateson and Punnett, during the course of experiments on the inheritance of comb form in fowls. Each of the common varieties of poultry possess a characteristic type of comb. The Wyandotte breed, among others, has a low, regular, papillate comb known as the "rose" comb; Brahmas and some of the varieties of game fowls have a narrower, higher, three-ridged comb known as the "pea" comb; while Leghorns and breeds of similar origin have "single" combs, consisting of a single upright blade. Each of these types can be bred quite true (Fig. 29). Crosses made experimentally between rose-combed and single-combed varieties showed that rose was dominant over single and that there was a clear segregation into three-fourths rose and one-fourth single in the F_2. In crosses between pea-combed and single-combed birds, pea comb was also found to be dominant over single, and a simple $3:1$ ratio appeared in the F_2. A new and interesting result, however, was obtained when rose was crossed with pea, for the F_1 birds showed a new comb form different from either the rose or the pea. This was known as "walnut" comb from its resemblance to half of a walnut meat and had previously been noted as characteristic of the Malay breeds of fowls, a race unrelated to the types from which the new walnut comb was obtained. When the F_1 walnut-combed birds were bred together, a still more remarkable result was manifest, for in the F_2 generation there appeared not only walnut-, rose-, and pea-combed fowls but *single-combed* ones as well. After large numbers of F_2 birds had been bred and classified, it was found that these types occurred in the following proportions: $\frac{9}{16}$ walnut, $\frac{3}{16}$ rose, $\frac{3}{16}$ pea, $\frac{1}{16}$ single.

This was recognized as the ratio to be expected in F_2 from a cross of parents differing in *two* factors. The doubly dominant class in F_2 was apparently walnut, while the numbers of singles obtained indicated that this type contained both of the recessive factors involved, a conclusion supported by the fact that the F_2 singles when bred together produced only single-combed progeny in subsequent generations. The following explanation of these results was offered: The walnut comb depends on the presence of *two* dominant factors, R and P. One of these

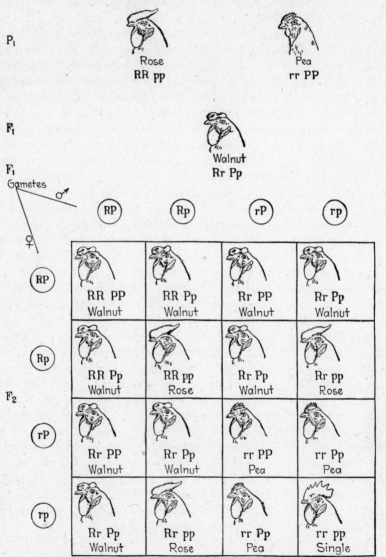

FIG. 29.—Diagram showing interaction of factors for comb form in fowls. The cross of a pure rose-comb bird with a pure pea-comb one gives all walnut-combed offspring. The 16 possible combinations of the F_1 gametes, with their genotypes and the phenotypes resulting from factor interaction, are shown in the F_2 checkerboard.

factors alone (R) produces the rose comb; the other alone (P) produces the pea comb. The combination of the recessive alleles of these factors produces the single type of comb *rp*. These assumptions are illustrated in the diagram in Fig. 29.[1]

The similarity between the F_2 results in this diagram and the common two-factor case explained on page 65 will be readily noticed. The mode of inheritance of the factors for rose and pea does not differ at all from the usual Mendelian scheme, for they display complete independence of assortment. The differences which distinguish this and similar cases from ordinary dihybrid inheritance are that (1) the F_1 resembles neither parent and (2) *two new types* appear in F_2. One of these new characters (walnut comb), therefore, evidently results from an interaction between two independently inherited dominant factors, while the other (single comb) results from the interaction of their two recessive alleles. These peculiarities are not due to a new method of inheritance but simply to the circumstance that both factors involved happen to express themselves in the same part of the organism, in this case the comb.

Fruit Shape in Squashes.—In the summer squash, *Cucurbita Pepo*, races breeding true to different fruit shapes have been isolated. The spherical form behaves as a recessive to the flat or disk form (Fig. 26). A cross of two spherical-fruited races from different ancestry, however, produced in F_1 only *disk*-fruited offspring, and in F_2 *three* types of plants appeared: nine-sixteenths with disk fruits, six-sixteenths with spherical fruits, and one-sixteenth with *elongate* fruits. This ratio shows that two pairs of factors are involved. Interaction between the two dominant alleles gives rise to disk and between the two recessives produces the new combination elongate, while either factor alone results in the sphere shape. Thus:

P_1	Sphere	$\times$	Sphere
	$AAbb$		$aaBB$
F_1		Disk	
		$AaBb$	
F_2 $\frac{9}{16}$ Disk	$\frac{3}{16}$ Sphere	$\frac{3}{16}$ Sphere	$\frac{1}{16}$ Elongate
$A(a)B(b)^2$	$A(a)bb$	$aaB(b)$	$aabb$

The peculiarities here are (1) the resemblance of F_1 to neither parent, (2) the appearance of *one* new type in F_2, and (3) the phenotypic resemblance of two different genotypes in F_2. As in the case of comb form, the factors affect the same character, which is thus influenced by an interaction between two pairs of independent factors.

[1] The checkerboard scheme in this diagram, which is similar to that employed in the study of a simple dihybrid, is a useful means of finding the various genotypes resulting from combinations of the gametes formed by complex heterozygotes of this sort. The relative proportions of the different types of individuals to be expected may be read off directly.

[2] Factor symbols enclosed in parentheses represent alternative genotypes. Thus $A(a)$ indicates that the genotype may be either AA or Aa.

Flower Color in Sweet Peas (Complementary Factors).—A similar type of interaction has been found between two factors affecting flower color in the sweet pea (*Lathyrus odoratus*). This plant occurs in a number of true-breeding varieties, all descended from the wild sweet pea of Sicily, which bears a purple flower with red wings. While studying a number of the different cultivated varieties, Bateson and Punnett found that purple flower color is dominant over white and gives a typical 3:1 ratio in the F_2. They also observed that the white types bred true, as was to be expected, and that crosses between white varieties usually produced white-flowered progeny. In one instance, however, where two pure white varieties were crossed, there resulted quite unexpectedly no white offspring at all but only *colored-flowered* plants. The flowers of these F_1 hybrids were very similar in color to the wild Sicilian ancestor of the cultivated sweet pea. When such purple-flowered F_1 plants were self-fertilized, they produced an F_2 generation consisting of about nine-sixteenths purple-flowered plants and seven-sixteenths white-flowered ones. All the F_2 white individuals bred true when self-fertilized. The purples, however, were evidently of several different types, for a few bred true; others produced colored- and white-flowered plants in the proportion of three-fourths colored to one-fourth white; while still others produced offspring of which about nine-sixteenths were colored and seven-sixteenths white.

This result, like the inheritance of comb shape, may also be explained by segregation of two independent factor pairs, but the type of interaction between them is somewhat different, for no new traits appear in the F_1 or F_2. The fact that purple flower color occurs in nine-sixteenths of the F_2 plants suggests that it appears only when two independent dominant factors are present together and that it results from some sort of interaction between them. White flower color may thus evidently be due to the absence of either or both of these factors. Denoting one of the factors by C (color) and the other by P (purple), it may be assumed that one white parent was of the genotype $CC\ pp$ while the other was $cc\ PP$. Neither the color factor alone nor the purple factor alone is, by this assumption, able to cause the production of color in the flowers. The cross between two such white types produces the heterozygote $Cc\ Pp$, which bears colored flowers, since it contains both the factors for color and purple. When this hybrid forms its gametes, the factors C and P segregate independently, and the gametes formed may be written CP, Cp, cP, and cp. The combinations between these types of gametes and the resulting flower colors of the F_2 plants are shown in Fig. 30.

The ratio here is obviously the normal $9:3:3:1$ expected in F_2 when the parents differ in two factors, but with the last three terms added together ($9:7$). The peculiarity of this ratio arises from the fact that *all* plants which lack either factor are white, regardless of the condition as to the other factor. Thus three F_2 plants are white because they lack the color factor; three are white because they lack the purple factor; while one white lacks both of these.

A study of the genotypes of the plants with colored flowers also explains why they breed so differently in later generations. One of them (with the genotype $CC\ PP$) breeds true to purple. Four (with the genotypes $Cc\ PP$ or $CC\ Pp$) produce about three-fourths purple and one-fourth

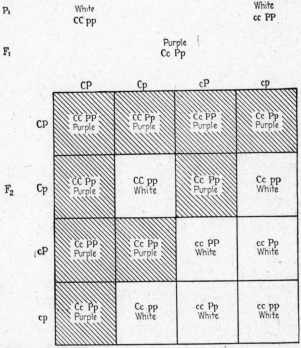

FIG. 30.—The 9:7 ratio. Checkerboard showing the expected composition of the F_2 from a cross of two white-flowered sweet peas which produce all purple-flowered plants in F_1.

white offspring when inbred, since they are homozygous for one of the factors. Four others (with the genotype $Cc\ Pp$) produce nine-sixteenths purple and seven-sixteenths white, just as did the F_1. Such factors as C and P, which are similar in their individual effect but are both necessary to the production of another and different character, are called *complementary* factors. In the sweet pea, again, the complications are due not to any change in the principles of inheritance but to (1) the dependence of one factor on another and (2) the expression of two different factors in the same part.

The interaction of two factors such as C and P to produce a character different from that which results from either one alone may be made clearer by a simple chemical comparison. When a colorless solution of an alkali (such as potassium hydroxide) and a colorless solution of an "indicator" (such as phenolphthalein) are brought together, a light-red color appears. Here the chemical interaction of two colorless substances results in the production of color. The alkali may be compared to the material, whatever it is, which is furnished by the factor C; and the indicator, to that furnished by the factor P.

This illustration may be more than a mere analogy, for Blakeslee has found that in the yellow daisy, *Rudbeckia hirta*, the cross of two yellow-coned races produces a purple-coned F_1 and the ratio of $\frac{9}{16}$ purple-coned to $\frac{7}{16}$ yellow-coned in F_2. When placed in dilute alkali, the cones of one of the parental yellow races turn reddish; those of the other race, blackish. The yellow-coned types in F_2, although identical in appearance, could be similarly differentiated by treatment with alkali into three-sixteenths of one type and four-sixteenths of the other. Evidently yellow results from chemically different processes in the two types; the combination of the two carries the reaction to a further stage (purple) than is possible with either factor alone, and this reaction may be simulated by the addition of alkali instead of the addition of another factor.

In sweet peas and several other plants it is now known that two white races which on crossing give colored progeny each contain a *different* necessary component of the anthocyanin pigment. The combination of these components gives color, whether they be combined by crossing or as extracts in vitro. It is thus reasonable to suppose that in sweet peas the factor C leads to one of these components and P the other. The identification of a chemical substance with an immediate effect of a genetic factor has been made in a few cases.

Reversion.—The method of inheritance of flower color in sweet peas suggests an explanation for the numerous instances among domesticated animals and plants in which crosses between true-breeding varieties produce progeny resembling a remote ancestor more than they do either parent. Plant and animal breeders have noted these peculiar "throwbacks" or "reversions" for many years, but in the absence of any satisfactory explanation they have regarded reversion as the expression of some mysterious force which caused the retention and subsequent reappearance of a remote ancestral trait. It is now known that such reversion may be explained in terms of ordinary Mendelian inheritance, for the reappearance of an old trait is usually due to the reunion of the two or more factors, necessary for its production, which had become separated in the history of the plant or animal. Thus, in the sweet pea, it is plain from the experiment cited above that purple flower color depends on at least two factors and that white flower color results when either is changed. It is easy to imagine that one white variety arose when in the purple type a mutation occurred from C to c; while the second white variety arose when P changed to p. Thus the two elements necessary for purple color became separated into two different strains. When these strains were crossed, the two complementary factors were reunited, and the primitive or "reversionary" flower color appeared.

Coat Color in Rodents (the 9:3:4 Ratio).—A similar but more complex case of factor interaction and reversion has been worked out in breeding experiments with "fancy" varieties of the common house mouse, where not only two but a number of factors have been found to interact in producing what appears to be a simple character. The ancestral or original coat color of this species is seen in the grayish-brown or grizzled pattern of our ordinary wild mice. When closely examined, this is found to be due to the presence of two pigments in the fur. The individual hairs are for the most part black with a narrow yellow band near the tip. The underside of the animal is usually much lighter, the hairs being cream or yellow, with some black or gray at the base. This inconspicuous and hence protective coloration, which is known as the "agouti" pattern, characterizes nearly all of the wild rodents, such as the Norway rat, the wild rabbit, the guinea pig, the gray squirrel, and many others.

A number of variations which have taken place in this wild gray or agouti coat coloration have been preserved under domestication and have given rise to the many color varieties of mice known to fanciers. The commonest and most familiar variation is the albino, in which the coat is white and the eyes are pink or blood color because of the entire absence of pigment from the iris. Albinos always breed true, and this variation has been found to behave as a simple recessive to any color. Another variation in coat color probably arose through the disappearance of all yellow pigment from the agouti pattern, leaving the fur solid black. Black is recessive to the wild gray type and breeds true. When black mice are crossed with ordinary albinos, the progeny are usually *all agouti* like the wild type. When these F_1 agoutis are inbred, their progeny consist, on the average, of nine-sixteenths agouti animals, three-sixteenths black, and four-sixteenths albino (Fig. 31). This, like the 9:7 ratio encountered in sweet peas, apparently indicates a difference of two factors in the parents. Here, however, the last two terms of the ordinary 9:3:3:1 ratio have been added together, indicating that two of the ordinarily different classes of the dihybrid F_2 zygotes cannot be distinguished. The results are explained on the assumption that the parents differ in (1) a factor, C, necessary for the development of any color, which the black mice contain but which is lacking in the albinos;

and in (2) a factor for the agouti pattern, A, which results in a banding of the black hairs with yellow. Since the black mice cannot contain this factor A (or they would appear agouti), it must have come from the albino parent, where, in the absence of the ability to develop any color at all, it could have no visible expression. The recombination of these two factors, one for color and the other for the agouti pattern, reconstitutes the genotype of the wild mouse, and a "reversionary" type results.

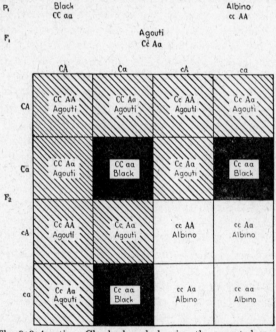

FIG. 31.—The 9:3:4 ratio. Checkerboard showing the expected composition of the F_2 from a cross of black and albino mice which produce all agouti animals (wild type) in F_1.

This case is, therefore, similar to that of flower color in sweet peas in that (1) two independently inherited factors both affecting the same part (in this case coat color) interact to produce a single character; and (2) this interaction produces reversion in the F_1 generation, followed by the reappearance in the F_2 of both of the parental colors as well as the reversionary type. It differs somewhat from the previous case, for in sweet peas *three* of the F_2 genotypic classes have the same appearance, producing a 9:7 ratio, whereas in mice only *two* of the F_2 genotypic classes are indistinguishable, thus producing a 9:3:4 ratio.

Epistasis.—One of the first complications which was encountered in the discussion of unit inheritance was the fact of dominance, by which the presence of one factor of a pair was obscured or hidden. It sometimes happens that when two *different* factors, which are not alleles, both affect the same part or trait of the organism, the expression of one factor covers up or hides the expression of the other. A factor which thus masks or prevents the expression of another is said to be *epistatic* to it, and the factor which is hidden is said to be *hypostatic*. This masking effect is known as *epistasis* and is similar to dominance except that it occurs between different factors instead of being the two members of an allelic pair.

In Squashes (*the* 12:3:1 *Ratio*).—In summer squashes there are three common fruit colors, white, yellow, and green. In crosses between white and yellow and between white and green, white is always found to be dominant; and in crosses between yellow and green, yellow is always found to be dominant. Yellow thus acts as a recessive in relation to white but as a dominant in relation to green. There is evidently a factor for white, W, which is epistatic to those for yellow and green; and so long as it is present, no color is produced in the fruit, regardless of whether or not factors for color are present. Where this factor for white is lacking, however (in plants which are ww), the fruit color will be yellow if the factor for yellow, Y, is present and green if it is absent. Green-fruited plants may thus be represented by the double recessive genotype $ww\ yy$; yellow-fruited plants by $ww\ YY$, and white-fruited ones either by $WW\ YY$ or by $WW\ yy$.

The truth of this assumption that there are two independent factor pairs, one epistatic over the other, may be tested by crossing a homozygous white from a race which is known to carry yellow, $WW\ YY$, with a green, $ww\ yy$. Here the F_1 plants, $Ww\ Yy$, are white-fruited. They should produce four types of gametes, WY, Wy, wY, and wy, and the F_2 expected from a cross between two such F_1 plants is indicated in Fig. 32.

Three-fourths of the plants in this generation will evidently carry W and will thus appear white-fruited no matter what the rest of the genotype may be. Of the one-fourth which have no factor for white, however, three-fourths, or three-sixteenths of the whole, will carry yellow and thus appear yellow; and one-fourth, or one-sixteenth of the whole, will not, and will thus appear green. The occurrence of white, yellow, and green in the F_2 in approximately the ratio expected on the assumption (12:3:1) is actually realized in breeding experiments. The essential fact here is that the white factor masks everything which is hypostatic to it, so that the factor for yellow, which segregates quite independently of white, produces a visible effect only in that fraction of the F_2 which lacks the white factor.

In Poultry (*the* 13:3 *Ratio*).—It has already been noted that the white plumage of White Leghorn fowls is almost completely dominant over the colored plumage of black, barred, or other colored varieties. The white plumage of some other white varieties, however, such as White Wyandottes or White Plymouth Rocks, has been found to be *recessive* to colored plumage and to be due to a factor distinct from that which produces the white of Leghorns. Experiment shows that White Leghorns contain a color factor and with it a factor which inhibits its expression. They are genetically colored birds which are unable to develop their true color. Denoting such an inhibiting factor by I and the color factor by

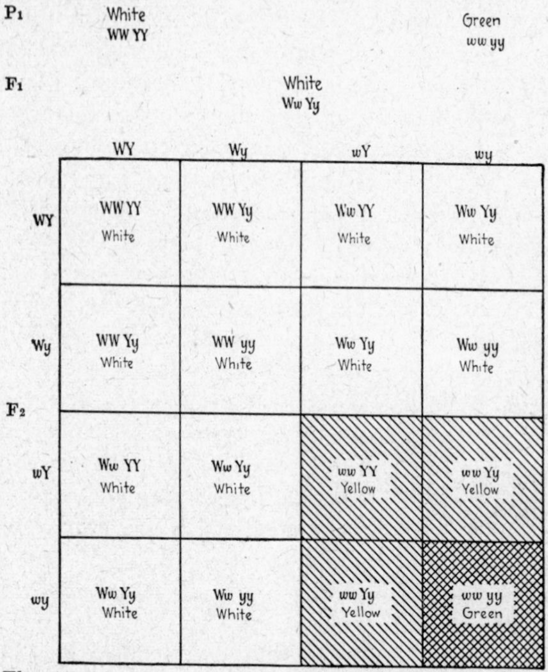

P_1	White WW YY		Green ww yy
F_1		White Ww Yy	

	WY	Wy	wY	wy
WY	WW YY White	WW Yy White	Ww YY White	Ww Yy White
Wy	WW Yy White	WW yy White	Ww Yy White	Ww yy White
wY	Ww YY White	Ww Yy White	ww YY Yellow	ww Yy Yellow
wy	Ww Yy White	Ww yy White	ww Yy Yellow	ww yy Green

F_2

Fig. 32.—The 12:3:1 ratio. Checkerboard showing the expected composition of the F_2 from a cross of a white-fruited squash plant which carries yellow, with a green-fruited one.

C, the White Leghorn is $II\ CC$ and the White Wyandotte is $ii\ cc$. A test of this hypothesis by crossing White Leghorns with White Wyandottes produces a curious result. The F_1 chickens from such a cross are white with small, dark flecks and resemble the F_1 birds produced by crossing White Leghorns with colored fowls. When these F_1 whites are bred together, however, white *and colored* chicks appear in F_2 in the proportion of about $13/16$ white (or white with small, dark flecks) to $3/16$ colored. Although this ratio is not like that of any of the other two-factor ratios which have been discussed (9:3:3:1, 9:7, 9:3:4, and 12:3:1), it may be explained in the same way as these with the additional assumption that the inhibiting factor I is epistatic to or hides the segregation of the color factor C.

On the assumption made, the F_1 fowls from the cross of dominant white by recessive white should be of the genotype $Ii\ Cc$ and should form gametes IC, Ic, iC, and ic in equal numbers. When F_1 fowls are bred together, these gametes should recombine at random, producing the genotypes shown in Fig. 33.

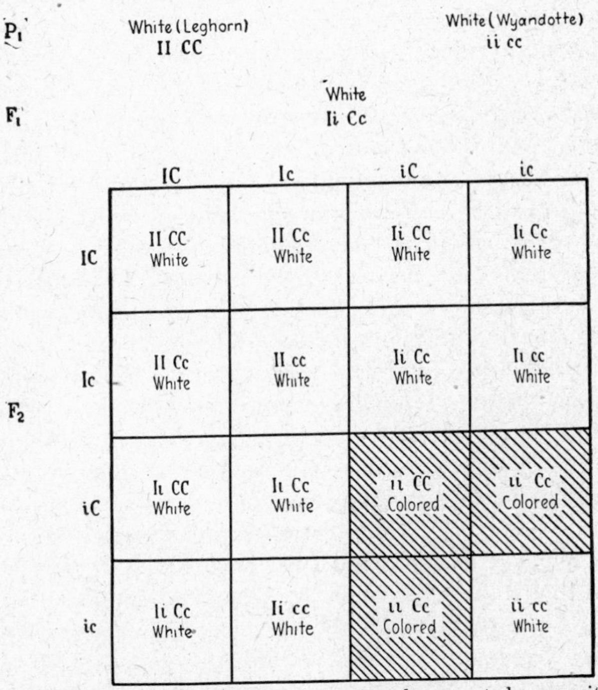

P_1 White (Leghorn)   White (Wyandotte)
    II CC   ii cc

F_1 White
    Ii Cc

	IC	Ic	iC	ic
IC	II CC White	II Cc White	Ii CC White	Ii Cc White
Ic	II Cc White	II cc White	Ii Cc White	Ii cc White
iC	Ii CC White	Ii Cc White	ii CC Colored	ii Cc Colored
ic	Ii Cc White	Ii cc White	ii Cc Colored	ii cc White

(F_2)

Fig. 33.—The 13:3 ratio. Checkerboard showing the expected composition of the F_2 from a cross of a variety with dominant white plumage and one with recessive white plumage, in fowls.

In determining the appearance of these F_2 chickens, it should be remembered that, wherever I is present, pigment development is inhibited, so that fowls which inherit I are white, whatever other factors they may receive. There are 12 such types among the 16 shown in the F_2 checkerboard. The segregation of the Cc pair, which determines the presence or absence of color, can therefore be observed only in those 4 types, among the 16, which do not receive I. Of these, 3 should receive C and be colored (shaded on the checkerboard), and 1 should not receive C and should, therefore, be white. In appearance, then, 13 out of every 16 F_2 chickens should be white and 3 colored; and the actual results are in close accord with this expectation. The peculiarity in this case lies in the ability of the dominant white factor I to mask the segregation of the Cc pair.

The complications introduced by epistasis are comparable with those produced by dominance, that is, two or more genotypes are indistinguishable in appearance. In cases of epistasis, however, there are always two or more factors involved, each of which affects the same part of the organism. This same condition occurred in cases of interaction such as that observed in comb shape in fowls, but in these latter *both* factors are expressed, producing a new or different condition of the part. In epistasis, on the contrary, the competition of two factors for expression in one part results in the apparent triumph of one and the suppression of the other, so that the original traits are recovered but in modified ratios.

Analysis of Coat Color in Mice.—A thorough study of the variations in a group of related characters in any organism will usually reveal an intricate series of interactions between the component factors. As an example we shall choose the house mouse, for in this animal a large number of spontaneous variations have provided the opportunity for a genetic analysis of the factors affecting coat color. Many such factors have been studied and their interrelationships made out. C is the fundamental color factor, necessary for the production of any pigment in the coat. Another factor, A, or gray, determines the development of the agouti pattern. Its recessive allele, a, is present in the nonagouti mice, such as blacks or browns. Still another, B, governs the development of black pigment and is dominant over its allelic condition of brown or chocolate, b. Many varieties are spotted with white in a blotched or piebald pattern, and such mice contain a factor, s, which is recessive to self or solid color, S. Another factor, d, brings about a clumping of the black and brown pigment granules in the hairs and makes these colors appear faded or *dilute*, as opposed to the normal fully pigmented form, D. Another factor reduces the amount of black and brown pigment in the fur, giving it a pale and washed-out appearance, and also reduces the pigment in the iris, making the eyes appear reddish or pink like the eyes of albinos. This factor, which is called pink eye (p) from its most noticeable effect, is recessive to the normal dark-eyed, intense-colored condition, P. These factors all segregate sharply and may occur in any combination. There are also several other factors affecting coat color which will be omitted for the sake of simplicity. Some of these combinations result in characters which are distinctive and have been given names of their own. Thus the nonblack agoutis are called "cinnamon," or brown agouti; the dilute blacks, "blue"; the dilute browns, "silver fawn"; and so on. Table VII lists these various factor combinations, together with the type of coat color produced by each.

All of these types are recessive to the wild coat and appear to have arisen from it by mutation of one or more factors. Thus at any time the wild type may be reconstituted by bringing into combination all of the alleles of the factors which are responsible for these new types. *In fact, the wild coat color itself is found to depend on the presence and inter-*

TABLE VII.—INTERACTION OF FACTORS FOR COAT COLOR IN MICE

Factors						Gametic formula	Phenotype
C	A	B	D	P	S	CABDPS	Wild-type agouti
			D		s	CABDPs	Spotted agouti
				p	S	CABDpS	Pink-eyed agouti
		B			s	CABDps	Pink-eyed, spotted agouti
			d	P	S	CABdPS	Dilute agouti
					s	CABdPs	Spotted, dilute agouti
				p	S	CABdpS	Pink-eyed, dilute agouti
	A				s	CABdps	Pink-eyed, spotted, dilute agouti
			D	P	S	CAbDPS	Cinnamon
					s	CAbDPs	Spotted cinnamon
				p	S	CAbDpS	Pink-eyed cinnamon
		b			s	CAbDps	Pink-eyed, spotted cinnamon
			d	P	S	CAbdPS	Dilute cinnamon
					s	CAbdPs	Spotted, dilute cinnamon
				p	S	CAbdpS	Pink-eyed, dilute cinnamon
C					s	CAbdps	Pink-eyed, spotted, dilute cinnamon
			D	P	S	CaBDPS	Black
					s	CaBDPs	Spotted black
				p	S	CaBDpS	Pink-eyed black
		B			s	CaBDps	Pink-eyed, spotted black
			d	P	S	CaBdPS	Dilute black
					s	CaBdPs	Spotted, dilute black
				p	S	CaBdpS	Pink-eyed, dilute black
	a				s	CaBdps	Pink-eyed, spotted, dilute black
			D	P	S	CabDPS	Brown
					s	CabDPs	Spotted brown
				p	S	CabDpS	Pink-eyed brown
		b			s	CabDps	Pink-eyed, spotted brown
			d	P	S	CabdPS	Dilute brown
					s	CabdPs	Spotted, dilute brown
				p	S	CabdpS	Pink-eyed, dilute brown
					s	Cabdps	Pink-eyed, spotted, dilute brown
c	with any other factors					c........	Albino, may be of any of 32 genotypes above

action of all of the factors named. Thus, in order to produce the agouti pattern there must be present the factors for color (C), agouti (A), black (B), dark eye (P), dense color (D), and solid color (S). With regard only to these factors the genotype of the wild mouse may be written *AA BB CC DD PP SS.* These factors all show essentially complete dominance, so that their heterozygous condition will give the same result as is produced by the homozygous form here given. Thus an animal with the genotype *AaBbCcDdPpSs* would also be agouti in appearance. The factors named do not include all that are known, nor is it believable that more than a small sample of the factors affecting coat color in mice have been studied. Were knowledge complete, it is probable that the list of factors necessary for the production of the agouti pattern would be much longer and that the letters of the alphabet would be exhausted in attempting to write the genotype of the wild mouse. Here, then, is a clear and convincing example of factor interaction. In order that the apparently simple pattern characteristic of wild house mice may be developed, there must be present at least six factors (probably many more) each of which has a definite effect on coat color. If any single factor is missing or changed, a coat pattern differing more or less widely from the wild type results.

This type of factor interaction is not exceptional but is found whenever numerous variations in a single aspect of the organism are carefully analyzed. Such analyses have been made for several groups of characters in maize. More than a dozen factors affecting the color of the plant are known. The normal color is green, which, like the agouti pattern of mice, results from the combined action of the alleles of all these factors. If one factor is changed, the plant is white instead of green; if another changes, the leaves become red or purple in the sun; whereas changes in various other factors produce brown, yellow, and various combinations of these colors in striped or blotched patterns. In fact, it may be accepted as a general rule that the characters of a plant or animal depend on multiple and finely balanced interactions between a very large number of factors.

Multiple Alleles.—All of the cases which we have discussed up to this point involve factors which act as alternative conditions in inheritance, forming two members of a single *pair* of alleles. Many cases are now known in which the same factor occurs in more than two alternative states. The common pink-eyed white (albino) rabbit (Fig. 34, bottom) has long been known to act as a simple recessive to the colored type (Fig. 34, top). Crosses of colored with albino rabbits produce only colored progeny, which, when inbred, produce colored and albino young in the ratio of $\frac{3}{4}$ colored to $\frac{1}{4}$ albino. Color, C, and albinism, c^a, thus form a pair of alleles. There is another form of albinism in rabbits known as Himalayan albinism (Fig. 34, center). Himalayans have pink eyes and their fur is white except for the feet, tail, ears, and tip of the nose, which are black or dark brown. When these are crossed with fully colored rabbits, the F_1 is colored, and in

Fig. 34.—Three alleles of a gene for coat color in rabbits. Top, colored; center, Himalayan albinism; bottom, complete albinism. (*From Castle, in Journal of Heredity.*)

the F_2 there are ¾ colored and ¼ Himalayan. Himalayan albinism, c^h, and color are therefore alleles. It is interesting to see what happens when Himalayan is crossed with albino. If Himalayan and albino are due to different factors, each type should carry the allele of the other, and reversion to full color should occur in F_1. Actually the cross of Himalayan by albino produces *all* Himalayan in F_1 and $\frac{3}{4}$ Himalayan and $\frac{1}{4}$ albino in F_2. Reversion does not occur. Other experiments show that the factor for Himalayan and the factor for albinism are never present in the same gamete; a colored animal may carry *either* Himalayan *or* albino but never both. It is evident that Himalayan and albino are allelic to each other and that both are allelic to color. The members of such a system of three or more alternatives are known as *multiple alleles*.

Many such series of alleles are known. In mice there are four alleles in the albino series: C, full color; c^{ch}, dilute color or chinchilla; c^h, extreme dilution; and c^a, albino. Black agouti mice with different members of this series appear as follows:

$AABBCC$	Black agouti (wild type)
$AABBCc^{ch}$ or Cc^h or Cc^a	Black agouti, *i.e.*, the C allele, is dominant to all the others, at least in the combinations known
$AABBc^{ch}c^{ch}$	Light agouti; base of hairs full black, tips cream
$AABBc^{ch}c^h$	Chinchilla agouti; base of hairs brownish, tips nearly white
$AABBc^{ch}c^a$	Chinchilla agouti; as above
$AABBc^hc^h$	Extreme dilute agouti; base of hairs light slate, tips white
$AABBc^hc^a$	Dusky white; base of hairs dirty white, tips white
$AABBc^ac^a$	White with pink eyes

Crosses between members with different alleles (except C) are intermediate in color between the parent types. Thus light agouti by extreme dilute produces all chinchillas, of a color about midway between those of the parents, showing that the alleles (below C) do not show dominance. Such F_1 animals $(c^{ch}c^h)$ bred together produce one-fourth light agouti $(c^{ch}c^{ch})$, one-half chinchilla $(c^{ch}c^h)$, and one-fourth extreme dilute (c^hc^h). There is no reversion in any of the crosses within this series. Members of such a series with unlike alleles, for example, $c^{ch}c^h$, are known as *compounds*, to distinguish them from other heterozygotes.

The absence of dominance is characteristic of most series of multiple alleles but is not a constant feature. In mice there are five alleles in the so-called agouti series of coat colors as follows: (1) A^Y, yellow; A^L, agouti with light belly; A, wild type, that is, agouti with gray belly; a^t, black and tan, that is, black back with light belly; a, nonagouti, that is, self black.

Of this series yellow is dominant to all the other colors; agouti light belly is dominant to A, a^t, and a; agouti gray belly is almost completely dominant to black and tan, the compound Aa^t having an agouti back but a lighter belly than the wild type; A and a^t are both dominant to a. Thus the compounds A^YA^L, A^YA, A^Ya^t, and A^Ya are all yellow. The homozygote A^YA^Y does not survive to birth; this allele is known to have also a recessive lethal effect (see p. 113). All other combinations are fully viable, so that normal ratios are obtained. For example, A^ra (yellow) by a^ta (black and tan) produces one-half yellows (A^ra^t and A^ra), one-fourth black and tans (a^ta), and one-fourth blacks (aa).

Multiple alleles have been found in many animals. In other rodents (guinea pigs, rats, rabbits) several alleles of the albino series are known in each.

In *Drosophila melanogaster* at least 14 alleles of the gene for white eye color are known. The homozygotes form a graded series of increasing shades of yellow and red beginning with the lowest member, white (ww), and proceeding through ivory, pearl, tinged, honey, buff, apricot, cherry, eosin, blood, coral, and wine to the wild-type red. Red is dominant to all other alleles; compounds are in general intermediate

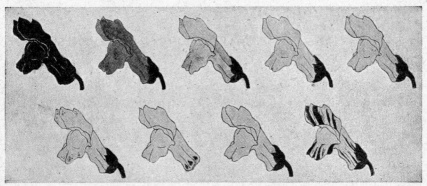

Fig. 35.—A series of nine alleles of the gene *Pal* affecting flower color in the snap-dragon (Antirrhinum), from normal red (upper left) through pale shades to red-striped (lower right). (*After Baur.*)

between the pure parent types crossed. In Drosophila it has been possible to establish the important fact that alleles arise from mutations at the *same* locus in a chromosome. In the paired homologous chromosomes they are thus always opposite each other and are probably modifications of the same gene locus.

Several series are known in plants. The most extensive of these, as reported by Baur in the snapdragon, has nine members, all affecting the anthocyanin colors of the flowers and leading from the normal red through various paler shades to ivory color with red stripes (Fig. 35). Each member appears to be dominant to those lighter than itself. In maize, Emerson has found several such series. The clearest case involves the alleles of the "sun-red" gene, which in combination with other factors affect the colors of aleurone, plant, pericarp, and silk (Table VIII). In this case the alleles affect many different parts and in some compounds each allele produces its own effect and a mosaic expression results, as in $A_1{}^ba_1$.

TABLE VIII.—RELATIONS OF THE a_1 ALLELES TO ALEURONE, PLANT, PERICARP, AND SILK COLOR IN MAIZE* (*After Emerson, Beadle, and Fraser*, 1935)

Alleles of A	Aleurone color with $C R Pr$	Plant color		Pericarp color		Silk color with $P sm$
		With $B Pl$	With $B pl$	With Pl_{rch}	With P	
A_1A_1	Strong purple	Purple	Sun red	Cherry	Red	Salmon
A_1a_1	Strong purple	Purple	Sun red	Cherry	Red	Salmon
$A_1A_1{}^b$	Strong purple	Purple	Sun red	(Cherry)	Brown	Green
$A_1a_1{}^p$	Strong purple	Purple	Sun red	Cherry	Brown	(Green)
$A_1{}^bA_1{}^b$	Strong purple	Purple	Sun red	(Cherry)	Brown	Green
$A_1{}^ba_1{}^p$	(Strong purple)	(Purple)	(Sun red)	(Cherry)	(Brown)	(Green?)
$A_1{}^ba_1$	Strong purple	Purple	Sun red	(Cherry)	Brown	(Green?)
$a_1{}^pa_1{}^p$	Pale purple	Reddish brown	Green	Brown	Brown	(Green?)
$a_1{}^pa_1$	Pale purple	Reddish brown	Green	Brown	Brown	(Green?)
a_1a_1	White	Brown	Green	Brown	Brown	Green

* Combinations not tested directly are given in parenthesis.

The Human Blood Groups.—An interesting and important series of multiple alleles has been studied in man, and these too show the peculiar relationship that in a compound each allele produces its own effect. The character affected by these alleles is the property (antigen) of the normal red blood cells by which they respond to specific components in the blood serum (antibodies). Landsteiner discovered in 1900 that in certain cases when the red blood cells of one person were placed in the blood serum of another the cells were clumped or agglutinated. This reaction occurred only when the cells of certain individuals were placed in serum from certain other persons. It was found that in respect to blood cells there are two such antigens, A and B, and two serum antibodies which agglutinate them. It was found that all persons could be classified into four groups with regard to the antigen property of the blood—those with antigen A (group A), those with antigen B (group B), those with both A and B (group AB) and those with neither antigen (group O). Persons of group A have no antibody which agglutinates A cells but do have antibodies which agglutinate B cells; those of group B

TABLE IX

Blood group	Serum agglutinates blood cells of group	Cells agglutinated by serum of group
AB	None	O, A, B
A	B, AB	O, B
B	A, AB	O, A
O	A, B, AB	None

have no antibodies which agglutinate B but do have antibodies which agglutinate A; those of group AB have neither type of antibody; those of group O have both types of antibody.   When blood cells from persons of one group are placed in serum from persons of the same or another group the reactions occur as shown in Table IX.

Large numbers of persons have been classified into these four groups by means of the agglutination test, and the distribution of the blood groups in the offspring of parents of known blood groups has been studied. The evidence shows that these blood properties are determined by a series of three allelic genes A, a^B, and a as follows:

Group	Genotype
AB	Aa^B
B	a^Ba^B or aa^B
A	AA or Aa
O	aa

A is a factor for the production of antigen A, a^B for antigen B, and a for neither antigen.

The existence of these three factors in man and the ease of recognizing the blood groups has obvious practical applications in blood transfusion, cases of disputed parentage, and identification of persons, but these need not concern us here.   What is significant for genetics is that allelic factors, affecting fundamental serological properties of the blood, act in such a way that in the compound Aa^B each factor produces its own characteristic and specific effect to the full so that the cells contain both antigens A and B; A and a^B on the other hand each show complete dominance over a, the lack of both antigens.   The case is unique among examples of factor interactions.

Duplicate Factors.—Not only have changes in the same gene been found to produce different effects, as in multiple allelic series, but different though independent factors have been found with the same or similar effects.   Factors with the same expression are known as *duplicate factors*. Their discovery has pointed the way to an explanation of some of the most complex cases of inheritance.

In Bursa (the 15:1 Ratio).—One of the simplest instances of duplicate factors is involved in the inheritance of capsule or pod form in the shepherd's-purse, Bursa, as reported by G. H. Shull.   One race of this species has characteristically triangular capsules, whereas in another they are ovoid or top shaped.   When these two types are crossed, the F_1 plants all have triangular capsules, the dominance of this shape being complete.   In the F_2, however, there are ordinarily found to be about 15 plants with typical triangular capsules to every 1 with ovoid capsules. This F_2 ovoid plant breeds true in subsequent generations, whereas of the F_2 triangular plants some breed true, others produce triangular and ovoid plants in the ratio of 3:1, and others produce these types in the ratio of 15:1. Remembering that where parents differing in two factors are crossed, the double recessive type appears in only one-sixteenth of the F_2 progeny (as opposed to one-fourth in a single-factor cross), the hypothesis at once suggests itself that the triangular capsule of Bursa is caused by two dominant duplicate factors or by either one of them

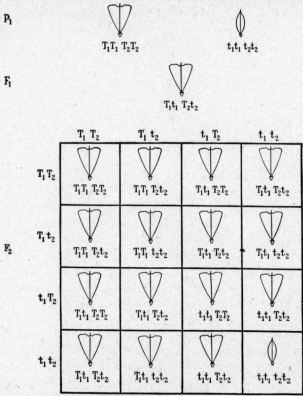

Fig. 36.—The 15:1 ratio. Checkerboard showing the expected composition of the F_2 from a cross between a type of shepherd's-purse (Bursa) with triangular capsules (homozygous for two duplicate factors) and a type with top-shaped capsules. (*After G. H. Shull.*)

alone and that the ovoid type is due to the recessive alleles of both of these. The 15:1 ratio is thus still another modification of the 9:3:3:1 ratio, the first three terms here being indistinguishable from each other. Representing these two factors for triangular capsule by T_1 and T_2, the genotypes and phenotypes of the F_2 are shown in the checkerboard in Fig. 36.

The hypothesis of duplicate factors not only explains this peculiar ratio but makes it easier to understand the differences in breeding behavior which have been found to exist between the various triangular types occurring in F_2. Seven plants out of sixteen (those which are homozygous for either T_1 or T_2 or both) should breed true to triangular capsules in later generations. Four plants have only one of the triangular factors represented and that in a heterozygous condition (T_1t_1 t_2t_2 or t_1t_1 T_2t_2), so that these plants may be expected to produce offspring about three-fourths of which have triangular capsules and one-fourth ovoid ones. The remaining four are heterozygous for both factors (T_1t_2 T_2t_2) and should thus produce offspring, when inbred, in about the ratio of 15:1, just as does the F_1 hybrid. These expectations have been borne out by actual breeding tests.

In Wheat.—A somewhat more involved case was brought to light during some breeding experiments on wheat by Nilsson-Ehle. He found that the red color of the grain in certain varieties was dominant to the white or colorless condition of the grain in other varieties. After red and white races had been crossed, however, these colors appeared in various ratios in the F_2 generations. From some crosses he obtained a normal one-factor ratio of ¾ red to ¼ white. In other F_2 counts, however, the ratio was apparently 15 red to 1 white, and in still others 63 red to 1 white. By comparison with the shepherd's-purse it may be inferred that the red color may be due to the operation of one or two, or even of three, independent factors, any one of which, or all together, may produce the color; and that white is due to the absence of all these. Breeding tests show that the red plants which, when crossed with white, produce a ratio of 3 red to 1 white in the F_2 do indeed possess but a single factor pair for red; whereas the reds which give the 15:1 and the 63:1 ratios possess two and three factor pairs for red, respectively.

Denoting these various factors for red by R_1, R_2, and R_3, we may represent the results of crosses by checkerboards as before. A cross of "double red" and white is shown in Fig. 37.

According to the assumption, the presence of a single factor for red (either R_1 or R_2) is sufficient to cause the development of red color in the grains. Fifteen of the F_2 types in the checkerboard have either R_1 or R_2 or both and are red, while only one out of the 16 has neither, and this is the double-recessive white plant. The cross of a "triple red" with a white can be shown in the same way, with the appearance of the white plant in the F_2 expected only once in every 64 individuals.

In this example it is significant that red is not completely dominant over white, for plants in which there are two red factors have darker grains than those with one; plants with three are darker than those with two; and so on, which indicates that these duplicate factors have *cumulative* effects. This conception, through its extension in the theory of multiple factors, has a very important bearing on the modern explanation

of the inheritance of quantitative or size characters, a subject which will
be treated in detail in a later chapter. The important point to be
emphasized in the present connection, however, is that the same effect
may be produced by several different factors which are inherited quite
independently of one another in typical Mendelian fashion.

The possible method of origin of such duplicate genes will be discussed
later. Cases of duplicate factors are known chiefly in plants, where

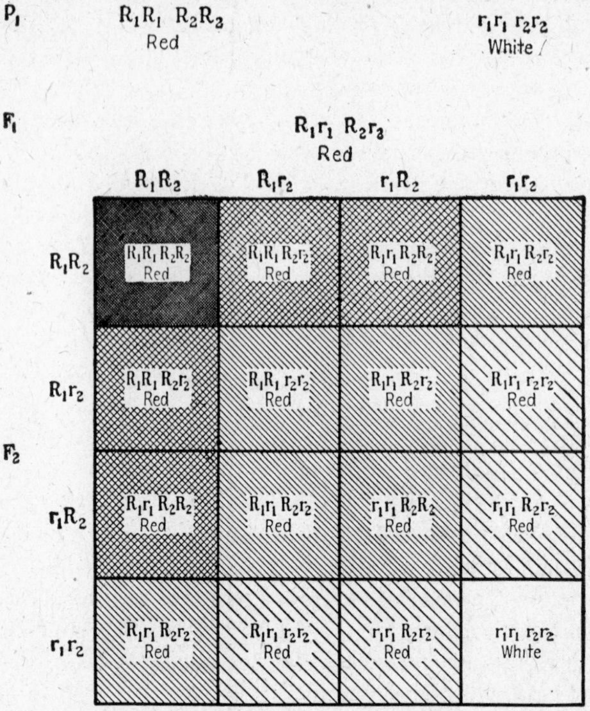

P_1	$R_1R_1\ R_2R_2$ Red		$r_1r_1\ r_2r_2$ White

F_1 $R_1r_1\ R_2r_2$
Red

F_2	R_1R_2	R_1r_2	r_1R_2	r_1r_2
R_1R_2	$R_1R_1\ R_2R_2$ Red	$R_1R_1\ R_2r_2$ Red	$R_1r_1\ R_2R_2$ Red	$R_1r_1\ R_2r_2$ Red
R_1r_2	$R_1R_1\ R_2r_2$ Red	$R_1R_1\ r_2r_2$ Red	$R_1r_1\ R_2r_2$ Red	$R_1r_1\ r_2r_2$ Red
r_1R_2	$R_1r_1\ R_2R_2$ Red	$R_1r_1\ R_2r_2$ Red	$r_1r_1\ R_2R_2$ Red	$r_1r_1\ R_2r_2$ Red
r_1r_2	$R_1r_1\ R_2r_2$ Red	$R_1r_1\ r_2r_2$ Red	$r_1r_1\ R_2r_2$ Red	$r_1r_1\ r_2r_2$ White

Fig. 37.—Diagram showing the result of a cross between a red-kernelled and a white-kernelled wheat, where the red color is due to the operation of either or both of two factors, R_1 and R_2.

duplication of the whole chromosome set (ploidy) is known to occur,
whereas in animals only one case of such duplicate factors is known
(the inheritance of leg feathering in fowls) and ploidy in animals is
very rare.

Modifying Factors.—Of the several factors which interact to produce a
given phenotype, some contribute a greater share than others to the
total effect, and in some cases certain of these factors appear merely to
modify the effect of another, or main, factor, having little or no effect
when the "main" factor is not present. Thus in certain strains of mice
there occurs a form of white spotting known as "variegated" (Fig. 38).

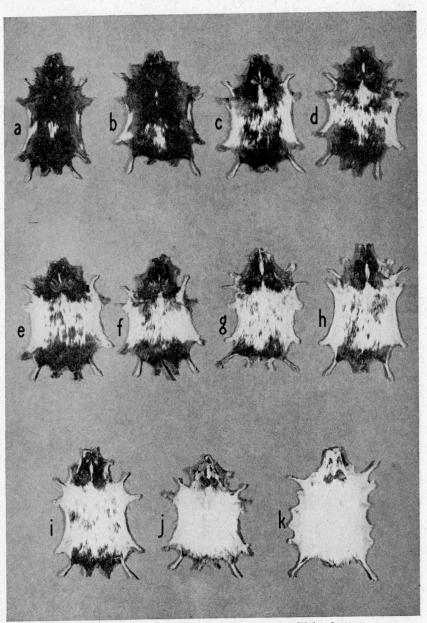

Fig. 38.—Variation in spotting of mice due to modifying factors.

Such variegated mice are heterozygous for a dominant spotting factor. Animals homozygous for this factor, WW, have a severe anemia and die soon after birth; when they live long enough to develop hair, they are white with black eyes, that is, the white spotting covers the whole coat. The degree of white spotting of the heterozygotes, however, depends not only on the presence of W but upon a number of other multiple factors which determine the degree of expression of W. If several of these modifying factors are present with W, the coat has much white; if few or none are present, the coat has little or no white. These modifying factors have little or no effect in ww mice; even when several of them are present the animal is unspotted unless W is also present. One effect of these modifying factors is thus to determine the degree of expression or dominance of the factor W. When all of the modifiers are present, the cross of $Ww \times Ww$ produces offspring in the ratio of $\frac{3}{4}$ white ($\frac{1}{4}$ WW, $\frac{2}{4}$ Ww): $\frac{1}{4}$ unspotted (ww); when part of them are present, the offspring consist of one-fourth white (WW), one-half variegated (Ww), and one-fourth unspotted (ww); and when none are present, the progeny are one-fourth white (WW) and three-fourth unspotted (Ww and ww). This is a clear-cut demonstration of the fact that dominance in one pair of 's is determined by the interaction of other factors in the genotype.

In Drosophila likewise modifying factors are known which have little or no effect on eye color except when combined with one allele of the white-eye series (eosin); in this combination they dilute or lighten the eye color.

Such factors as the above may be called *specific modifiers* since their effects are produced only upon a specific genotype.

Of more frequent occurrence are cases in which factors have a less specific or general modifying effect. In mice and many other mammals there is another form of white spotting known as pied. Pied mice differ from unspotted ones by having a recessive gene, s, but ss mice may vary from almost self-colored to nearly all white with black eyes. Other independent spotting factors determine these differences in extent of spotting; as more of them are combined with ss the coat becomes whiter, although when ss is replaced by its normal allele, S, the other spotting factors still produce white-spotting effects, but to a lesser degree. Thus a mutual modifying effect is exerted by s upon the effect of the other factors and vice versa.

Such cumulative effects of factors and of modification of the effects of one factor by others have been noted so frequently that it is probable that all factors partake to some extent of the nature of modifiers. The distinction between "modifiers" and other factors is thus purely a formal one and is used for convenience only.

Multiple Effects of a Single Factor.—Not less important, perhaps, than the cooperation of many factors in producing a phenotype is the effect of a single factor upon many different characters. A number of instances of this manifold effect have come to light, and it is probably the rule with all factors. A factor has frequently been spoken of as though it affected but a single trait in the individual, expressing itself in some more or less definite and limited way, such as by a difference in eye color, or flower color, or the presence or absence of horns. Although it is convenient to name and refer to a factor by its most peculiar or striking manifestation, this custom should not conceal the fact that its most noticeable expression may not be its only one or even always its most important one.

A simple example of the widespread effect of a single factor may be seen in one of the traits which Mendel himself studied. He noted that the plants which bore purple flowers had also reddish spots in the axils of the leaves and bore seeds with gray or brown seed coats. His evidence showed that this type differed by one factor from the type which had white flowers, green stems and leaf axils, and white seed coats. It is easy to see that in this case the factor affected pigment development in general and that the many differences between purple- and white-flowered plants were but local expressions of one fundamental difference. The same differences may be noted between the colored- and white-flowered varieties of many cultivated plants, such as the Jimson weed, the columbine, and others.

Of less obvious nature are the examples in which a single factor is known to affect different parts of the organism in a variety of apparently unrelated ways. Thus in the wild Jimson weed the large seed capsules are covered with sharp spines, whereas in one variety which has been bred under cultivation spines are lacking, and the capsules are smooth. This difference is conspicuous and behaves as a single unit in inheritance, the spiny type being dominant. These two types also differ, however, in many other characters, such as the length of the internodes, the stoutness of the stems, the angle of branching, the relative development of the short lateral branches, and other particulars. Here one factor evidently affects all sorts of traits all over the plant body.

Finally in the flour moth, Ephestia, it has been shown that a single factor (p. 377) affects the color of the larval skin, testes, brain, and eyes of the adult; the viability; the reaction of the animal to temperature; and other traits.

All of the diverse effects of a single factor may not be shown under a single set of conditions. One factor in Drosophila, known as "bent" from a peculiar effect which it has on the shape of the wings, is expressed under ordinary conditions in various changes in the wings and in a shortening and twisting of the legs; but when bent flies are reared in a cold atmosphere, a number of other peculiarities appear. The compound eyes become speckled and roughened because of irregularities in the hairs between the facets; one of the veins in the wing appears broken; and the pattern of the bristle arrangement on the thorax is disturbed. The bent factor itself is not altered by the lower temperature, but many effects of this factor which are not apparent at ordinary temperatures are made visible.by the cold.

These considerations serve to emphasize the conclusion already stated several times, that the real unit of inheritance is not the developed character which is visible and measurable and which, as has been seen, may be variable and complex, but an invisible something in the cell called a factor or gene. Not only is the organism formed under the cooperative influence of a large number of these factors, but each factor, itself a distinct unit, exerts a widespread influence on many parts of the organism. The extreme extension of this view may be seen in the idea that many fundamental characters of the organism are determined by factors acting on the whole animal or plant rather than on single parts.

Lethal Factors.—In the examples thus far cited, we have considered some of the ways in which the genetic factors express themselves in the characters of the organism and have seen that many of them interact with and modify the expression of others. There is still another group of factors which produce such an extreme modification that at some point in its course they stop the development of the individual, and death ensues. Factors which have a fatal effect of this sort are termed *lethal* and are now recognized as of rather frequent occurrence among all sorts of animals and plants. They exhibit their peculiar effects, however, only when present in a homozygous condition. Lethal factors in the heterozygous condition may be carried with impunity by perfectly normal individuals, but that portion of the offspring of such individuals in which segregation has brought two lethals together is killed.

Albino Plants.—The complications introduced by the presence of lethal factors may be illustrated by a common occurrence in the breeding of corn and of sorghum. When the self-fertilized seeds from an apparently normal green plant are sown in the field, it sometimes happens that among the seedlings a number of spindling white plants are found which soon die because they lack chlorophyll, which is essential in the manufacture of food and hence in the life of the plant. When seeds from a plant which has produced such "albino" seedlings are sown and the numbers of green and white seedlings are counted, it is often found that the green seedlings outnumber the white by about three to one (Fig. 19). The parent plant was apparently heterozygous for a factor for white (absence of chlorophyll), which is lethal when homozygous. Here the cause of the lethal effect produced by two white factors acting together is plain, since they prevent the development of a substance essential in the metabolism of the plant.

In Mice.—In most cases, however, the specific effect of the lethal cannot be ascertained, and it is known only that the ratios ordinarily expected from a given mating are altered by the death of a portion of the progeny. The first case of this sort was found among house mice. The yellow variety of this species is peculiar in that it *never breeds true.* Matings between two yellows produce progeny of which about *two-thirds* are yellow like the parents, while *one-third* are of another color (black, brown, or gray). When yellows are bred to nonyellows, about half the young produced are yellow, while half are nonyellow. The latter ratio is that which is to be expected from the mating of a heterozy-

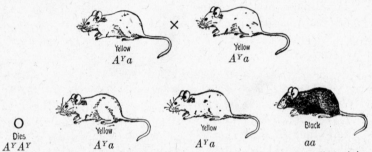

FIG. 39.—Inheritance of a lethal factor in mice. A mating of yellow by yellow giving one-fourth dead embryos, one-half yellow mice, and one-fourth non-yellow ones.

gote with a recessive and suggests that yellow mice are heterozygous. When two such heterozygous yellows are mated, however, it would be expected that one-fourth would be pure yellow, one-half heterozygous yellow, and one-fourth nonyellow; but apparently *only the two latter classes* are born from such matings, and these occur in the proportion (as expected) of two yellow to one nonyellow. It has been found that all three classes of individuals are probably formed and begin their development but that the pure yellows die in an early embryo stage and only the heterozygous yellows and the nonyellows live to be born (Fig. 39). In conformity with this explanation the litters born from matings between yellows are smaller by about one-fourth than litters from yellow by nonyellow. The inheritance of yellow may be represented as follows:

$$A^Y = \text{a dominant factor for yellow (see p. 102)}$$
$$a = \text{a recessive factor for nonyellow}$$

Parents...................	Yellow $A^Y a$	$\times$		Yellow $A^Y a$	
Gametes...................	A^Y, a			A^Y, a	
Progeny...................	$A^Y A^Y$	$A^Y a$		$A^Y a$	aa
	¼ Pure yellow	¼ Yellow		¼ Yellow	¼ Nonyellow
	die		live		live

In explanation of this case it is assumed that the union of two yellow factors produces a reaction which is fatal in some way to the developing embryo. A mouse which inherits a factor for yellow can survive only if it receives also the allelic factor for nonyellow. The expression of the character yellow depends, therefore, on the simultaneous presence of the factor for yellow and of its normal allele.

A large number of factors which express themselves in this way are known in the plants and animals which have been most thoroughly studied; for example, maize, snapdragon, and Drosophila. In the last, hundreds of lethal factors have been distinguished. In the fowl the "creeper" or short-legged condition behaves like yellow in mice. The homozygotes are very abnormal; their growth is retarded and they die at about seventy-two hours of development. In mice, brachyury, or the short-tailed variation, shows the same peculiarity. The homozygotes show many striking changes from the normal type and die regularly on about the tenth day after fertilization. In most of the cases cited the factor concerned has a dominant effect on external characters such as coat color, leg length, or tail length but a recessive effect on viability, since death results only when two factors are present. In Drosophila many of the "lethals" with dominant morphological effect have turned out to be not single factors but defective or deficient sections of chromosomes, and other cases may prove to be of the same nature.

No sharp line can be drawn between lethals and other factors, for all grades of lethal effect have been encountered, from those which cause death of the gamete (in certain plants), the fertilized egg, and early or late embryos or seedlings to those which affect the mature individual. Moreover, many recessive factors partake of the nature of lethals, since individuals homozygous for them are less viable than the "normal" or wild type. The effects of some of these factors on development will be discussed in a later chapter (XVI). Their importance at this point is in illustrating a new type of factor expression which may greatly modify the results of breeding experiments.

Factor Expression in Development.—The characteristics of the developed organism are not only influenced by a complex of interacting genetic factors but depend to a considerable extent upon the environment in which these factors act during development. A rough distinction may be drawn between the external environment—those various agencies outside the body of the organism which may have an influence upon it, such as temperature, light, gravity, chemical substances, and so on—and the internal environment, including all those stimuli which have their origin within the body itself.

External Environment.—Attention has already been called to the profound effect which differences in the external environment produce on the visible characteristics of genetically similar individuals.   Soil conditions, moisture, temperature, food, parasites, and similar agencies may in some cases so alter the expression of genetic factors as to mask or obscure their action entirely.

In Drosophila a character, "abnormal abdomen," although due to a dominant factor, appears only in flies which not only have this factor but which have also been reared on a *moist* culture medium.   The same character when due to a different factor depends on just the opposite conditions for its maximum expression.   The factor for duplicated legs produces its specific effect only in flies reared at low temperatures, while the effects of the factors for vestigial wings, bar eyes, and others are greatly modified by the temperatures at which development proceeds.   Such cases of interaction between a genetic factor and a particular set of environmental conditions warn one to use great care in ascribing a given effect either to the environment or to a genetic factor exclusively.

Fig. 40.—A normal and a dwarf mouse of the same age.   The difference depends on a gene which affects the amount of a pituitary hormone, deficiency of the hormone producing dwarfism.   (*From Keeler, Courtesy of Harvard University Press.*)

Internal Environment.—In the higher animals the various internal secretions—those which enter the blood from the ductless glands and which are called *hormones*—have a marked influence upon many physical and mental features.   Some of these hormones regulate and correlate the general processes of development, and the attainment of normal maturity depends upon their presence in proper amount.   Others regulate growth in particular tissues or regions, and abnormalities in the supply of these results in such conditions as goiter, abnormalities of the bones, and other specific defects.   These secretions provide one item of the general environment within which the genes act.   A hormone itself may often be one channel through which a gene affects general characters; and there is undoubtedly a complex series of interactions between the genetic factors, the endocrine secretions, and the other agencies of the internal environment during development.

One clear case which may be taken as an example is the inheritance and development of dwarfism in the house mouse (Fig. 40).   Dwarf mice appear as about one-fourth of the progeny in litters from parents heterozygous for a recessive factor *dw*. The dwarfs stop growing at about two weeks of age and reach only about a third of the size of their normal litter mates, and although otherwise healthy they are always sterile. The anterior lobes of the pituitary glands of the dwarfs are deficient, as well as the cortex of the adrenal gland. When anterior pituitary glands from normal rats are implanted into the dwarfs, they begin to grow and continue to gain weight as the gland implantations continue. Under continued treatment they reach almost the size of normal mice of the same age, and the males may become fertile. It has been shown that the dwarf factor interferes with the production of the growth hormones of the anterior pituitary, although another hormone from this gland, which influences sexual maturity, is apparently not affected. Through this means, the factor affects all the structures of the body. The artificial supply of the normal secretion replaces the action of the normal gene, and this shows that the normal gene is responsible for many of the complex interactions which take place during growth.

Many of the ways in which genetic factors interact in influencing the sexual characters, the sex organs and their secretions, and the general course of development will be discussed in later chapters.

Complexity of the Problem.—The examples used to illustrate the various types of factor expression and interaction are only a few of the many which investigation during the past forty years has brought to light. Mendelism was hailed as a means of simplifying the problems of heredity, but as knowledge has increased, it has been found to involve all sorts of unsuspected complications. These have often been so intricate and obscure as to suggest, at first, that they were unexplainable in simple terms, but advancing knowledge has brought them one by one into harmony with the underlying principles enunciated by Mendel.

REFERENCES

BATESON, W., and R. C. PUNNETT. 1906. Comb characters. Report to Evolution Committee of the Royal Soc. II, pp. 11–16.

BAUR, E. 1930. Einführung in die Vererbungslehre. 11th ed. Berlin. (Contains excellently illustrated account of genetic analysis of *Antirrhinum*, snapdragon.) See also Bibliotheca Genetica **4.** Berlin.

BLAKESLEE, A. F. 1921. A chemical method of distinguishing genetic types of yellow cones of Rudbeckia. Zeitschr. Ind. Abst. Vererb. **25.**

CASTLE, W. E. 1930. Genetics and eugenics. 4th ed. Cambridge (Mass.).

DARWIN, C. 1876. The variation of animals and plants under domestication. 2d ed. New York.

DUNN, L. C. 1936. Description of agouti and albino series of allelomorphs. J. Genet. **33:** 443–453.

———. 1937. Genetic analysis of variegated spotting in the house mouse. Genetics **22:** 43–64.

—— and D. R. CHARLES. 1937. Analysis of quantitative variations in the pied spotting of the house mouse. Genetics **22** : 14–42.

EMERSON, R. A., G. W. BEADLE, and A. C. FRASER. 1935. A summary of linkage studies in maize. Cornell Univ. Agr. Exp. Sta. Memoir **180**.

KEELER, C. 1931. The laboratory mouse. Cambridge (Mass.).

LINDSTROM, E. W. 1931. The genetics of maize. Bull. Torrey Bot. Club **57**.

LITTLE, C. C. 1913. Experimental studies on the inheritance of color in mice. Carnegie Inst. Washington Publ. **179**.

NILSSON-EHLE, N. 1908. Einige Ergebnisse von Kreuzungen bei Hafer und Weizen. Bot. Notiser.

ONSLOW, MURIEL. 1925. The anthocyanin pigments of plants. 2d ed. Cambridge (England).

SHULL, G. H. 1914. Duplicate genes for capsule form in *Bursa bursapastoris*. Zeitschr. Ind. Abst. Vererb. **12**.

SINNOTT, E. W. 1927. A factorial analysis of certain shape characters in squash fruits. Amer. Nat. **61** : 333–344.

——, and G. B. DURHAM. 1922. Inheritance in the summer squash. Jour. Heredity **13**.

SMITH, P. E., and E. C. MACDOWELL. 1930. An hereditary anterior-pituitary deficiency in the mouse. Anat. Rec. **46**.

SNYDER, L. M. 1934. Principles of Heredity. New York. (Good account of blood group inheritance.)

STERN, C. 1930. Multiple Allelie. Handbuch der Vererbungswissenschaft. Berlin.

PROBLEMS

125. Can pure stocks of the following be produced: yellow mice; walnut-combed fowls; blue Andalusian fowls? Explain.

126. How could you most easily distinguish the various genotypes among the walnut-combed F_2 birds in the checkerboard in Fig. 29?

127. A strain of black, solid-colored mice has bred true for 10 generations, except for one albino which appeared in the second generation. In the sixth generation a black- and white-spotted mouse is born in this strain. The breeder's explanation is that the blacks have been carrying white as a latent character and that, through long association, the two traits have affected or "contaminated" each other, resulting in a black-and-white animal. Criticize this explanation and offer an alternative one.

128. The difference between dark and blue eyes in man is probably determined by a single factor, but there are many shades of brown and of blue eyes. How would you explain these minor differences?

129. Can you suggest a chemical or physical explanation for the multiple effects of a single factor such as Mendel found in purple-flowered peas?

130. In mice how would you recognize a recessive trait which has also a lethal effect?

131. Describe one or more instances in man where the expression of an inherited defect has been modified by training or environment.

132. Can an albino mouse be heterozygous for another member of the albino series of alleles? Explain.

133. How would you determine whether a dwarf mouse contained the gene for dwarfism described on page 115?

Note.—In certain breeds of sheep both sexes bear horns, but in others horns are absent from both. In crosses between the two, the horned condition is dominant in males and recessive in females. White fleece is dominant over black in both sexes and in all breeds.

134. If a homozygous horned, white ram is bred to a homozygous hornless, black ewe, what will be the appearance of the F_1 and the F_2 generations as to horns and color?

135. A horned, black ram bred to a hornless, white ewe has the following offspring: Of the males, one-fourth are horned, white; one-fourth horned, black; one-fourth hornless, white; and one-fourth hornless, black. Of the females, one-half are hornless, black and one-half hornless, white. What are the genotypes of the parents?

Note.—In man, assume that baldness, S, is dominant over nonbaldness, s, in males but recessive in females.

136. A brown-eyed, bald man whose father was nonbald and blue-eyed marries a blue-eyed, nonbald woman whose father was bald and all of whose brothers were also bald. What will be the probable appearance of their children as to eye color and baldness?

Note.—In poultry the factors for rose comb, R, and pea comb, P, if present together, produce walnut comb. The recessive alleles of both, when present together in a homozygous condition, produce single comb.

137. What will be the comb character of the offspring of the following crosses, in which the genotypes of the parents are given?

$Rr\,Pp \times Rr\,Pp$	$Rr\,Pp \times Rr\,pp$
$RR\,Pp \times rr\,Pp$	$Rr\,pp \times rr\,Pp$
$rr\,PP \times Rr\,Pp$	$Rr\,pp \times Rr\,pp$

Note.—In the following five questions, all of which concern comb form in poultry, determine the genotypes of the parents:

138. A rose crossed with a walnut produces offspring three-eighths of which are walnut, three-eighths rose, one-eighth pea, and one-eighth single.

139. A walnut crossed with a single produces offspring one-fourth of which are walnut, one-fourth rose, one-fourth pea, and one-fourth single.

140. A rose crossed with a pea produces six walnut and five rose offspring.

141. A walnut crossed with a single produces one single-comb offspring.

142. A walnut crossed with a walnut produces one rose, two walnut, and one single offspring.

143. If one of the walnut parents in the preceding question were crossed with one of its single-comb offspring, what would *their* offspring be like?

Note.—In poultry, feathered shanks, *F*, are dominant over clean, *f*; and the white plumage of Leghorns, *I*, is dominant over black, *i*.

144. What will be the appearance of the offspring of the following crosses, in which the genotypes of the parents are given:

$$ff\,Rr\,Pp \times Ff\,Rr\,pp$$
$$Ff\,ii\,Rr\,pp \times ff\,II\,Rr\,Pp$$

145. A feather-shanked, rose-comb bird crossed with a clean-shanked, pea-comb one produces 25 feathered, pea offspring; 24 feathered, walnut; 26 feathered, rose; and 22 feathered, single. What are the genotypes of the parents?

146. A breeder has a homozygous race of feather-legged, black, rose-comb birds and another of clean-legged, white, pea-comb ones. He wants a race of black birds which have clean legs and walnut combs. What proportion of the F_2 raised from a cross between these two races will be what he desires in *appearance?* What proportion of these birds will be homozygous for the desired characters?

147. If the disk-fruited F_1 squash plants resulting from a cross of sphere $\times$ sphere (p. 89) are crossed with elongate-fruited plants, what will be the fruit shape of their offspring?

148. A certain disk-fruited squash plant crossed with a spherical-fruited one produces offspring of which three-eighths are disks, one-half spheres, and one-eighth elongates. What are the genotypes of the parents?

Note.—In sweet peas, factors *C* or *P* alone produce white flowers, the purple color being due to the presence of both these factors.

149. What will be the flower color of the offspring of the following crosses, in which the genotypes of the parents are given?

$$Cc\,Pp \times cc\,Pp \qquad\qquad cc\,Pp \times CC\,pp$$
$$Cc\,Pp \times Cc\,PP \qquad\qquad Cc\,pp \times cc\,Pp$$

150. In the checkerboard (Fig. 30) what will be the flower color of the offspring of each of the nine purple-flowered plants if selfed?

Note.—In the following three crosses of sweet peas what are the genotypes of the parents?

151. A white-flowered plant crossed with a purple produces offspring of which three-eighths are purple and five-eighths white.

152. A purple-flowered plant crossed with a white one produces offspring of which one-half are purple and one-half white.

153. A white-flowered plant crossed with another white produces offspring of which three-fourths are white and one-fourth purple.

Note.—In maize, factors *C* and *R* are both necessary for the production of red aleurone color, the absence of either resulting in white aleurone. If factor *P* is present in addition to *C* and *R*, the aleurone is purple, but *P* has no effect in the absence of either *C* or *R* or both.

154. In maize, what is the aleurone color of the offspring of the following crosses, the genotypes of the parents being given?

$Cc\,Rr\,pp \times cc\,Rr\,Pp$ $CC\,rr\,Pp \times Cc\,Rr\,pp$

$cc\,RR\,Pp \times Cc\,Rr\,pp$ $Cc\,Rr\,Pp \times Cc\,Rr\,Pp$

Note.—In the following three questions, all of which refer to aleurone color in maize, find the genotypes of the parents.

155. A purple plant crossed with a white produces offspring of which one-eighth are purple, one-eighth red, and three-fourths white.

156. A purple plant crossed with a red produces offspring of which nine thirty-seconds are purple, nine thirty-seconds red, and seven-sixteenths white.

157. A purple plant crossed with a white produces offspring of which three-eighths are purple and five-eighths white.

Note.—In maize, factor W prevents the appearance of any color in the aleurone at all, and its presence thus results in white aleurone. Its recessive allele w allows the development of color.

158. What will be the aleurone color of the offspring of the following crosses, the genotypes of the parents being given?

$Ww\,Cc\,Rr\,Pp \times ww\,cc\,rr\,pp$ $ww\,Cc\,rr\,Pp \times WW\,cc\,rr\,Pp$

$Ww\,cc\,Rr\,pp \times Ww\,cc\,Rr\,pp$ $ww\,cc\,Rr\,pp \times Ww\,Cc\,rr\,PP$

Note.—The effect of the factors C, A, B, D, P, and S and their recessive alleles on coat color in mice is as follows (see Table VII): C, colored; c, albino; AB, black agouti (wild type); Ab, cinnamon (brown agouti); P, normal dark eyes; p, pink eyes; aB, black; ab, brown; D, normal dark color; d, dilute color; S, solid or self color; s, spotted with white.

159. In mice what will be the coat color of the offspring of the following crosses, in which the genotypes of the parents are given?

$Cc\,Aa\,Bb \times CC\,aa\,Bb$

$Cc\,Aa\,BB\,Dd \times cc\,Aa\,Bb\,Dd$

$CC\,aa\,Bb\,dd\,Pp \times Cc\,aa\,Bb\,Dd\,pp$

$CC\,AA\,BB\,Dd\,Pp\,SS \times Cc\,aa\,Bb\,DD\,Pp\,ss$

Note.—In the following five crosses, which deal with coat color in mice, find the genotypes of the parents.

160. An agouti animal crossed with another agouti produces offspring of which nine-sixteenths are agouti, three-sixteenths black, three-sixteenths cinnamon, and one-sixteenth brown.

161. A cinnamon animal crossed with an albino produces offspring of which three-eighths are agouti, one-eighth black, and one-half albino.

162. A black animal crossed with an agouti produces offspring of which nine thirty-seconds are agouti, nine thirty-seconds black, three thirty-seconds cinnamon, three thirty-seconds brown, and one-fourth albino.

163. A dilute agouti animal crossed with a pink-eyed, spotted black produces three agouti offspring, one spotted agouti, two dilute agouti, two dilute, spotted agouti, four cinnamon, one spotted cinnamon, two dilute cinnamon, and four albinos.

164. An agouti animal crossed with a dilute pink-eyed, spotted brown produces one dilute black, one spotted agouti, and one pink-eyed cinnamon.

Note.—In summer squashes the factor for white fruit color, *W*, is epistatic to that for yellow, *Y*; *WY* and *Wy* plants are white, *wY* plants yellow, and *wy* plants green.

165. What is the color of the fruit in the offspring of the following crosses, the genotypes of the parents being given?

$$Ww\,Yy \times Ww\,yy \qquad ww\,YY \times Ww\,yy \qquad Ww\,yy \times ww\,Yy$$

Note.—In the following three questions, which deal with fruit color in squashes, find the genotypes of the parents:

166. A white plant crossed with a yellow one produces offspring of which one-half are white, three-eighths yellow, and one-eighth green.

167. A white plant crossed with a green one produces offspring of which one-half are white and one-half yellow.

168. A white plant crossed with another white one produces offspring of which three-fourths are white, three-sixteenths yellow, and one-sixteenth green.

Note.—In stocks, factor *C*, in the absence of factor *R*, produces cream-colored flowers; *c* produces white ones; *C* with *R*, red ones; *C* with *R* and *V*, violet ones, but *V* has no effect in the absence of either *C* or *R* or both. Factor *H* causes the plant to be hairy, but it is operative *only in the presence of both C and R*. Its recessive allele, *h*, causes a smooth condition. White-flowered and cream-flowered plants are thus always smooth, and red-flowered and violet-flowered ones may be either hairy or smooth.

169. In stocks, what is the appearance of the offspring of the following crosses, the genotypes of the parents for flower color and plant surface being given?

$$CC\,Rr\,VV\,Hh \times Cc\,rr\,Vv\,HH \qquad Cc\,rr\,vv\,Hh \times cc\,RR\,Vv\,hh$$
$$Cc\,Rr\,Vv\,Hh \times Cc\,Rr\,Vv\,Hh \qquad Cc\,Rr\,Vv\,Hh \times cc\,rr\,vv\,hh$$

Note.—In the following three questions, which deal with flower color and plant surface in stocks, find the genotypes of the parents:

170. A cream smooth plant crossed with a white smooth one produces offspring of which three-eighths are violet smooth, one-eighth red smooth, and one-half white smooth.

171. A violet smooth plant crossed with a white smooth one produces offspring of which one-sixteenth are violet hairy, one-sixteenth violet smooth, one-sixteenth red hairy, one-sixteenth red smooth, one-fourth cream smooth, and one-half white smooth.

172. A violet hairy plant crossed with a red smooth one produces one white smooth plant, one cream smooth one, and one red smooth one. What are the chances of getting a violet hairy plant out of this cross?

173. What will be the plumage color of the offspring of the following crosses in poultry, the genotypes of the parents being given (p. 97)?

$$Ii\,Cc \times ii\,Cc \qquad\qquad ii\,Cc \times Ii\,CC$$
$$II\,cc \times ii\,cc \qquad\qquad Ii\,cc \times ii\,Cc$$

174. In rabbits full color (C), Himalayan albinism (C^h), and albinism (c^a) form a series of multiple alleles with dominance in the order given. What will be the appearance of the offspring of the following crosses:

(*a*) colored × Himalayan (homozygous)
(*b*) F_2 from (*a*)
(*c*) Himalayan × albino
(*d*) F_2 from (*c*)
(*e*) F_1 from (*a*) × F_1 from (*c*)

175. In maize there are several factors which affect plant color. Three of these are *sun red*, *weak sun red*, and *dilute sun red*, their intensities being in the order named. Following are the results of crosses between these three types (data from Emerson): sun red × dilute sun red gave all sun red in F_1 and 998 sun red to 314 dilute sun red in F_2; weak sun red × dilute sun red gave all weak sun red in F_1 and 1,300 weak sun red to 429 dilute sun red in F_2; sun red × weak sun red gave all sun red in F_1 and 71 sun red to 16 weak sun red in F_2.

Explain these results, stating the relationship among these three plant colors.

Note.—In mice the following genes affecting coat color form a series of multiple alleles: A^L, agouti light belly; A, agouti (gray-belly, wild type); a^t, black and tan (black back, light belly); a (black, nonagouti); Aa^t animals are agouti with light belly; otherwise dominance is complete in order given. C is colored; cc, albino.

176. What will be the appearance of the offspring of the following crosses:

(*a*) $A^L A \times A\,A$
(*b*) $A^L A^L \times A\,a$
(*c*) $A\,a^t \times A\,a$
(*d*) $A^L A \times a^t a$

177. What are the genotypes of the parents in the following crosses:

(*a*) Agouti light belly × agouti light belly giving one-fourth agouti, one-half agouti light belly, one-fourth black and tan.

(*b*) Agouti light belly × agouti giving one-half agouti light belly; one-fourth agouti; one-fourth black.

(*c*) Albino × agouti giving all agouti light belly in F_1; and in F_2 three-sixteenths agouti, three-eighths agouti light belly, three-sixteenths black and tan, and one-fourth albino.

178. What will be the appearance of the offspring from the following crosses in mice (*cf.* p. 102):

(a) $AA\ Cc^{ch} \times AA\ Cc^a$
(b) $AA\ c^{ch}c^h \times AA\ c^hc^h$
(c) $AA\ c^hc^a \times AA\ c^{ch}c^{ch}$
(d) $AA\ Cc^h \times AA\ c^{ch}c^a$

179. What crosses would you make to determine the genotypes as to albino and agouti alleles of the following mice: (a) agouti; (b) extreme dilute black and tan; (c) chinchilla light-bellied agouti? What would be the genotype of one animal or pure stock which could be used to make progeny tests for all of these genes at once?

180. From the data on inheritance of capsule shape in the shepherd's-purse, calculate the expected results in F_3 from self-fertilizing each of the 15 F_2 types with triangular capsules in Fig. 36.

181. In wheat, determine the genotypes of the parents in the following crosses:
(a) Red × white giving three-fourths red and one-fourth white;
(b) Red × red giving seven-eighths red and one-eighth white.

182. In each of two different strains of maize, plants have been found which, when selfed, produce about three-fourths normal green and one-fourth lethal white ("albino") seedlings. If two such albino-producing plants, one from each strain, are crossed, the F_1 is found to be all green, but certain of the F_2 populations are approximately nine-sixteenths green and seven-sixteenths white. Explain, giving genotypes.

183. In maize, plant A when crossed with plant B produced 255 green and 89 white offspring but when selfed produced 153 green and 118 white offspring. What are the genotypes of these two plants? What should plant B produce when selfed?

184. A green maize plant when selfed produces about fifteen-sixteenths green and one-sixteenth white (lethal) seedlings. Explain.

185. In mice what will be the appearance of the offspring from the following crosses (A^Y = yellow):

$$CC\ A^YA\ Bb \times CC\ A^YA\ bb$$
$$Cc\ A^YA\ BB \times Cc\ A^YA\ Bb$$
$$cc\ A^YA\ BB \times Cc\ A^YA\ BB$$

186. In Drosophila crosses of Dichaete winged flies × Dichaete always give two-thirds Dichaete to one-third normal winged offspring. Dichaete × normal gives one-half Dichaete and one-half normal. How would you explain these results?

187. In poultry the following results were obtained:

	Progeny	
	Short-legged	Normal
a. Short-legged × short-legged	1,972	955
b. Short-legged × normal	1,676	1,661

Explain these results, giving genotypes of animals involved.   Explain how you would test your hypothesis (*a*) by statistical methods; (*b*) by obtaining what additional facts?

188. What will be the phenotype, as to blood groups, of offspring of parents of the following genotypes for blood groups:

$$Aa \times a^B a$$
$$Aa^B \times a^B a$$
$$a^B a \times a^B a$$

189. If a person of blood group AB marries one belonging to group O, what will be the blood groups of their children?

Note.—In the three following problems on blood groups, determine the genotypes of the parents.

190. One parent is group A and the other group B, but all four groups are represented among the children.

191. Both parents are group A, but three-fourths of the children belong to group A and one-fourth to group O.

192. One parent is AB and the other B, but of the children one-fourth are A, one-fourth AB, and one-half B.

193. In the two following cases of disputed paternity, determine the true father of the child:

(*a*) The mother belongs to group B, the child to O, one possible father to A and the other to AB.

(*b*) The mother belongs to group B, the child to AB, one possible father to A and the other to B.

194. In the choice of donors for blood transfusion, a patient's brother or sister is often selected.   Would these be more likely to be successful donors if both parents belonged to blood group AB or if both belonged to group O?   Explain.

195. If both parents belong to blood group AB, what proportion of their children would be expected to be of such a type as to be able to give blood to their parents?

196. A given F_2 population consists of 1,250 *B* and 350 *b* individuals.   Does this fit better a 3:1 or a 13:3 segregation?   Decide this by calculating $S.E._d$ for each ratio.

197. By calculating χ^2 and *P* determine whether the following F_2 population fits better a 3:3:1:1 ratio or a 27:21:9:7 ratio:

AB	*Ab*	*aB*	*ab*
285	245	90	84

CHAPTER VI

MULTIPLE-FACTOR INHERITANCE

The traits of organisms which we have thus far considered are definite and easily recognized ones. The characters which Mendel studied in peas, the comb types in poultry, and the coat colors of mice are readily distinguished by contrast with their alternatives. Factor interaction, linkage, and other causes may introduce complications, but the classification of a given segregating population and a determination of the ratios which it exhibits are for the most part easy tasks. In a cross between a wild gray house mouse, for example, and a pale, pink-eyed, spotted, brown one, segregation and recombination will produce a wide range of different coat colors in F_2, but each is a distinct type and with but little practice may be placed in its proper class.

Quantitative Characters.—Even casual observation, however, will disclose many traits where alternatives are not easily distinguishable and where there are all degrees of intermediate conditions between one extreme and the other. Such traits are often termed quantitative in distinction to the simpler qualitative ones. Examples are those involving the length, weight, and girths of the body, the number of multiple parts such as petals or appendages, and the degree of fertility, yield, intelligence, strength, or development in any other character, including most of those which are economically important. It is obvious that characters of this sort, involving differences in degree, cannot be analyzed by the simple methods used for qualitative ones. In studying stature, for example, it is impossible to divide men into "tall" and "short," or even into "tall," "medium," and "short," for if a large random group of people is examined, it will not be found to be composed of definite groups but of individuals representing every gradation in height from very short to very tall.

Such characters often show in inheritance the same absence of clearly marked classes. If a homozygous "large" individual is crossed with a homozygous "small" one, the F_2, if extensive enough, includes some individuals as small as one grandparent, some as large as the other, and others ranging all the way between. Here there is evidently no clean-cut segregation into distinct classes which can be recognized and counted, and the problem of determining the method of inheritance of such traits must evidently be approached by a somewhat different method from

125

that of ordinary Mendelian analysis. Indeed, such characters were long thought to constitute important exceptions to Mendel's laws.

It is obvious, however, that there is no hard-and-fast difference between qualitative and quantitative characters. Color, which in many cases shows definite alternative inheritance, as in the case of pea flowers, may in others appear in a series of intensities which grade almost imperceptibly into each other and which show slight differences in the quantity of pigment present. The series of eye-color alleles in Drosophila, running from white through successive intensifications of pigment to red, or the similar series of flower-color factors in Antirrhinum (Fig. 35) are examples. Similarly, shape sometimes presents simple qualitative differences and sometimes a more complex intergrading series. The primary sex difference is usually a definite and discontinuous one, but, as we shall see, intermediate forms are often found, and maleness and femaleness are now recognized as matters of degree. Many characters which under certain conditions may be easily described in "qualitative" terms may be typically "quantitative" under others.

The Multiple-factor Hypothesis.—The absence of clear-cut segregation into definite and readily recognizable classes, which is the main difference between the inheritance of typical quantitative characters and that of the ones which we have chiefly considered thus far, may perhaps best be explained by a study of the manner of inheritance of one of those traits which is sometimes a simple qualitative one but at other times behaves in a more complex manner. In a previous chapter (p. 105) the operation of *duplicate* factors, such as those discovered for capsule shape in Bursa by Shull and for kernel color in wheat by Nilsson-Ehle, has been described. The latter case is particularly illuminating. Here red is not completely dominant over white, but the hybrids may show various intensities of color. In some crosses of red with white a simple 3:1 ratio is found, indicating a single gene difference, but some of the reds are as dark as the red grandparent, and others resemble the F_1 in being less intense. In other crosses a 15:1 ratio of red to white is found in the F_2. Here there are a few which are as dark red as the red grandparent, a considerable number which are of about the same shade as the F_1, and some which are even paler than the F_1. The conclusion seems obvious (and is supported by a study of F_3 generations raised from these various types) that there are here two pairs of genes for red, neither completely dominant over white and either capable of producing red kernels, but that the four members of these pairs are cumulative in their effect, the dark reds being due to the presence of four genes, the next in intensity to three, those like the F_1 to two, and the pale reds to but one. Representing one of these factor pairs by AA and the other by BB, the original dark-red parent is $AABB$ and the white one $aabb$. The F_1 is $AaBb$, intermediate in color. The checkerboard in Fig. 37, p. 108, shows the genotypes of the F_2 plants, with the number of red genes possessed by each class. Only 1 of the 15 reds has all four genes and is thus dark red; 4 have three genes; 6 have two; 4 have one; and one-sixteenth of the whole population has none.

In still other cases Nilsson-Ehle found that $^{63}\!/_{64}$ of the F_2 plants were red kerneled and only $\frac{1}{64}$ white, a condition which suggested *three* independent genes for red. Here the range in intensity of the red was even more marked, as was to be expected. If the red parent is represented by the genotype *AABBCC* and the white by *aabbcc*, the F_1 (*AaBbCc*) should evidently be essentially uniform and intermediate between the parents in color, both of which expectations are realized. In the F_2 there should also be a marked increase in the range of color types. The relative proportions of the various groups may readily be calculated. A few individuals ($\frac{1}{64}$) may be expected to have six genes for red, others ($^{6}\!/_{64}$) five, others ($^{15}\!/_{64}$) four, others ($^{20}\!/_{64}$) three, others ($^{15}\!/_{64}$) two, others ($^{6}\!/_{64}$) one, and a few ($\frac{1}{64}$) none at all (resulting in white kernels). Although it is not always possible to distinguish these six classes of reds by their appearance, it is evident that there are *few* of either extreme type and *many more* of the intermediate grades, and segregation in later generations indicates the essential correctness of this three-factor hypothesis.

In the uniform but intermediate character of the F_1 and the marked increase in variability of the F_2, red kernel color of wheat in this case behaves essentially like an ordinary quantitative character. That the nature of its inheritance is truly Mendelian is proved not only by an analysis of the results of this cross but by a comparison between it and the obviously simpler results (3:1 and 15:1 segregations) for the same character in related races. From a study of such cases as this Nilsson-Ehle (and East independently) proposed the Multiple-factor hypothesis for the inheritance of quantitative characters. This assumes that there is a *series of independent genes* for a given quantitative trait, and that these genes are cumulative in their effect. Dominance is ordinarily absent, the F_1 appearing as a blend of the characters of the two parents. If instead of a unit of color (as in wheat kernels) each gene should contribute a unit of height, weight, or other typically quantitative trait, the relations between parents, F_1, and F_2 would be essentially like those just described for kernel color.

As a typical example we may take the inheritance of ear length in maize, as studied by East. He worked with two relatively pure types: one, long-eared Black Mexican sweet corn and the other, short-eared Tom Thumb popcorn. In Fig. 41 are shown the parental types and the F_1 and F_2 generations following a cross between them. The ears have been arranged in classes differing by 1 cm. in length, and under each class is given the number of individuals in that class. Thus in the F_1 there was one plant in which the ear was 9 cm. long, there were 12 in which it was 10 cm., and so on. Each of the pure types evidently varied somewhat in ear length, presumably because of environmental differences, and the

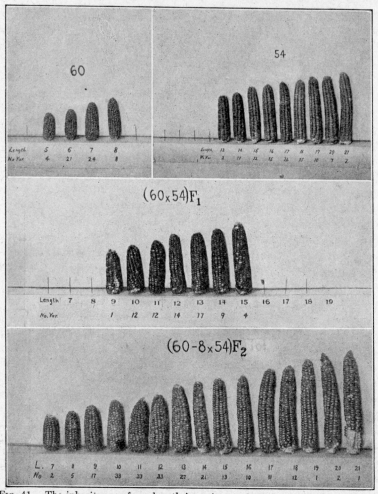

Fig. 41.—The inheritance of ear length in maize, as shown by the results of crossing a short-eared variety of popcorn with a long-eared variety of sweet corn. Ears showing the range in length of the parent types are pictured above, with the F_1 and F_2 generations below. (*From East.*)

F_1 shows about the same degree of variability, although it is essentially intermediate between the two parental types. In the F_2, however, there is a much greater range, from plants with ears as short as the shorter eared grandparent to those with ears as long as the longer eared grandparent. There are relatively few of these extreme types, and a relatively large number of those which have intermediate ear length essentially like that of the F_1. This situation is similar in its essentials to that of kernel color in wheat, and although segregation into a series of distinct classes is impossible to demonstrate, the marked increase in variability of the F_2 as compared with the F_1 finds its simplest explanation in the independent segregation of a series of "multiple factors," each affecting ear length and all of them cumulative in their effect.

Analysis of Quantitative Inheritance.—To study the inheritance of traits like ear length in maize, where simple segregation is lacking and an intergrading series of forms is found, a technique adapted to an analysis of quantitative data must be employed.

Most quantitative traits cannot readily be described by words such as "tall," "short," "heavy," "light," "high," "low," "weak," or "strong," because of the existence of all grades of intermediates. Evidently, the only way in which a satisfactory determination and description of such characters can be made is by *measurements*. By this means every individual has a quantitative description of its particular character whereby it may easily be compared with other individuals of the same kind. The series of measurements which have thus been gathered in any study of the inheritance of size must then be classified and simplified by methods of statistical analysis if they are to be handled easily and their meaning presented in precise and understandable form. The application of statistical methods to living things is known as *biometry* and has developed into an important branch of biological investigation. Before it is possible to understand the inheritance of quantitative characters, it is necessary, therefore, to master certain of the more important methods of biometrical analysis and learn to extract from the "raw" data themselves a few of the simplified measures, or *constants*, which are commonly used in problems of this sort. The concern here is with biometry, not as an end in itself, but as a convenient mathematical tool which may be used in dealing with quantitative characters.

Biometrical Constants.—Even in a group of individuals which is known to be homozygous for a given size character, all the members are not exactly alike, for quantitative characters are greatly influenced in their expression by the environment. Bean plants belonging to the same pure line or race, for example, which are similar in their entire genetic constitution, differ markedly in vine height, pod size, yield of fruit, and other quantitative traits according to the conditions of temperature, moisture, and soil fertility under which they have grown. Similarly among animals, proper feeding results, even in the same race, in a much greater development of such characters as body weight, milk production, and egg yield than does a ration which is deficient in some component necessary to maximum development. Even when every attempt is made to secure complete uniformity, both in the genetic constitution of the individuals studied and in the various factors of their environment, there is almost always a variation among them with regard to any quantitative character. If the inheritance of such a character is to be studied by crossing individuals from one group with those from another (tall plants with dwarf ones, say) and the results of this cross followed to later generations, it is important to obtain a single quantity which shall represent, as accurately as possible, that size character for that particular group, free from the fluctuations shown by individual members. Such a quantity is the *average* or *mean*, and its determination for a given group is an important step in biometrical analysis.

It is also useful to obtain a measurement of the *variation* which a given group of individuals displays, for not only does this often serve to indicate purity of type, or influence of the environment, but a study of the comparative variability of parents and offspring has given valuable clues as to the method of inheritance of quantitative characters. The mean tells nothing of variation, for two populations may have the same mean but may differ greatly in the extent to which their members vary around it; and other constants, especially the *standard deviation* and the *coefficient of variability*, must be determined.

Measurement of type and measurement of variation are thus two of the primary objects of a biometrical analysis of size inheritance or, indeed, of any statistical study of quantitative characters. The method by which the necessary statistical constants are determined is described at the end of this chapter.

Biometrical Analysis of Some Quantitative Traits.—An application of biometrical methods may now be made to the case of ear-length inheritance in maize, already described. In Table X are classified, in 1-cm. classes, the 57 individuals of the pop race studied, the 101 individuals of the Black Mexican race, the 69 individuals of the F_1 raised from a cross between these two, the 221 individuals of the F_2

TABLE X.—FREQUENCY DISTRIBUTION OF LENGTHS OF EARS IN CROSS OF LONG-EARED (60) AND SHORT-EARED (54) MAIZE (*From East*)

Line number	Class centers in centimeters for lengths of ears																	Mean, cm.	Standard deviation, cm.	Coefficient of variability, %
	5	6	7	8	9	10	11	12	13	14	15	16	17	18	19	20	21			
60	4	21	24	8														6.6 ± 0.07	0.81 ± 0.05	12.27 ± 0.78
54									3	11	12	15	26	15	10	7	2	16.8 ± 0.12	1.87 ± 0.09	11.13 ± 0.53
(60 × 54)F_1					1	12	12	14	17	9	4							12.1 ± 0.12	1.51 ± 0.09	12.48 ± 0.72
(60 × 54)F_2			2	5	17	33	33	33	27	21	13	10	11	12	1	2	1	12.6 ± 0.13	2.81 ± 0.09	$22 30 \pm 0.74$

obtained by crossing the F_1 plants. The mean, standard deviation, and coefficient of variation for each of these four groups are also presented.

It will be noted that even in the pure types the individuals vary somewhat in ear length, but these differences are presumably due to environmental conditions, which are very hard to equalize exactly. The mean ear length for each race, however, rather than the length of any one group of individuals may be taken as representative of the race as a whole. The means of the parent types differ by 10.2 cm. The variability of these two types, however, is low and of about the same magnitude. There are two noteworthy facts about the F_1: first, that its mean is approximately intermediate between that of the two parents (12.1 cm. as compared with 6.6 cm. and 16.8 cm.); and, second, that its variability is about as low as theirs (12.48 per cent as compared with 12.27 per cent and 11.13 per cent). The F_2 is different. Its mean is very close to that of the F_1, but *its variability has increased very greatly*, rising to 22.30 per cent. Some plants are found in this generation with ears as long as the mean of the sweet type and some with ears as short as that of the pop type, with others ranging all the way between. As stated above, these facts may best be interpreted by assuming that the two original races differ in a series of

FIG. 42.—Flowers showing the average corolla length of two varieties of *Nicotiana longiflora* (left and right) and an average flower from the F_2 of a cross between them (center). (*From East.*)

factors for ear length, that these lack dominance, and that their independent segregation in F_2 is responsible for the increased variability which this generation shows. Most quantitative traits that have been subjected to biometrical analysis show results essentially like these for ear length in maize and are now generally regarded as dependent upon a series of multiple factors.

The genetic complexity in a given case of quantitative inheritance may be roughly estimated by an analysis of the F_2 generation. If three factor pairs are responsible for a given size difference, it is evident that an individual as extreme as one of the grandparental types may be expected to appear only about once in sixty-four times. In the inheritance of most quantitative characters, however, the original types are recovered in the F_2 much less frequently than this, and it is therefore inferred that more than three factor pairs are involved. A rough guess as to their number can be made by determining the proportion of the F_2 which resembles one of the P_1 types. If four factor pairs are concerned, this parental type will reappear in approximately 1/256 of the individuals; if five, in about 1/1,024; if six, in about 1/4,096; and so on. If the number of factors is large, individuals like the grandparents will not appear in a small F_2 (as often happens). In the inheritance of corn ear length, for example, as shown in Table X, there are evidently few factors involved in the difference between the sweet and the pop types. In Table XI for corolla length in tobacco (Fig. 42), however, there seem to be more factors, for in a rather large F_2 the parent types do not reappear to all.

The inheritance of quantitative characters has now been studied in a considerable number of animal and plant species, and in most cases results essentially similar to those reported above have been obtained. Only rarely, however, is evidence sufficient to indicate at all definitely the number of genes concerned.

TABLE XI.—FREQUENCY DISTRIBUTION FOR COROLLA LENGTH IN A CROSS BETWEEN VARIETIES OF *Nicotiana longiflora* CAV. (*From East*)

	Class centers, millimeters																						
	34	37	40	43	46	49	52	55	58	61	64	67	70	73	76	79	82	85	88	91	94	97	100
P_1	1	21	140	49																			
P_1																		13	45	91	19	1	
F_1							4	10	41	75	40	3											
F_2						1	5	16	23	18	62	37	25	16	4	2	2						

Genetic Evidence for Multiple Factors.—The chief difficulty in making a multiple-factor analysis of quantitative traits lies in the fact that the various genes concerned all affect the same character, with the result that it is difficult to demonstrate their individual existence and independence. Conclusive proof that such genes actually exist is furnished only when we are able to isolate them and study their individual effect just as we do for those which determine other characters.

In a few cases, as in the inheritance of height in peas studied by Mendel, there is evidence that a single gene produces a marked and easily recognizable difference in a quantitative trait. In this same species it has now been shown (de Haan) that there are at least three pairs of genes, independently inherited, which determine plant height and that the particular effect of each of these is distinguishable from that of the others. In oats, there are three distinct dwarf types, each produced by a different gene; and a considerable number of other cases might be cited where several genes, each recognizably distinct in its action, affects a single quantitative character.

Still more definite evidence has been obtained from linkage experiments, where it can be shown that genes affecting size are definitely linked with genes for qualitative characters and thus evidently occupy definite positions in the chromosomes. Lindstrom, for example, has demonstrated the presence of a major gene for fruit size in one of the chromosomes of the tomato and has determined its linkage relations with three other genes there; and he has shown that genes influencing fruit size occur in at least two other chromosomes. Lindstrom has also reported that specific genes controlling number of rows of kernels on the ear of maize are present in at least four of the chromosomes of this species.

In Drosophila a series of genes affecting body size have been isolated and their linkage relations determined. Among these are two "giant" genes and two "dwarf" ones. In Drosophila, too, Warren has been able to establish the existence of genes for egg size in all four linkage groups, and to prove that they differ in the intensity of their effect and behave in inheritance like ordinary genes, segregating purely, showing independent assortment with those size and other genes which occur in different chromosomes, and showing linkage with those which occur in the same chromosome.

In beans Sax finds that a gene which increases seed weight by 5 or 6 centigrams is linked with a gene for pigmentation of the seed coat. Hoshino has shown linkage between a gene for flower color and one for flowering time in garden peas and presents evidence that flowering time is determined by two genes, one linked with flower color and the other independent of it.

In Datura characters such as height of plant, area and thickness of leaves, shape of capsules, diameter of vessels, size of starch grains, width of vascular bundles, and many others have been found to be influenced by most, or all, of the 12 pairs of chromosomes, suggesting that genes controlling these characters are numerous and widely distributed.

The Character of Gene Action in Quantitative Inheritance.—Most quantitative traits are relatively simple in their outward expression, and differences between them can readily be stated in units of measurement. The developmental processes which interact to produce these differences, however, may be very diverse. Thus in characters of body or organ size, the rate and the extent of cell multiplication and of cell enlargement, and the various other developmental processes which affect both of these, together determine the total amount of growth and thus ultimate size. Many distinct developmental processes are doubtless concerned in the determination of size differences. There is evidence in a few cases that these processes, to some extent, at least, are independent both genetically and developmentally, and it is therefore to be expected that a very considerable number of genes will ordinarily be concerned in the inheritance of a quantitative trait.

The particular effect of a given gene in quantitative inheritance is ordinarily difficult to distinguish because of the large number of genes involved, and our knowledge of the part played by each is not nearly so complete here as it is for simpler traits. There is every reason to believe, however, that these multiple genes are not all alike in their effects but that some primarily influence one developmental process and others another. A number of cases have already been cited where, as in plant height in peas, the particular effect of each of several different genes may be distinguished. This may be shown even more clearly in the effects of genes that control quantitative differences in the distribution rather than in the amount of growth. Thus in the inheritance of fruit shape in Cucurbita at least three genes controlling the ratio of length to width have been found, each with its distinct effect. In many other cases of shape inheritance similar differences may be recognized. It is therefore to be expected, in other cases of quantitative inheritance where the effects of single genes are too small to be distinguishable, that each of these, too, is specific in character.

Furthermore, the same gene seems not to have the same effect in every individual but to be influenced in its expression by the rest of the genotype in which it occurs. It seems clear that a gene affecting a quantitative trait does not add a given *absolute amount* to that trait (as is often assumed) but rather contributes a certain *percentage*. This is to be expected from what we know as to the nature of growth, which is ordinarily an exponential or "compound-interest" process, and evidence pointing to the same conclusion is derived from a study of populations segregating for size. Thus the F_2 from a cross between races showing a quantitative difference usually does not show a symmetrical distribution when plotted in classes which are arithmetically equal (as it should if genes had the same effects in large as in small individuals) but is asymmetrical or "skewed" (Fig. 43A), the mean being higher than the median (p. 147). This is what we should expect to happen if the segregating genes for size were multiplicative rather than additive in their cumulative effect, with the same gene producing a larger effect in a large individual than in a small one. It is as though the quantitative traits were sums of money accumulating at compound interest and that the segregating genes determined the interest rates at which the accumulation is going on. That this is essentially what happens is further shown by the fact that if such a segregating F_2 population is plotted in classes which are logarithmically equal (a method which corrects for much of the percentage effect of gene action) a much more nearly symmetrical distribution results (Fig. 43*B*).   The problem of gene action in quantitative inheritance is doubtless far more complex than such a simple picture would indicate, but the student should realize at least that the multiple-factor hypothesis does not imply a constant absolute effect for each gene. Here, as elsewhere, the developmental effect of a gene is conditioned by many other genes.

It often happens that in crosses between two relatively pure types, which differ in a size character, the F₁ approaches the larger parent rather closely, or even exceeds it, although subsequent analysis shows little evidence of dominance in the series of size genes.   Such a result is due to the general increase in size which is characteristic of highly heterozygous individuals.   This phenomenon of *heterosis*, which will be discussed in more detail in a later chapter (p. 285) is apparently due to the

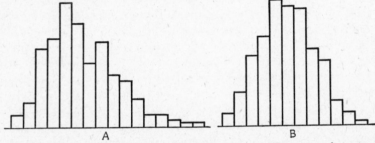

Fig. 43.—Frequency distribution of fruit weights in an F₂ from a cross between a race of squashes with heavy fruits and one with lighter fruits.   *A*, plotted with classes equal arithmetically; *B*, plotted with classes equal logarithmically.

combined effects of a series of many genes which influence vigor and size and produce their maximum effect in a heterozygous individual.   Hybrid vigor itself is thus interpreted in terms of multiple genes.

Significance of the Multiple-factor Hypothesis.—This conception of quantitative characters as controlled by series of multiple genes, therefore, seems well established, although from the nature of the traits concerned and the difficulty of identifying many of the genes, it is not so susceptible of clear demonstration as are many other genetic hypotheses. Its chief theoretical contribution has consisted in bringing quantitative or "blending" characters, at first thought to be radically different from qualitative ones, definitely under the operation of Mendelian principles.

In practical breeding it has also proved of service in interpreting the behavior of quantitative characters which are economically important. The fact that quantitative traits are apparently due to a series of independent genes will evidently result in differences in breeding behavior between individuals which are similar in appearance.   Two animals, for example, may have the same weight, but one may owe this to one group of genes and the other to another group, with a consequent recombination of genes in the offspring of a cross between them. Thus a basis is provided for a logical explanation of the often conflicting results obtained by selection. Under certain circumstances selection for a given quantitative character is no longer able to modify that character further; but if the selected race is crossed with a similar one from another source, selection among the progeny is often successful in modifying the character considerably. Evidently the first race contained only a limited number of genes for the character in question, and when these had become homozygous, no further change was possible. The introduction of *different* genes belonging to a series of multiple factors determining this character made it possible to obtain a stock with a larger number of genes and thus to establish the character on a permanently higher level.

Methods of Biometrical Analysis.—The object of biometrical analysis is to treat a mass of data in such a way that the essential facts which these embody may be expressed in very simple terms, usually by single values or *constants*. When two groups of individuals have been measured, it is thus possible to compare them readily and accurately by comparing their constants, whereas a comparison of the mass of original measurements themselves would lead only to vague and uncertain conclusions.

Several biometrical constants are of particular usefulness. One is the arithmetic average or *mean*, which expresses the type or character of a population for a given trait and makes possible a comparison, with regard to magnitude, of two populations. Other constants are the *standard deviation* and the *coefficient of variation*, which measure the variability of a population. The *standard error* serves as a measure of the reliability of a given constant. Other constants are employed in analysis according to the nature of the particular data and the problems involved.

The present discussion presents in elementary fashion some of the biometrical methods which are of particular value to students of genetics. For a more detailed discussion of this important subject the reader is referred to other sources (Davenport and Ekas, Fisher, Yule and Kendall).

Measurement.—Before biometrical analysis can be undertaken, it is obviously necessary to measure carefully all the individuals of the particular group which are to be studied for a given trait. That these original measurements should be made as accurately as possible goes without saying. No amount of statistical treatment will evolve sound results from unsound data. It should always be borne in mind that the statistical analysis of a mass of data adds nothing new thereto but merely reduces these data to a simpler form wherein we may be able to perceive certain relationships which would otherwise escape observation.

Classification.—The first step in simplifying the large and often confusing array of figures which results from the measurement of a group of individuals with regard to a given quantitative character is to arrange and classify them in a systematic fashion. In the figures for weight of 200 men, for example, which are given in Table XVII, at the end of this chapter, the lightest individual weighs 95 pounds and the others are scattered all the way along between that figure and the weight of the heaviest man, 195 pounds. If these 200 measurements are arranged in order, something has been done to simplify matters. However, a much clearer picture of the make-up of this particular group of men, as far as weight is concerned, is obtained, if, instead of studying these men as individuals, each of them differing from every other, they are divided into a comparatively small number of *groups* or *classes*, placing together in each class those who are nearly alike in body weight. In such a *frequency distribution* the relative numbers of individuals who are light, who are heavy, or who hold any given intermediate position are seen at a glance. What the limits of the classes are, provided the classes are numerous enough and of equal value, makes no great difference, although, of course, the division of a population into a large number of classes with narrow limits gives a correspondingly more accurate picture of its composition than a division into a smaller number of relatively wide classes.

In Table XII, the 200 weights presented in Table XVII have been arranged into eleven 10-pound classes, the class limits in each case being stated and the number of individuals which fall within that particular class being given. Thus, in the class which includes individuals weighing from 110 to 119 pounds there are 10 men, the weights of whom are 114, 115, 118, 111, 114, 116, 119, 112, and 119 pounds. In the next larger class are 31, and so on. The procedure in making such a classification is to establish arbitrarily the extent and limits of each class and then to check through the whole mass of data, placing each individual in its proper group.

TABLE XII.—CLASSIFICATION, FOR WEIGHT, OF THE 200 MEN
IN TABLE XVII

Class limits	90–99	100–109	110–119	120–129	130–139	140–149	150–159	160–169	170–179	180–189	190–199
Value of class center (V)..........	95	105	115	125	135	145	155	165	175	185	195
Number in each class (f).........	1	2	10	31	54	48	27	14	11	1	1

Thus the first man in Table XVII, whose weight is 135 pounds, would go in the class 130–139; the second, 156 pounds, in the class 150–159; and so through the list. An equally useful classification would result if the class limits were set at a different series of points, such as 145–154, 155–164, and so on. The number of individuals in the various classes will vary slightly, depending on the particular class limits chosen, but this variation is usually negligible. It is important, however, to decide exactly what the limits of each class shall be, so that no confusion may arise as to the placing of an individual. In the case here explained the third class, for example, includes all weights from 110.0 to 119.9 pounds, inclusive. An individual weighing 109.9 would go in the class below, one weighing 120.0 in the class above. It is also necessary to determine for each group its *class center*, the value which in later computations is

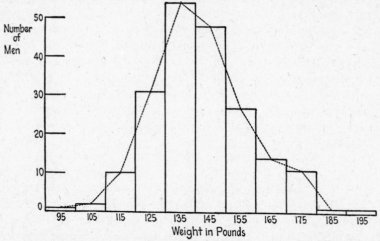

Fig. 44.—Frequency polygon and frequency curve showing variation in weight of 200 college students. A graphic representation of the data in Table XII.

used to stand for the weight of all the individuals in that class.[1] In the case cited it would be 115 pounds.

The Frequency Polygon.—When the original data have thus been classified, it becomes much easier to study the relative frequency of the various weights and so discern the character of the group as a whole. These facts may be brought out much more vividly, however, if, instead of studying the figures alone, a graphic representation of them is constructed, the so-called *frequency polygon* or *frequency curve*. If a horizontal line is divided evenly into segments or abscissas representing the number of classes into which the individuals have been grouped and if upon each of these segments is erected a column the height of which is proportional to the number of individuals in that class, a figure results

---

[1] The class center is taken to represent the average value of all the members of the class, and the larger the number in the class, the closer the class center will approximate this value.

which presents graphically the composition of the entire group. If the various class centers are united by lines, a frequency curve results. The polygon and the curve representing the body weight of the 200 men here studied are given in Fig. 44, which, it will be seen, is merely the graphic representation of the figures presented in Table XII.

The most striking characteristic of this group of individuals is that the various weights are not distributed at all evenly throughout the population; there are comparatively few very light and comparatively few very heavy men, but as a point midway between the two extremes is approached the size of the classes progressively increases until it reaches its maximum near the median line of the figure. In other words,

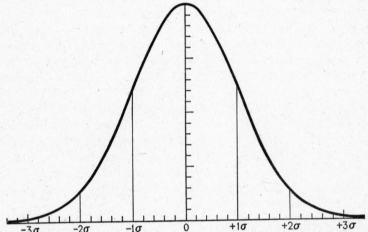

Fig. 45.—A normal curve. Perpendiculars are erected above and below the mean at points once, twice, and three times the distance of the standard deviation from the mean.

the bulk of this population consists of individuals that are intermediate in weight.

The Normal Curve.—Such a curve is found very commonly wherever a group of individuals is classified according to any quantitative character. It tends to approach what mathematicians call the *normal curve* (Fig. 45), a curve representing the relative frequency with which, according to the laws of probability, various consequences may be expected to ensue from the simultaneous action of many independent causes. For example, if six coins were to be tossed simultaneously, the chances of their all falling heads would be very slight and would be expected only once out of $(2)^6$ times, or 1 time in 64. The chance of throwing five heads and one tail is somewhat greater; of four heads and two tails greater still; and the combination of three heads and three tails is the most likely of all. The chances of two heads and four tails, one head and five tails, and six tails are progressively less and less.[1] The particular combination that appears in any given case is the result of six independent variables. The chance that they will all tend in the same direction is slight, and it is much more likely that some will tend one way and some another. Plotting the results of the interaction of these causes that may be expected on the basis of pure chance produces a curve which approaches more and more closely to the normal curve as the number of factors increases. The normal curve may be expressed by a rather complex equation which need not be considered here. Some of the properties of this curve, however, are of much importance biometrically and will be discussed later in this chapter.

That a group of individuals, classified for a given quantitative character, so commonly shows a curve like this leads one to suspect that such characters are affected by a series of factors or influences either in the environment or in the genetic constitution. Some of these factors tend in one direction and some in the other, the character, resulting from their interaction, usually finding its position at a point intermediate between the two extremes.

The division of a mass of data into classes and the plotting of these classes in a polygon or curve helps greatly in presenting a simple picture of the size relations of a given group. However, it is still far from providing the two determinations that are sought—a quantity that shall stand for the group as a whole, and another that shall measure the variation within the group. These two constants must be derived from a study of the classified data.

The Mode.—In an ordinary curve there is usually one class, commonly situated about midway between the two extremes, which contains more individuals than do any of the others. This is known as the modal class or the *mode.* For the group of men studied, the class from 130 to 139 pounds (Fig. 44) is the mode. Since the mode is the most populous and "fashionable" of all the classes, it may be taken as a rough indication of the *type* of the population as a whole. If a single individual were to be selected as typical of the group, it would probably be chosen from among the members of the modal class.

The Mean.—The mode, however, is often considerably nearer one extreme than the other, and there also may be two or more classes of

---

[1] The probable chances of each of these combinations, on the basis of 64 throws, correspond to the coefficients of the various terms in the expansion of the binomial $(a + b)^6$, which is: $a^6 + 6a^5b + 15a^4b^2 + 20a^3b^3 + 15a^2b^4 + 6ab^5 + b^6$. There would thus be 1 chance out of 64 for all heads, 6 chances for 5 heads and 1 tail, 15 chances for 4 heads and 2 tails, 20 chances for 3 heads and 3 tails, 15 chances for 2 heads and 4 tails, 6 chances for 1 head and 5 tails, and 1 chance for all tails. Plotting these coefficients gives a curve that begins to approach the normal one.

equal or almost equal size, so that, as a quantity which shall represent the group as a whole, the mode is not satisfactory. The figure that best serves this purpose is the arithmetical average, or *mean*. This constant may, of course, be obtained by adding the values for all the individuals and dividing this by the total number. A simpler method, and one substantially as accurate, is to classify the individuals (as has already been done for the group of men under consideration) and then to multiply the value of each class by the number within it, add these products, and divide by the total number of individuals. The value (class center) which is used to stand for the entire class is the one halfway between the two extremes included in the class. In the weight classes that have been used here, this value falls at 105 pounds, 115 pounds, 125 pounds, and so on. $\bar{m}$ is commonly employed to denote the mean, V the value of a given class center, f the number of individuals in a class (the class frequency), and n the total number of individuals. Σ is the mathematical symbol for summation. Thus

$$\bar{m} = \frac{\Sigma fV}{n}.$$

TABLE XIII.—THE DETERMINATION OF THE MEAN (LONG METHOD)

V	f	fV
95	1	95
105	2	210
115	10	1,150
125	31	3,875
135	54	7,290
145	48	6,960
155	27	4,185
165	14	2,310
175	11	1,925
185	1	185
195	1	195
Total..............	200	28,380

In determining these biometrical constants the classes are arranged in a vertical, rather than in a horizontal, column as in the plotted curve. In Table XIII the class centers of the group of men being studied, for weight, are thus placed under V with the corresponding number of individuals at the right of each class center, under f. The third column (fV) contains the products of each class value by its class frequency. Using the formula given above, the mean is

$$\frac{28,380}{200} = 141.9 \text{ pounds}[1]$$

[1] A simpler method of determining the mean will be explained later.

This is the average weight of the group under consideration and gives important information as to this particular trait in these individuals. The mean often lies within the modal class but in an asymmetrical curve may be far on either side of the mode.

The Average Deviation.—More difficult to arrive at is a measure of variation. Two populations may have the same mean but may differ markedly in their variability. In one the individuals may be grouped in a fairly compact body, with the extremes not far apart, and in the other they may be dispersed over a much greater distance. Two frequency curves, one with high and one with low variability, are shown in Fig. 46. An inspection of the frequency curve will give a general idea of the degree of variability, but to measure this requires: first, the establishment of a definite point with reference to which variation can be determined; and, second, a measurement of the deviation of each individual from this point. The mean is the most obvious point from which to measure variation. Once this has been established, it is a simple matter to determine the deviation of each individual (or class) from this mean and

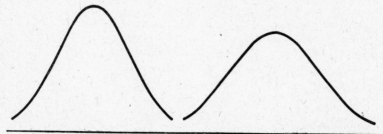

Fig. 46.—Differences in variability indicated graphically. At left a curve representing a population of comparatively low variability. At right, one representing a population of the same size but greater variability.

thus to arrive at the *average* amount of deviation displayed by the population as a whole. Letting d represent the deviation of an individual or class from the mean, the *average deviation* will be $\Sigma fd/n$. This quantity may be used as an approximate measure of variation. In Table XIV the V and f columns are as before, but there have been added the columns d, giving the deviation of each class from the mean, and fd, the product of the deviation of each class by the number of individuals in it. The sum of the column fd divided by the total number of individuals will thus give us the average deviation from the mean. This will be, in the example, 2,572.4/200, or 12.86 pounds.

The Standard Deviation.—A more accurate method of measuring variation, however, is to square the deviations and then extract the square root of their sum. The reason may be suggested by the familiar

TABLE XIV.—THE DETERMINATION OF THE AVERAGE DEVIATION AND THE STANDARD DEVIATION (LONG METHOD)

V	f	d	fd	fd²
95	1	46.9	46.9	2,199.61
105	2	36.9	73.8	2,723.22
115	10	26.9	269.0	7,236.10
125	31	16.9	523.9	8,853.91
135	54	6.9	372.6	2,570.94
145	48	3.1	148.8	461.28
155	27	13.1	353.7	4,633.47
165	14	23.1	323.4	7,470.54
175	11	33.1	364.1	12,051.71
185	1	43.1	43.1	1,857.61
195	1	53.1	53.1	2,819.61
	200		2,572.4	52,870.00

$$\text{Average deviation} = \frac{\Sigma fd}{n} = \frac{2,572.4}{200} = 12.86 \text{ pounds}$$

$$\sigma = \sqrt{\frac{\Sigma fd^2}{n}} = \sqrt{\frac{52,870}{200}} = \sqrt{264.35} = 16.26 \text{ pounds}$$

example of shooting at a target. A shot to be 6 inches from the bull's-eye must be somewhere within a total area of approximately 1 square foot. If the deviation from the bull's-eye is twice as great, or 1 foot, the total area within which the shot may lie is not twice as great as before but the square of twice, or four times as great, since the area within a 1-foot radius of the center is approximately 4 square feet. Thus it is four times as hard to get within 6 inches of the bull's-eye as it is to get within a foot of it; and in comparing the rifle score of two persons (their "variability" in marksmanship), it is evidently fairer to square the distance of each shot, average these squared values and then extract the square root of this average, than to average the actual distances themselves. This is the method commonly followed in biometry and the resulting constant is known as the standard deviation, σ, its formula being:

$$\sigma = \sqrt{\Sigma fd^2/n}.$$

To obtain this it is necessary to add another column to the table, that of the squared deviation of each class multiplied by its class frequency, or fd^2. This may, obviously, be obtained by multiplying the d and fd columns, and such a column has been added to Table XIV. The standard deviation in the example is thus $\sqrt{52,870/200}$, or 16.26 pounds.

The Short Method.—The determination of mean and standard deviation in this way usually involves, as here, complex fractional values and much arduous calculation. A much simpler method has been devised which is just as accurate and which avoids the use of fractions (Table XV). This method, briefly, is to *assume* that the mean falls on an even class value, to measure the deviation from this assumed mean, *a*, and to make the necessary corrections at the end of the calculation. The mean may be assumed at a class which by inspection can be seen to be rather close to the true mean. If this is done, the deviations will be relatively small, but some will be plus and some minus, involving an extra operation in calculating. It is a common practice to assume the mean at the smallest class or at zero, so that all the deviations are plus in sign. These deviations should be treated as units regardless of the actual class intervals and the calculations made on the basis of these units, thus avoiding the necessity for large numbers if the class interval is more than 1. The proper correction can be made by multiplying at the proper time by the class interval, *i*, which will bring the results back to the unit of measurement employed. The class interval in our example is 10, since the classes used are 10-pound classes.

In Table XV the columns are arranged as in the long method (Table XIV), but the mean is assumed to be at the lowest class value, and the intervals are units instead of tens. Deviation from the assumed mean is represented by d' to distinguish it from the true deviation, d. The d', fd', and fd'^2 columns are evidently obtained much more easily than by the long method.

The sum of the fd' column divided by the total number of individuals and multiplied by the class interval gives the average deviation from the assumed mean, in the units employed. It will be evident that this represents the difference between the assumed mean and the true mean, so that, by adding this quantity to the assumed mean, the true mean is easily determined.

The formula for the mean by the short method is thus:

$$\bar{m} = a + i\left(\frac{\Sigma fd'}{n}\right)$$

In the present example $\bar{m} = 95 + 10(^{938}\!/_{200}) = 141.90$ pounds the same value as was obtained by the long method.

The short method is equally valuable in determining the standard deviation. The fd'^2 column is found as in the long method but, as with the mean, a correction must be applied before it is used. This is done by subtracting from the sum of the fd'^2 column the square of the correction factor, $(\Sigma fd'/n)^2$, before the square root is extracted. The final result must, of course, be multiplied by the class interval to bring it back to the units of measurement employed.

The formula for the standard deviation by the short method is thus:

$$\sigma = i\sqrt{\frac{\Sigma fd'^2}{n} - \left(\frac{\Sigma fd'}{n}\right)^2}$$

In the present example this is

$$10\sqrt{\frac{4,928}{200} - (4.69)^2} = 16.26 \text{ pounds}[1]$$

This is the same value as was obtained, much more laboriously, by the long method.

TABLE XV.—THE DETERMINATION OF THE MEAN, STANDARD DEVIATION, AND COEFFICIENT OF VARIATION (SHORT METHOD)

V	f	d'	fd'	fd'^2
95	1	0	0	0
105	2	1	2	2
115	10	2	20	40
125	31	3	93	279
135	54	4	216	864
145	48	5	240	1,200
155	27	6	162	972
165	14	7	98	686
175	11	8	88	704
185	1	9	9	81
195	1	10	10	100
	$n = 200$		$\Sigma fd' = 938$	$\Sigma fd'^2 = 4,928$

$a = 95$ pounds
$i = 10$

$$\bar{m} = a + i\left(\frac{\Sigma fd'}{n}\right) = 95 + 10\left(\frac{938}{200}\right) = 141.90 \text{ pounds}$$

$$\sigma = i\sqrt{\frac{\Sigma fd'^2}{n} - \left(\frac{\Sigma fd'}{n}\right)^2} = 10\sqrt{\frac{4,928}{200} - (4.69)^2} = 16.26 \text{ pounds}$$

$$v = \frac{\sigma \times 100}{\bar{m}} = \frac{16.26 \times 100}{141.90} = 11.46 \text{ per cent}$$

The Coefficient of Variation.—The standard deviation is, of course, always in terms of the units used (pounds in our example), and its useful-

[1] Wherever the original measurements are grouped into classes to each of which is assigned the value of its mid-point, a slight error is evidently introduced, since we assume that the value of the mid-point is always the mean of all the individuals in the class. Where number of individuals is high or the classes relatively few, Sheppard's correction may be applied. (Yule and Kendall, p. 140.)

ness lies in comparing the variability of groups of individuals with regard to the same character. It is often necessary, however, to compare variability in one character with variability in another, for example, the variation in the weight of the men studied with the variation in their height; and for that purpose the standard deviation is useless, since pounds and inches cannot be compared. To avoid this difficulty, the *coefficient of variation*, *v*, is employed, which is merely the standard deviation divided by the mean and expressed as a percentage, its formula being

$$v = \frac{\sigma \times 100}{\bar{m}}$$

which in the example is 1,626/141.90 or 11.46 per cent.

Other Constants.—There are several other constants employed by biometricians and sometimes useful in genetics, the derivation of which will be briefly discussed here.

The *mode* has already been mentioned. It is the class which contains the largest number of individuals. In genetically pure populations, where the individuals differ only because of environmental causes; in populations segregating for many genes; or in any other group the members of which differ because of a series of chance factors, the curve will approach symmetry and the mode will lie near its center. Sometimes, however, there are two modes, separated by classes of smaller size, forming a two-humped or bimodal curve; and more rarely the curve may be multimodal. Such a condition indicates that the population consists of a mixture of two or several markedly different types.

It is often important to know the point which divides a population into two equal parts, half of the individuals lying above and half below. This point is known as the *median*. It can readily be found by arranging the individuals in order of magnitude and determining the position of the middle one or the point between the middle pair. Where grouping into classes has been made, the class in which the midmost individual must be can easily be found. The position of the median in this class may be determined by first finding what proportion of the individuals in it are necessary, when added to the sum of the individuals in all the classes below this, to complete half the total population; and then by adding to the lower limit of the class this same proportion of the entire class range. Thus if the class in which the midmost individual lies ranges from 30 to 34.99 mm. and contains 15 individuals and if 3 of these, added to all below, will make up 50 per cent of the whole, then $\frac{3}{15}$ of the distance from 30 to 35, or 31, is the median.

Where the curve is perfectly symmetrical, the mean and the median obviously are the same. Most populations, however, show some asym-

metry or *skewness*, which occasionally becomes so marked that one side
of the curve slopes steeply up and the other gradually downward.   The
more skewed the curve is, the farther will the median be from the mean;
and this distance, expressed in relation to the variability of the population, may be used as a measure of the degree of skewness, a value which
it is often important to determine.   The most commonly used formula
for expressing the degree of skewness is

$$s = \frac{3(\bar{m} - m_d)}{\sigma}$$

where s is the degree of skewness and m_d the median.

Measures of Reliability.—The group of individuals from which
a given constant is derived (the 200 men here studied, for example)
are evidently only a small sample drawn from the entire population
of which they form a part.   How reliable a constant is will evidently
depend in part on how big the sample is.   A mean weight derived from
a sample consisting of only 10 men will command much less confidence
than one derived from a sample consisting of 1,000 men, for the bigger
the sample, the more accurately will it represent the entire population.
But this is not the only criterion of reliability.   If two samples are of
the same size but differ in variability, more confidence is to be placed in
constants derived from the less variable sample, since in such a group it
takes relatively few individuals to establish the character of the whole.

The Standard Error.—These two qualities, therefore—the size and
the variability of the sample or group studied—may be used to provide
a measure of the reliability of constants derived from it.   Such a measure
is the *standard error*, an understanding of which requires a brief discussion of probability and of the properties of the normal curve.

If a series of samples were to be drawn from the same population
as the one studied, the constants derived from them would not be the
same.   Another group of 200 college men would doubtless give a mean
weight somewhat different from 141.90 pounds.   If the differences
were due entirely to chance and the samples entirely random ones,
it is a fair assumption from our knowledge of probability that few samples
would be relatively low, and few relatively high, and that most would
be intermediate in value.   Furthermore, if a large group of these sample
means were plotted, they would be found to form the same normal
curve as did the individual measurements themselves.   The standard
error is *the standard deviation of such a curve*.   Since actually only one
sample is at hand, this curve cannot be constructed and analyzed.   From
the size and the variability of this single sample, however, the standard
deviation of a group of constants similarly derived may be calculated,
since the more variable the sample, in relation to its size, the more

variable might constants be expected to be which were derived from similar samples.

The formulas used to derive the standard error of the mean, standard deviation, and coefficient of variation are as follows:

Standard error of the mean,

$$\sigma_{\bar{m}} = \frac{\sigma}{\sqrt{n}}$$

In our example $\sigma_{\bar{m}}$ is thus $16.26/\sqrt{200} = 1.149$ pounds.

Standard error of the standard deviation,

$$\sigma_{\sigma} = \frac{\sigma}{\sqrt{2n}}$$

In our example σ_{σ} is thus $16.26/\sqrt{400} = .813$ pounds.

Standard error of the coefficient of variation,

$$\sigma_v = \frac{v}{\sqrt{2n}}\sqrt{1 + 2\left(\frac{v}{100}\right)^2}$$

Where v is small, 10 per cent or less, the quantity under the second radical may be omitted. In our example σ_v is thus .588 per cent.

Standard error of a ratio (p. 57) $\sigma_r = \sqrt{pq/n}$.

The standard error of a constant is placed directly after the constant with a $\pm$ sign between the two. Thus the mean in our example would be expressed as 141.90 ± 1.149 pounds; the standard deviation as $16.26 \pm .813$ pounds; and the coefficient of variation as $11.46 \pm .588\%$.

The usefulness of the standard error in measuring the reliability of a constant is dependent upon certain relations between the normal curve and its standard deviation. Normal curves may differ from each other considerably in variability, or, in other words, they may have very different standard deviations; but in one respect they are all alike, namely, in the proportion of their area (or the number of individuals which this represents) which is included between the mean and any multiple of the standard deviation. In Fig. 45 there is represented a typical normal curve, with perpendiculars erected below and above the mean at points once, twice, and three times the distance of the standard deviation from the mean. It can be proved that the area of the curve which is included between the perpendiculars at -1σ and $+1\sigma$ is .6826 of the whole; between -2σ and $+2\sigma$, .9544; and between -3σ and $+3\sigma$, .9974. Table XVI gives the percentages of the total area of the curve included between the limits set by various multiples of the standard deviation above and below the mean, and also the percentages of the curve lying outside these limits. Regardless of the absolute size of the standard deviation (and thus of the variability of the curve), these values are the same for all normal curves and thus theoretically for all populations which vary solely by chance for any quantitative trait.

The importance of this property of the normal curve for our present problem is now obvious; for if the value of the standard error of a constant is known (which is simply the standard deviation of a population of constants similarly derived), we shall have a criterion of the reliability of this constant. Since 68.26 per cent of a normal curve (and thus of a population distributed purely by chance) may be expected to fall within the limits set by the mean plus its standard deviation and minus its standard deviation, we know the limits within which a constant derived from another sample may be expected to fall 68.26 per cent (approximately two-thirds) of the time. Thus when it is found that the mean weight of our group of men is 141.9 ± 1.149 pounds, this tells us that another sample from the same population would have, about two times out of three, a mean between 141.90 + 1.149 (143.049) and 141.90 − 1.149 (140.751). The standard error for the other constants is to be interpreted in the same way. Evidently the higher its standard error is, the less reliable is the constant. A mean of 10 ± .5 and 10 ± 5.0 are of markedly different value, since in the first, another sample will in two-thirds of the cases fall close to the determined figure (between 9.5 and 10.5), and the constant is thus to be relied upon as lying near the true mean for the whole population; whereas in the second the latitude is so great (between 5.0 and 15.0) that the constant is relatively valueless. The standard error, as a criterion of reliability, is thus an important adjunct to any biometrical constant, and the reason for its significance should be clearly understood.

The Probable Error.—The *probable error*, often used in biometrical work, is simply .6745 times the standard error. It measures the limits within which *half* the area of the normal curve will be included and thus within which the chance is *even* (rather than two out of three) that a constant derived from another sample will fall.

The Significance of Deviations from Expectation.—A knowledge of the standard error of a constant or other quantity is also useful in enabling one to judge whether a given deviation from some particular expectation is due merely to chance or is really a significant deviation which must be explained on other grounds. Table XVI is particularly useful here. The second column shows the percentages of the area of the normal probability curve which falls *within* limits set by ± various multiples of the standard deviation. The third column gives the percentages which would fall *outside* these limits. It is thus possible to determine how frequently any deviation from the mean expressed as a multiple of the standard deviation) may be expected to occur by chance alone, thus providing a means

TABLE XVI.—PERCENTAGES OF THE NORMAL CURVE LYING BETWEEN, AND
LYING OUTSIDE OF, THE LIMITS SET BY THE MEAN PLUS AND
MINUS VARIOUS MULTIPLES OF THE STANDARD DEVIATION

Multiple of standard deviation	Percentage of total area of normal curve lying between mean plus this multiple and mean minus this multiple	Percentage of total area of normal curve lying outside these limits
.2	15.86	84.14
.4	31.08	68.92
.6	45.14	54.86
.8	57.62	42.38
1.0	68.26	31.74
1.2	76.98	23.02
1.4	83.84	16.16
1.6	89.04	10.96
1.8	92.82	7.18
2.0	95.44	4.56
2.2	97.22	2.78
2.4	98.36	1.64
2.6	99.06	.94
2.8	99.48	.52
3.0	99.74	.26

of judging its significance. For example, if a given population, normally distributed, has a mean of 150 and a standard deviation of 10, we know that 68.26 per cent of the population lies between 140 and 160 (150 + 10 and −10) and that 31.74 per cent of it lies beyond these limits. This is the same as saying that a deviation of 10 or more will occur in 31.74 per cent of the cases. We also know that 83.84 per cent of the population lies between 150 ± 1.4 × 10 and thus between 136 and 164 and 16.16 per cent beyond these limits, which again is the same as saying that a deviation of as much as 14 (1.4 × 10) will occur by chance in 16.16 per cent of the cases. Between 150 ± 2 × 10, or between 130 and 170, lie 95.44 per cent of all the individuals, so that only 4.56 per cent of the time will there be expected to be a deviation as great as 20 by chance alone. If a deviation as great as this, in proportion to its standard error, is found, the probability is very slight (only about one chance out of 22) that it is due to chance alone, and we are justified in attributing it to some other factor.

In genetics, the commonest use of this relation between the normal curve and its standard deviation is in comparing observed ratios with theoretically expected ones. In an earlier chapter (p. 57) a ratio of 78:22 per cent, based on an observation of 500 individuals, was compared with the theoretical expectation of 75:25 per cent. The deviation here is 3 per cent, and the standard error of the ratio 75:25 per cent with 500 individuals is 1.936 per cent. Hence the deviation is 1.55 times as great as the standard error of such a ratio, and an inspection of Table XVI shows that as large a deviation is expected in more than 10.96 per cent of similar cases and is thus probably to be explained as the result of chance alone, indicating that the fit of observation with expectation is reasonably close and that this population may therefore be regarded as an example of a 3:1 ratio.

The Significance of Differences.—By another formula, it is possible to estimate whether the difference between two populations, the constants and standard errors for which are known, is really significant or only the result of chance. This is done by comparing the difference with the standard error of the difference. The latter is the square root of the sum of the squares of the standard errors of the two constants. It may be expressed thus:

$$\sigma_d = \sqrt{\sigma_a{}^2 + \sigma_b{}^2}$$

where σ_d is the standard error of the difference, σ_a that of one constant, and σ_b that of the other.

If, for example, one mean (or other constant) is 155 ± 6 and another 140 ± 8, the question arises whether this is a really significant difference or merely a chance one. The difference is $155 - 140$, or 15. Applying the formula above, the standard error of the difference is $\sqrt{(6)^2 + (8)^2}$, or 10. The difference is thus 1.5 times its standard error, and one of this size would thus be expected to occur by chance more than 13 per cent of the time (Table XVI). It is thus probably not significant. In general, a difference is not usually regarded as significant unless it is at least twice its standard error.

REFERENCES

CASTLE, W. E., and J. C. PHILLIPS. 1914. Piebald rats and selection. Carnegie Inst. Washington Publ. **195.**

DAVENPORT, C. B., and M. P. EKAS. 1936. Statistical methods in biology, medicine and psychology. New York.

DE HAAN, H. 1927. Length factors in Pisum. Genetica **9.**

EAST, E. M. 1910. A mendelian interpretation of variation that is apparently continuous. Amer. Nat. **44.**

——. 1916. Studies in size inheritance in Nicotiana. Genetics **1.**

—— and H. K. HAYES. 1911. Inheritance in maize. Connecticut Agr. Exp. Sta. Bull. **167.**

EMERSON, R. A., and E. M. EAST. 1913. The inheritance of quantitative characters in maize. Nebraska Agr. Exp. Sta. Res. Bull. **2.**

FISHER, R. A. 1936. Statistical methods for research workers. 6th ed. Edinburgh.

HOSHINO, T. 1915. On the inheritance of flowering time in peas and rice. Jour. Coll. Agr. Tohoku Imp. Univ. **6.**

LINDSTROM, E. W.   1932.   First-chromosome genes in the tomato.   Genetics **17**.

NILSSON-EHLE, H.   1908.   Einige Ergebnisse von Kreuzungen bei Hafer und Weizen. Bot. Notiser.

PEARSON, KARL.   1924.   Tables for statisticians and biometricians.   Part I.   Cambridge (England).

SAX, K.   1923.   The association of size differences with seed-coat pattern and pigmentation in *Phaseolus vulgaris*.   Genetics **8**.

SHULL, G. H.   1914.   Duplicate genes for capsule form in *Bursa bursapastoris*. Zeitschr. Ind. Abst. Vererb. **12**.

SINNOTT, E. W.   1937.   The relation of gene to character in quantitative inheritance. Proc. Nat. Acad. Sci.   Washington **23**.

WARREN, D. C.   1924.   Inheritance of egg size in *Drosophila melanogaster*.   Genetics **9**.

YULE, G. UDNY, and M. G. KENDALL.   1937.   An introduction to the theory of statistics. 11th ed.   London.

PROBLEMS

198. The F_1 generation from pure parent types differing in a size character is usually no more variable than the parents.   Explain.

199. If two pure types, differing in a size character, are crossed, is it possible for individuals in the F_2 to be more extreme than either grandparent? Explain.

200. Why is it, when selection has ceased to be effective in producing changes in a given stock, that if this stock is crossed with another similar one, selection among the subsequent offspring is often able to produce a marked change?

201. As a result of crosses involving a size character, it is often found that F_3 families raised from selfed F_2 plants differ markedly in their variability.   Some are almost as low as the original parents, some a little higher, and some as high as the F_2 itself.   None exceeds the F_2 in variability, however.   Explain these facts.

202. It frequently happens that one character of a plant, such as number of seeds, is much more variable than another character, such as weight of seeds. What explanations for this difference can you suggest?

203. Certain groups of individuals, when their frequency distribution is plotted, show a bimodal or multimodal curve.   What different explanations can you make for this fact?

Note.—Assume that in man the difference in skin color between negro and white is due to two pairs of factors; that *AA BB* is "black" and *aa bb* "white"; and that any three of these factors produce "dark" skin; any two, "medium"; and any one, "light."

204. What will be the skin color of the offspring from a mating of white with black?   From a mating of two individuals genotypically like these F_1 offspring?

205. What are the genotypes of the parents in the two following matings of negroes: medium × light, giving one-eighth dark, three-eighths medium, three-eighths light, one-eighth white; medium × light, giving one-half medium and one-half light?

206. Can two negroes have white-skinned offspring? Can two white-skinned people have dark-skinned offspring? Explain.

207. Assume that the red kernel color of a certain race of wheat is due to the presence of three independent factors A, B, and C. Any one of the factors singly will cause the red color. White is $aa\ bb\ cc$. What are the genotypes of the parents in each of the following crosses: red × red giving 3 red to 1 white; red × red giving 15 red to 1 white; red × red giving 63 red to 1 white; red × red giving 7 red to 1 white; red × white giving 1 red to 1 white; red × white giving 3 red to 1 white; red × white giving 7 red to 1 white; red × white giving all red.

208. Assume that the difference between a race of oats yielding about 4 grams per plant and one yielding 10 is due to three equal and cumulative multiple factor pairs $AA\ BB\ CC$. Cross one type with the other. What will be the phenotypes of the F_1? of the F_2?

209. Assume that in squashes the difference in fruit weight between a 3-pound type and a 6-pound type is due to three factor pairs AA, BB, and CC, each factor contributing $\frac{1}{2}$ pound to fruit weight. Cross a 3-pound plant ($aa\ bb\ cc$) with a 6-pound one. What will be the phenotypes of the F_1? of the F_2?

210. In the following squash crosses, what will be the range in fruit weight of the offspring, on the previous assumption?

$Aa\ Bb\ CC \times aa\ Bb\ Cc$ $Aa\ Bb\ Cc \times Aa\ Bb\ Cc$
$AA\ bb\ Cc \times Aa\ BB\ cc$ $aa\ BB\ cc \times AA\ BB\ cc$

211. A breeder has three squash plants each of which bears 4-pound fruits. Plant 1, when selfed, breeds true to 4-pound fruits. So does plant 2. In plant 3 the offspring range from 3 to 5 pounds. Plant 1 crossed with plant 2 gives offspring all of 4 pounds, but *their* offspring when inbred range from 3 to 5 pounds, and selection cannot increase this above 5 pounds. Plant 1 crossed with plant 3 gives offspring which range from $3\frac{1}{2}$ to $4\frac{1}{2}$ pounds, and selection among *their* offspring can raise the fruit weight to 6 pounds. Plant 2 crossed with plant 3 gives offspring which also range from $3\frac{1}{2}$ to $4\frac{1}{2}$ pounds, but selection among their offspring is able to raise fruit weight only to 5 pounds. Give genotypes for these three parent plants which will explain these results.

212. Assume in the following five problems that the difference between a corn plant 10 decimeters high and one 26 decimeters high is due (insofar as it is caused by inheritance) to four pairs of equal and cumulative multiple factors, the 26-decimeter plant being $AA\ BB\ CC\ DD$ and the 10-decimeter one $aa\ bb\ cc\ dd$. What will be the size and genotype of an F_1 from a cross between these two pure types? Give the limits of variation in height which the offspring of the following crosses will show:

$Aa\ BB\ cc\ dd \times Aa\ bb\ Cc\ dd$ $AA\ BB\ Cc\ DD \times aa\ BB\ cc\ Dd$
$aa\ BB\ cc\ dd \times Aa\ Bb\ Cc\ dd$ $Aa\ Bb\ Cc\ Dd \times Aa\ bb\ Cc\ Dd$

213. Two 14-decimeter corn plants, when crossed, give nothing but 14-decimeter offspring. Two other 14-decimeter plants give one 18-decimeter, four 16-decimeter, six 14-decimeter, four 12-decimeter, and one 10-decimeter plants. Two other 14-decimeter plants when crossed give one 16-decimeter, two 14-decimeter, and one 12-decimeter plants. What genotypes for each of these 14-decimeter parent plants would explain these results? By selection in any of these families would it be possible to get a plant taller than 18 decimeters?

214. A breeder has a number of plants which are 14 decimeters high. He crosses some of these together, selfs their offspring, and selects among their offspring for increased tallness, for several generations. His results are as follows:

Two throw all 14-decimeter offspring, and selection fails to raise their height.

Two others throw offspring varying from 10 to 18 decimeters, and selection among these fails to raise the height above 18 decimeters.

Two others throw offspring varying from 12 to 16 decimeters, and selection is able to raise the limit to 22 decimeters.

Two others throw offspring varying from 10 to 18 decimeters, and selection is able to raise the limit to 22 decimeters.

Two others throw offspring varying from 10 to 18 decimeters, and selection is able to raise the limit to 26 decimeters.

Explain, by giving parents' genotypes for height, why these results obtain.

215. A breeder has a 26-decimeter starchy and a 10-decimeter sweet corn. Starchiness is dominant over sweetness and is due to a single factor. He wants a 26-decimeter sweet corn. Assume that height is due to four factor pairs, as before. If he wants this new type of corn in two years, how many plants should he raise in the F_2 of the cross between tall starchy and short sweet to be reasonably sure of getting it? If he has more time, what would you advise him to do in order not to have to raise such a big crop in the F_2 and subsequent generations?

216. Suppose that the difference between a 26-decimeter and a 10-decimeter corn plant is caused by four pairs of multiple factors (as in the previous examples) and that the difference between a one-stalked and a nine-stalked corn is also due to four other pairs of cumulative multiple factors. A breeder has a nine-stalked 10-decimeter race and a one-stalked 26-decimeter race. He wants for silage corn a pure race 26 decimeters high, with nine stalks. If he wants it in two years, how many plants should he raise in the F_2? By spending more time how can he get it more easily?

217. A breeder has a race of plants which has been self-fertilized for 10 generations. He has repeatedly tried to increase the flower size of this race by selection, but to no avail. Explain why this is so. Finally, he crosses this race with another which is exactly similar to it in flower size. The hybrids resemble their parents, but by selection among the offspring of the hybrids the breeder is able in a few generations to increase the flower size considerably. Explain why this is so.

218. Find the mean, standard deviation, coefficient of variability, and their standard errors, of the heights in Table XVII.

219. Find the mean, standard deviation, coefficient of variability, and their standard errors, of the chest girths in Table XVII.

220. In what relative order do the variabilities of these men, in weight, height, and chest girth, stand?

221. Suppose that one long inbred strain of spotted mice has for mean and standard deviation of the percentage of white on the dorsal surface 10.3 and 1.98, determined from 200 individuals; and another strain, 23.7 and 3.01, from 317 individuals. Are the means significantly different? Standard deviations? Coefficients of variation?

TABLE XVII.—WEIGHT, HEIGHT, AND CHEST GIRTH OF 200 MEN

(Data from Department of Physical Education, Connecticut State College)

Weight, pounds	Height, inches	Chest, inches	Weight, pounds	Height, inches	Chest, inches	Weight, pounds	Height, inches	Chest, inches	Weight, pounds	Height, inches	Chest, inches
135	67	35	121	65	32	142	65	40	130	67	35
156	72	40	118	64	32	143	69	35	135	67	33
163	69	39	130	68	37	158	73	36	119	64	31
128	65	34	146	70	39	127	65	34	139	67	37
126	70	34	137	60	37	195	71	41	130	66	35
142	70	36	159	68	38	144	69	35	144	59	38
156	70	37	154	72	37	130	66	34	119	64	34
152	67	38	131	69	32	133	67	38	172	73	40
156	68	38	124	68	38	133	66	35	136	64	37
144	68	35	134	65	36	161	68	38	137	66	33
157	69	34	150	70	38	141	69	39	137	70	35
162	73	35	131	67	36	152	67	35	136	67	33
147	67	33	129	66	35	114	66	34	136	68	36
124	65	32	156	67	37	141	66	37	133	65	35
114	63	35	134	68	35	130	67	35	136	66	36
152	68	37	111	64	34	130	68	33	143	69	37
127	69	32	171	71	41	175	72	39	185	74	40
146	70	35	135	66	36	140	70	37	135	73	36
130	66	36	140	68	34	127	66	35	148	68	35
115	65	34	141	64	37	124	64	34	142	68	36
135	66	36	145	66	34	116	64	34	147	68	40
131	68	35	122	66	32	125	67	36	149	68	37
174	69	38	123	64	36	145	67	33	139	62	37
130	65	35	121	65	31	155	67	39	112	64	34
151	66	38	140	64	34	128	63	35	170	69	41
176	71	37	140	67	34	131	66	35	148	67	37
140	71	37	137	66	33	147	67	37	123	69	36
133	68	36	165	72	38	142	67	36	144	67	38
127	66	36	135	69	36	148	72	38	141	65	38
142	68	36	162	73	36	150	68	33	142	67	34
135	64	36	128	68	36	131	66	34	142	67	34
126	69	36	130	68	33	135	68	35	122	66	33
148	70	37	156	72	38	139	63	34	121	61	32
139	68	36	144	68	38	125	64	32	148	71	38
123	66	36	132	68	35	173	74	37	157	72	38
150	71	39	173	70	39	154	69	39	107	62	33
160	71	39	152	70	33	134	65	32	148	67	38
140	67	37	136	70	35	151	69	37	176	69	39
134	68	36	128	69	34	158	66	37	135	70	37
153	69	40	134	71	33	135	66	38	119	66	35
135	68	33	120	65	34	135	67	35	95	62	30
141	70	33	148	69	34	127	67	33	174	66	39
127	63	33	162	67	35	165	68	39	133	67	35
144	72	33	145	65	38	153	69	38	150	69	37
130	66	32	166	73	41	169	70	38	141	69	36
123	65	32	142	68	38	165	68	39	138	69	36
141	65	35	122	67	35	140	67	34	122	64	32
134	69	32	126	64	36	150	67	35	166	69	39
160	67	38	109	68	34	153	68	37	160	71	36
133	66	32	149	68	35	141	69	35	171	69	40

CHAPTER VII

THE PHYSICAL BASIS OF INHERITANCE

As has been pointed out in an earlier chapter, the only physical link between one generation and the next in sexual reproduction is the pair of gametes, one from each parent, which by their fusion produce the first cell of the new individual. These gametes differ greatly in size, structure, and method of development. In the lowest organisms they may be essentially like the rest of the cells of the body, but in the higher ones they have become specialized in various ways. Gametes agree, however, in one important particular—each is a *single cell*. This cell, like the others which compose the bodies of organisms, is a minute but distinct bit of protoplasm, consisting of a nucleus and cytoplasm. It is evident, however, that since this cell is the bridge across which the entire inheritance of a parent is transmitted to its offspring, it must possess a highly complex organization. This organization has been shown to inhere chiefly in the many genes which direct the development of the great number of complex characters of the adult. These self-perpetuating genes pass through the gametes from generation to generation, and thus form the basic units of heredity and of reproductive organization.

Highly complex as each of these minute sex cells necessarily must be, we have no reason to believe that it differs radically from any of the other cells which compose the plant or animal body. All the vital activities of living organisms—metabolism, growth, reproduction, and the rest—have their basis in protoplasm and necessitate therein a high degree of physical and chemical complexity. Inheritance is merely one of the manifestations of protoplasmic activity, and an understanding of the mechanism of inheritance requires a knowledge of the general structure and activities of protoplasm as these find expression in living cells.

With regard to many of the fundamental problems relating to cells we are still entirely in ignorance, but cytological research has given us a picture of some of the more obvious details and, particularly in recent years, has thrown much light upon the relationship between the phenomena of cellular structure and activity (particularly as exemplified in gametes) and the facts of inheritance. A study of the physical basis of inheritance, therefore, should begin with a brief consideration of the

157

more important facts as to the structure of the cell and its component parts.

The Cell.—The bodies of all plants and animals consist of cells (Fig. 47) diverse in size, shape, structure, and function but alike in their more fundamental characteristics. They are, in general, very small. Ordinarily cells range from 0.1 to 0.01 mm. in diameter, many of them being very much more minute. In a cubic inch of some kinds of tissue there may thus be billions of cells. Each typically consists of a denser mass of protoplasm, the *nucleus*, surrounded by cytoplasm. The vegetative cells of plants normally have a large central vacuole or

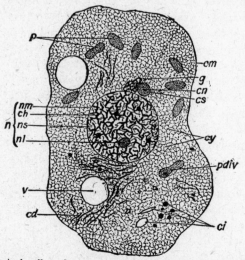

Fig. 47.—A typical cell. *cd*, mitochondria; *ch*, chromatin; *cm*, cell membrane; *cn*, centriole; *cs*, centrosphere; *cy*, cytoplasm; *g*, Golgi apparatus; *n*, nucleus; *nl*, nucleolus; *nm*, nuclear membrane; *ns*, nuclear sap; *p*, plastids; *pdiv*, plastid dividing; *v*, vacuole. (*From Shull, La Rue, and Ruthven.*)

sap cavity and are surrounded by a rather rigid wall of cellulose. Animal cells usually lack a pronounced wall, and their vacuoles, even when present, are relatively small.

The Nucleus.—The nucleus seems to be the directive center of most of the activities of the cell. The fact that male gametes in animals and plants ordinarily consist chiefly of a nucleus and yet are equivalent to female gametes as carriers of inheritance indicates that this part of the cell is of major importance in the transmission of traits from parent to offspring, and much evidence from other sources supports this conclusion.

In cells which are not in the process of division, the nucleus is provided with a definite nuclear membrane. This surrounds a clear and homogeneous nuclear sap in which is suspended a network or *reticulum* of much denser substance, consisting chiefly of a material which stains very readily and was early given the name *chromatin*. Portions of this threadlike reticulum stain much more readily than others, and some observers regard the thread as consisting of granules or small masses of chromatin suspended upon an axis of *linin*. Present evidence indicates that the differences between these materials are more apparent than real and that the nuclear network consists of a single substance which differs in its appearance and staining reactions at different times and under different conditions. This chromatin network, or more minute structures included in it, is now looked upon as the actual seat of the hereditary factors themselves and has therefore been subjected to the closest scrutiny.

In addition to this reticulum most nuclei contain one or more dense, usually rounded bodies, the nucleoli.

The Cytoplasm.—The protoplasmic material of the cell outside the nucleus is known as the *cytoplasm*. Its groundwork is a clear, viscous, colorless liquid, but in this occur various differentiated protoplasmic structures as well as numerous bodies which appear to be nonprotoplasmic in nature, such as oil globules, starch grains, and other objects, which seem to be chiefly nutritive.

In most animal cells there is distinguishable a series of fibrils or platelike bodies, the *Golgi apparatus* or *Golgi material*, which seems to have a specific character.

In animal cells there also usually occurs a definite *centrosome* or *central body*, ordinarily surrounded by a system of "cytoplasmic rays," the *aster*. The central body seems to take a leading part in cell division, but its absence in cells of higher plants indicates that it is not essential in this process. It is found in many lower plants, and similar structures occur in the motile gametes of certain higher ones. Of particular importance, especially in plants, are the relatively large *plastids* of various sorts, notably chloroplasts, chromoplasts, and leucoplasts, which have specialized functions and are found only in certain cells. Almost universally present also are many smaller bodies, sometimes granular or in the form of tiny rods or threads, most of which are included under the general names of *chondriosomes* and *mitochondria*. As to the manner of inheritance of these bodies there is no general agreement, but in many cases they seem clearly to be the primordia of plastids, and they may play an important part in the inheritance of those rather rare traits in plants which are transmitted through the cytoplasm of the gametes. These are discussed in Chapter X.

Somatic Cell Division.—The structures just described are those visible while the cell is in the so-called resting condition, when it is metabolically active but is not in any stage of division. The process of cell division, whereby growth is made possible, involves radical changes in the appearance and arrangements of the parts of the cell and makes manifest certain structures which seem to be of the utmost significance in inheritance but which are usually invisible at other times. The division of an ordinary body or *somatic* cell should first be understood as the basis for a consideration of the somewhat different situation in cells which give rise to gametes. The process seems to be initiated and controlled largely

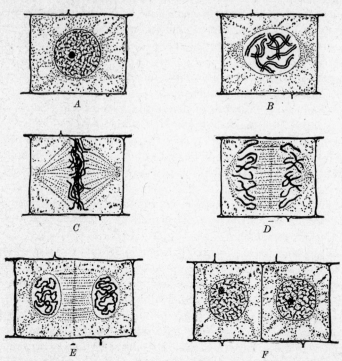

Fig. 48.—Diagram of cell division by mitosis. *A*, resting cell, the chromatin of the nucleus in a fine network. *B*, *prophase*, the chromatin is gathered into long thread-like double chromosomes. *C*, *metaphase*. The split chromosomes arrange themselves in a plane across the equator of the cell, and the spindle, with its two poles, is formed. *D*, *anaphase*. The chromosome halves separate, one complete set (eight in this case) going to one pole and the other set to the other pole. *E*, *telophase*. Each new group of chromosomes arranges itself into a thread, and a new cell wall begins to appear between the groups. *F*, two complete new cells, each with a nuclear content equal and similar to that of *A*.

by the nucleus. The nuclear division itself is commonly called *mitosis* (Fig. 48), although this term is now often used for the entire act of cell division.

As the first indication of imminent division the nuclear reticulum resolves itself into a definite thread or spireme, which is broken up into separate pieces, the chromosomes, each of which is split longitudinally into two. (In animal cells the centrosome has divided into two before this time, the halves migrating to two poles at opposite sides of the nucleus.) These stages are together called the *prophase* of mitosis (Fig. 48*B*).

The nuclear membrane at this stage breaks down, and the space occupied by the nucleus is now largely filled with a spindle-shaped mass of fiber-like structures, converging to two opposite poles. In the equatorial plane of the cell between the poles the chromosomes, now usually much shortened, become dispersed, and to each half chromosome is seen to be attached a spindle fiber which appears to connect it with the adjacent pole. This stage is the *metaphase* of mitosis (Fig. 48*C*).

The two halves of each of the original chromosomes now separate, *one member going to each pole.* In this process separation always begins at the point of fiber attachment, the points in the two halves being exactly opposite. The result of this activity is the aggregation at each pole of a group of chromosomes, similar in number and all other visible respects to the single set of mother-cell chromosomes from which they arose. This stage of polar migration of chromosomes is known as the *anaphase* (Fig. 48*D*).

The members of each of these polar groups of chromosomes now ordinarily lose their identity and fuse into a new nuclear reticulum which becomes surrounded by a membrane and thus reorganizes a daughter nucleus exactly like that of the mother cell. Meanwhile (in most plants) a new wall is laid down in the equatorial plane of the cell between the nuclei; or (in animals) the cytoplasmic mass is divided by a cleavage furrow going inward from the periphery. This final stage in division is known as the *telophase* (Fig. 48*E*).

The Chromosomes.—The most noteworthy feature of this mitotic process is the extreme exactitude with which the chromosomal material is divided into two equal parts, one of which is distributed to each of the daughter cells. The protoplasmic bodies are roughly divided *en masse*, but (except for the centrosomes) there seems to be no mechanism for insuring an exact equipartition. These facts early suggested that the chromosomes, rather than the rest of the nucleus or the cytoplasm, are of particular importance as carriers of hereditary material; and a great body of evidence, both genetic and cytological, has been amassed which confirms this conclusion. The structure and division of these bodies therefore assume a particular significance in the study of heredity.

In diploid organisms the chromosomes occur in pairs and the members of each pair are alike (with one significant exception in animals and some plants, p. 173). Their number in every body cell of every individual of a species is always the same (barring rare chromosome aberrations) but may differ greatly from species to species. Furthermore, the two members of a chromosome pair are often visibly different in size or in shape from the members of other pairs; and although the chromosomes may lose their individualities in the resting nucleus, the fact that in every successive division they reappear in the same number and with the same characteristic sizes and shapes suggests that there is a continuity of specific materials embodied in each of them which persists through every mitotic division and thus is present in every cell of the body (Fig. 49).

FIG. 49.—Individuality of the chromosomes. Chromosomes of a plant louse (*A*), beetle (*B*), and seed plant (*C*), showing similarities between the members of the same pair of chromosomes and differences between the pairs. (*From The Cell in Development and Heredity, by E. B. Wilson, 3d ed., copyright 1925, by The Macmillan Company. Reprinted by permission.*)

That an individual chromosome is not a homogeneous body but possesses qualitative differences in its material is also indicated by the frequent constrictions or swellings along its axis and by differences in staining reactions at various points. The fact, too, that in every mitosis the spindle fiber is always attached at one particular point on the chromosome indicates that this point must be specifically differentiated. This

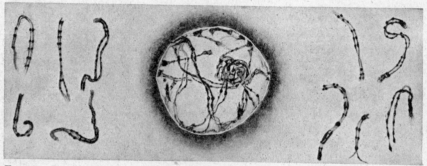

FIG. 50.—Pairs of chromosomes after synapsis, in Gasteria, showing well-marked chromomeres. (*From Wm. Randolph Taylor.*)

concept of the individuality and continuity of chromosomes throughout every cell of an individual has been of great significance in the development of modern theories as to the physical basis of inheritance.

The evident importance of these nuclear bodies has led to an extensive study of their structure, but the technical difficulties involved in making such minute objects visible has made it difficult to get an exact description of them. In many cases the chromosome, particularly in the early stages of mitosis, seems to consist of an axis along which is distributed a series of minute chromatic bodies, the *chromomeres* (Fig. 50), often showing persistent differences in size and distribution. In other cases the chromatic material seems to be in the form of a slender thread, the *chromonema* (Fig. 51), within the substance of a chromosome. These threads may be in a loose spiral in the prophase, when the chromosomes are relatively long, but in a much closer spiral as the chromosomes shorten during mitosis. The chromonema sometimes appears to persist through the resting phase of the nucleus, and many investigators believe that it constitutes the ultimate hereditary material.

Salivary Gland Chromosomes of Drosophila (Fig. 52).—In a few cases in insects, enormously enlarged chromosomes have been found in certain

Fig. 51.—Chromosomes of Gasteria showing spirally coiled chromonema in each. (*From Wm. Randolph Taylor.*)

somatic cells, and examination of these by Heitz and Bauer, Painter, Bridges, and others has revealed a pattern of structure within each chromosome and a wealth of detail never before observed. Such chromosomes are found in the salivary gland cells of Drosophila larvae, and here it has been found possible to identify the factors of heredity, the genes, with specific structures in the chromosome.

In Drosophila, as in many Diptera, the members of each pair of chromosomes lie side by side at somatic mitosis. In the resting salivary gland nucleus, the chromosomes consist of very long threads with cross striations of dense material, the two members of each pair lying closely apposed in somatic synapsis, so that each dark band appears to form a continuous line across both members of the pair. These darkly staining bands, apparently consisting chiefly of nucleic acid, differ in width and density and occur in a characteristic succession which is diagnostic for each section of each chromosome, so that it is possible to construct a map (Frontispiece) of each salivary chromosome, giving numbers to each section of bands and letters to each band in each chromosome. Bridges has recently counted about 1,000 distinct bands in the first (X) chromosome of Drosophila, and the total in all chromosomes may approach 5,000 or more, although the exact number is unknown. On high magnification some of the bands are resolved into dots, numbering 8 or 16 across each member of the pair, the dots in successive bands, according to Bridges, being connected by longitudinal threads on which the dots appear as beads on a string. "The salivary chromosome is thus essentially a bundle of parallel chromonemal threads, similar to that of ordinary chromosomes, except that the number of strands is supposedly higher

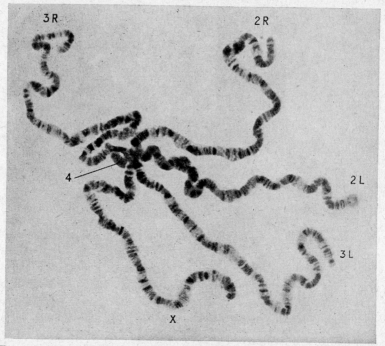

Fig. 52.—Photomicrograph of nucleus of salivary gland cell of *Drosophila melanogaster* female showing the X, the right and left arms of large autosomes (2R, 2L, 3R, 3L), and the small 4 chromosome. (*Courtesy of Dr. B. P. Kaufmann.*)

and the spiral coiling has practically vanished" (Bridges 1938). While the ultimate units of chromosome structure may prove to be even smaller, the elements in the cross bands of the salivary chromosomes constitute the nearest approach to ultimate morphological structure yet attained.

Meiosis (Fig. 53).—The cell divisions which immediately precede the formation of the sex cells differ in several significant respects from ordinary mitosis. The fusion of gametes in fertilization necessarily results in a doubling of nuclear material, most obviously shown in the doubling of chromosome number; a reduction of this material by half must evidently take place at some point in the life cycle before the

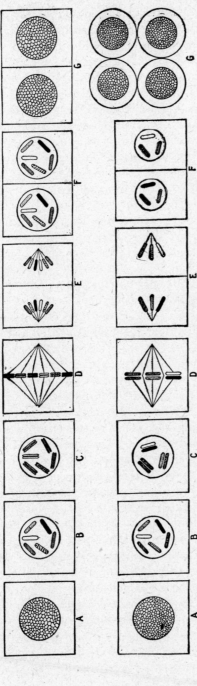

FIG. 53.—Comparison between mitosis in the body cells and in the meiotic divisions which precede the formation of the reproductive cells. The individual chromosomes are differently marked. In ordinary mitosis (upper row) it is evident that the chromatin is divided equally between the two daughter cells (*F* left and right). In the reduction divisions (lower row) the chromosomes do not split but align themselves in pairs (*C* and *D*) and one member of each pair goes to each pole (*E*), resulting in the formation of two cells (*F*), each with half as many chromosomes as the body cells. These by a subsequent equational mitosis give rise to four functional gametes (*G*). (*Modified from Sharp.*)

gametes are again formed. This "reduction division" occurs in the sex glands in animals immediately preceding gamete formation; and in the sporangia of higher plants incident to spore formation. The process, now commonly known as *meiosis*, has as its essential feature a reduction in the number of chromosomes from the double or *diploid* number characteristic of all somatic cells from the fertilized egg onward, to the halved or *haploid* number characteristic of gametes. A study of the chromosome complement of a somatic cell shows that its members are not all unlike but clearly separable into *pairs* of similar or *homologous* chromosomes. Investigation shows that each member of a pair was brought in by a different gamete, that is, one coming from the father and one from the mother, and that the essential feature in meiosis is their separation again in the gametes of the next generation. This is accomplished by two successive divisions through which a primary gamete-producing (or spore-producing) cell gives rise to four gametes (or spores). In the prophase of the first division the two members of each elongated pair approach each other side by side and become so closely associated (*conjugated*) that they sometimes seem to have fused into a single *bivalent* chromosome. This process of *synapsis*, which is often accompanied by a contraction of the chromosomes, is believed to be of a special significance as affording an opportunity for the interchange of material between homologous chromosomes.

During synapsis, or previously, each member of the bivalent pair splits longitudinally into two exactly equal daughter chromosomes or chromatids, so that for a time a *tetrad* is formed consisting of four chromatids. Between two of these four chromatids (derived from different members of the original pair) there form chiasmata or crosses where the chromatids exchange parts by a process known as crossing over (p. 197). The members of the tetrad now separate, two daughter chromosomes going to one pole, the two others to the opposite pole, so that each resulting cell gets two daughter chromosomes representing one original paternal or maternal homologue. At the next division, the members of each of these pairs of daughter chromosomes disjoin and each passes to a new daughter cell so that from one original cell with two chromosomes (one pair) four cells are derived, each with one chromosome. These two cell divisions, which occur in rapid succession, result in the *reduction* of the chromosome number to half the diploid number and in the *segregation*, at random, of one member of each chromosome pair to each gamete. The order in which these two divisions occur differs in different organisms. In some the reduction division (separation of the synapsed chromosomes) occurs first, as in the case illustrated; in others, the longitudinal split (equational division) occurs first. The essential results are the same in each case.

The significant feature of meiosis is the separation of two chromosomes of each pair. This does not restore the maternal and paternal groups of chromosomes intact, however, since the manner in which the two members of one pair separate has no effect on any other pair. Meiosis thus results in the formation of two cells, each with the haploid number of chromosomes and each with a representative of every chromosome pair; but between these cells the original parental chromosome sets have now been shuffled at random. This chromosomal mechanism pro-

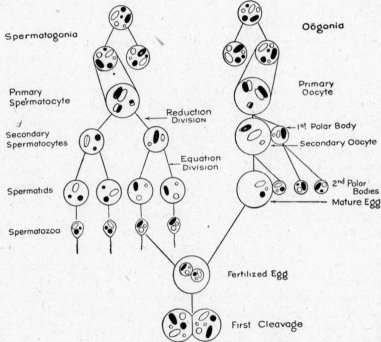

Fig. 54.—Diagram of spermatogenesis and oögenesis in an animal. (*After A. F. Shull.*)

vides the necessary basis for the segregation of genetic factors, and in its absence Mendelian heredity does not occur. The *meiotic* divisions are thus genetically the *segregation* divisions.

Gamete Formation in Animals.—Meiosis in animals (commonly known as *maturation*) occurs in the gonads and leads directly to the formation of gametes. The development of male gametes (*spermatogenesis*) and that of female gametes (*oögenesis*) differ in details and can best be considered separately.

Spermatogenesis (Fig. 54, left).—At a time preceding the sexual activity of the animal, in some cases by very long periods, there occurs in the testes of the male a series of cell divisions resulting in the formation of functional spermatozoa. The first step consists in the division of some of the cells (*spermatogonia*) lining the small tubules of which the testis is partly composed. By ordinary equational cell divisions the spermatogonia give rise to a second series of cells, the *primary spermatocytes*.

It is in these primary spermatocytes that the meiotic divisions take place, resulting in the production of *spermatids*, which, by elongation and shifting of the nucleus and addition of the small "middle piece" and the tail or flagellum, become converted each into a mature spermatozoon. Male gametes in animals are typically motile and consist chiefly of nucleus.

Oögenesis (Fig. 54, right).—The maturation of the egg follows a similar course except that the reduction division, instead of resulting in two functional cells of equal size, gives rise to one large functional cell, the *secondary oöcyte*, and to one small degenerate cell, the *first polar body* or *polocyte*. Each of these cells has the reduced number of chromosomes, and each subsequently divides equationally, the oöcyte to produce the large functional egg and another polar body; the first polar body usually into two polar bodies which disintegrate and disappear; or this second division may be suppressed.

Spermatogenesis produces four small gametes of equal size from a single spermatocyte; whereas in oögenesis a single large egg and usually three small degenerate cells (the polar bodies) are formed from each oöcyte. The difference between maturation in the male and in the female is chiefly in the larger amount of food accumulated in the egg cell. The two processes are identical in their essential function of producing gametes with one representative of each of the parental pairs of chromosomes.

Gamete Formation in Plants.—The life cycle in most plants is more complicated than in animals, and the formation of gametes, instead of following meiosis directly, may be considerably deferred.

The lowest of the four main divisions in the plant kingdom, the thallophytes, show a considerable diversity in this regard. In most of the green algae, meiosis occurs in the first two divisions of the fertilized egg, and thus almost all the vegetative cells of the plant, as well as its gametes, have the haploid number of chromosomes. In the brown alga, Fucus, almost exactly the opposite is true, since meiosis takes place just *before* the formation of the gametes and the cells of the plant body are thus all diploid, a condition essentially like that in animals. In many of the red algae the fertilized egg produces a group of spores (*carpospores*) each of which develops into a nonsexual plant, and these in turn bear nonsexual spores (*tetraspores*) in the formation of which meiosis is accomplished. The tetraspores develop into haploid sexual plants which ultimately bear gametes.

In plants above the thallophytes the "alternation of generations" is even more definite, a nonsexual diploid generation or plant, the *sporophyte*, bearing spores, in the formation of which meiosis occurs. These in turn grow into haploid sexual plants, *gametophytes*, which ultimately bear gametes, the fertilized egg developing into a sporophytic plant. There is thus an entire "generation" intercalated between meiosis and gamete production.

Among the seed plants, with which genetics has been chiefly concerned, the gametophytic generation has become very greatly reduced

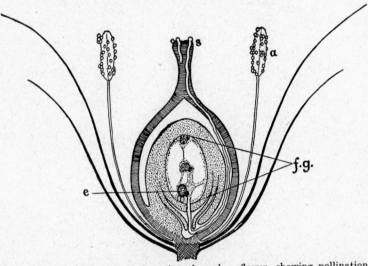

Fig. 55.—Diagram of a vertical section through a flower, showing pollination and fertilization. The anthers, *a*, have opened, liberating pollen grains, two of which have germinated on the stigma, *s*. The pollen tube from one of these has grown down the style and carried the two male gametes to the embryo sac or female gametophyte, *f. g.*, of the ovule, where one is fertilizing the female gamete or egg, *e*. From the union of their nuclei will develop the embryo of the seed, which grows into a new plant.

and is no longer an independent plant but is contained wholly within the reproductive structures of the sporophyte, which is the "plant" which we see. These reproductive structures are known as *flowers* (Fig. 55). Each consists, typically, of four sets of structures. Outside is a circle of protective parts, the *calyx*, and within this another circle of conspicuous and attractive parts, the *corolla*. Next occurs a series of "male" sexual organs, the *stamens*, each bearing an *anther*, which produces within itself a mass of single-celled *pollen grains*. Strictly speaking, however, the anther is not a sexual organ but is a sporangium, and the pollen grains are really microspores and not gametes, although they give rise directly to gametes. In the center of the flower is the "female" organ, the *pistil*, consisting of an *ovary*, *style*, and *stigma*. Within the ovary are one or more *ovules* which, after fertilization, develop into seeds. The ovule is really a sporangium, also, and produces within itself a megaspore which germinates into a very much reduced female gameto-

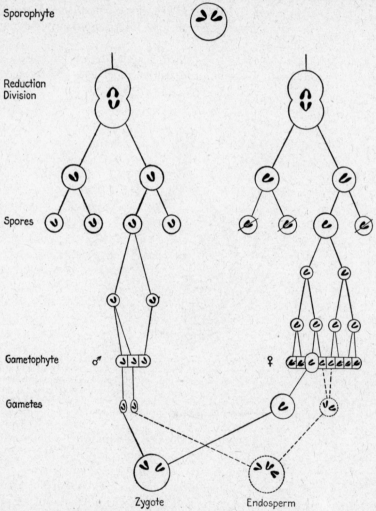

Fig. 56.—The life cycle of an angiospermous seed plant. Diagram showing chromosome reduction in formation of microspores (left) and megaspores (right); gametophyte development; gamete formation; and double fertilization. (*After Mohr.*)

phyte or "embryo sac," containing at least one egg cell, the true female gamete. Two other gametophyte cells, each with the reduced (haploid) chromosome number unite to form a diploid endosperm nucleus. The pollen grain (microspore) is carried by wind, insects, or other agencies to the stigma of the same flower or another of the same species and there germinates, its contents dividing into a small group of cells (in the higher plants only three), which represent the last vestige of the male gameto-phyte. From the germinating grain develops a *pollen tube* which pene-trates the style and enters the ovule in the ovary. Down this tube passes the contents of the pollen grain—one nonsexual nucleus and two other nuclei, the true male gametes. One of these gametes unites with the egg cell in the ovule, and from this fertilized egg develops the embryo of the seed. The second male nucleus unites with the endosperm nucleus and gives rise to the endosperm tissue of the seed which thus has three members of each chromosome set (triploid). This remarkable process of "double fertilization" (Figs. 55, 56) results in the formation of endosperm tissue, which partakes of both paternal and maternal inheritance; and in plants where the ovary wall and seed coat are thin and transparent, as in the kernel of maize, a direct effect of the male gamete on the char-acter of the endosperm is evident. Thus, if an ear of maize from a type normally bearing white endosperm is pollinated by pollen from a yellow race (yellow endosperm color being dominant over white), the endosperm of the seeds produced will be yellow. This direct effect of the male gamete on tissues other than embryonic ones is known as *xenia*.

Fertilization or Syngamy.—The union of the gametes in fertilization is of especial significance, since it brings about the intermingling of paternal and maternal hereditary material, which persists throughout the life of the new individual. It is accomplished by a great variety of means in animals and plants. In the lowest groups the gametes may be equal in size and similar in structure (an *isogamous* condition), but in the great majority of all animals and plants they are unequal (*heterogamous*), the male gamete being relatively small and consisting of little but a nucleus, and the female gamete (egg) being very much larger and possess-ing a considerable amount of cytoplasm in addition to its nucleus.

The essential feature in fertilization is the fusion of the nuclei of the gametes. A single male gamete penetrates the egg and (having lost whatever nonnuclear material it may have possessed) advances toward the egg nucleus, usually increasing in size as it goes. As they meet, the two nuclei may still be unequal in size, but there is good reason to believe that, as far as their chromosome content is concerned, they are equivalent. Fusion takes place shortly after the nuclei come into contact. By this union of the two haploid chromosome complements—one from the father and one from the mother—the diploid number is restored. From this fusion nucleus, or *zygote*, by successive equational divisions, are formed the nuclei of all the cells of the body which are quantitatively similar in chromosome content, however various they may be in other respects. It should be remembered that in each pair of chromosomes in the zygote one member has come from one parent and the other from the other parent.

In some forms the egg may sometimes develop directly into a new individual without having been fertilized, a process commonly called *parthenogenesis*. A well-known example of this in animals is the honeybee, where the haploid egg, if unfertilized, develops into a male (drone). In plant lice, however, the eggs under favorable conditions in summer remain unreduced (diploid) and develop parthenogenetically chiefly into females. Some produce males, and as unfavorable conditions ensue, normal meiosis again takes place and haploid eggs are formed which undergo normal fertilization and produce females.

Parthenogenesis may also sometimes be induced by artificial means and these instances in which the egg is able to develop without fertilization show that the male gamete is not indispensable. Under most conditions, however, it seems essential in providing the stimulus which initiates embryonic development; and its contribution of paternal genes is important in determining the character of the offspring and in providing for future variability.

In plants, somewhat similar situations obtain. In a number of cases (Datura, Lycopersicum, and others) normal unfertilized haploid eggs, under certain conditions, may produce embryos which develop into plants every cell of which is haploid. A considerable number of plants, of which the dandelion is a common example, undergo parthenogenetic development normally, but in these cases the egg remains diploid, owing to a failure of the usual meiotic process.

The Relations of the Chromosomes to Sex.—We must now take account of one important exception to the statements (1) that the chromosomes of the somatic cells of diploid organisms appear in pairs of homologous mates and (2) that, after the disjunction of the members of these pairs at synapsis, *all* gametes receive one member of each pair and are thus exactly equivalent in chromosome content. The discovery of this exception has led to the development of a chromosome theory of sex determination which has had an important influence on ideas concerning the physical basis of inheritance.

In the diploid body cells of animals and plants, chromosomes in general occur in pairs of homologous mates, and the two members of each pair seem to be exactly alike. In most of the higher plants, where the same individual produces both male and female gametes, *all* of the chromosomes normally occur in pairs. In most animals, on the other hand, and in a few plants, the male and female cells are produced by different individuals. This difference in function is usually accompanied by difference in structure between the male and the female individual, and the important fact has been established that this difference appears also in the chromosome constitution.

In some animals one sex is diploid, the other haploid. In the honey-bee the female (queen) has 32 chromosomes, the male (drone) 16. The reduction division in the male is omitted so that all the sperm have 16 chromosomes. Fertilized eggs thus produce females; unfertilized eggs which develop parthenogenetically produce haploid males. The haploid sex in such cases appears always to be the male. This type of sex differ-ence is known only in a few invertebrates.

Another type is of general occurrence in animals and in some dioecious plants. Here males and females differ by a single chromosome. In the squash bug, *Anasa tristis*, for example, Wilson found that females regularly have 11 pairs of homologous chromosomes, whereas males have 10 pairs, and one odd unpaired chromosome. The eggs consequently have each 11 chromosomes, while of the sperm half have 11 chromosomes and half have 10, since at reduction division the odd chromosome goes to either one pole or the other, at random. Fertilization of an egg (11 chromosomes) by a sperm with 11 chromosomes produces a *female* (22 chromosomes); fertilization by a sperm with 10 chromosomes produces a *male* with 21 chromosomes. The odd chromosome thus determines the sex of the individual which receives it, and it was consequently called the *sex chromosome* or X chromosome. The other chromosomes which are alike in males and females have been called *autosomes*. The case may thus be formulated:

$$\female = 10 \text{ pairs of autosomes} + 2 \text{ X chromosomes (or } \female = 10\,AA + XX)$$
$$\male = 10 \text{ pairs of autosomes} + 1 \text{ X chromosome (or } \male = 10\,AA + X)$$

In many other animals and in several plants males and females have been found to differ, not by the presence or absence of one whole chromo-some, but by the presence in one sex of a chromosome which is unlike its mate and unlike any chromosome in the opposite sex. In *Drosophila melanogaster* the female has four pairs of chromosomes (Fig. 57), the members of each pair being alike. In the male there is only *one* of the straight rodlike chromosomes, the place of the other member of this pair being taken by a rod with a hook-shaped or bent end. The rodlike mem-ber, which is alike in both male and female, is the sex or X chromosome; the unlike member of this pair in the male is known as the Y chromosome. The eggs all have four chromosomes (3 A + X); the sperms also have four chromosomes, but half have the rod-shaped X chromosome (3 A + X) and half have the bent Y chromosome (3 A + Y). Fertilization of any egg by an X-containing sperm produces a female (6 A + XX); fertilization by a Y-containing sperm produces a male (6 A + XY).

This type of sex-chromosome difference has been found in other species of Drosophila, in some fish and amphibia, and in mammals generally. In man, for example, there are 48 chromosomes (Fig. 58). In the female these appear as 24 pairs (23 AA + XX); in the male, as 23

FEMALE   MALE

X X   X Y

FIG. 57.—Diagram showing the four pairs of chromosomes in Drosophila. X designates the sex chromosomes. (*After Bridges.*)

pairs with one X and one Y chromosome (23 AA + XY). The sex of the offspring is determined at fertilization by the kind of sperm which happens to fertilize the egg. Since the number of males and females at birth is about equal, it is probable that X and Y sperm are produced in about

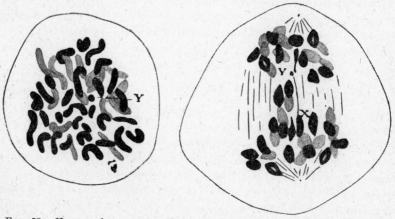

FIG. 58.—Human chromosomes. Left: spermatogonial plate of 48 chromosomes; right: anaphase of primary spermatocyle with the X-Y chromosomes and three other chromosomes not yet divided (note evidences of splitting for next division). (*From Evans and Swezy, courtesy of University of California Press.*)

equal numbers and that the chances of fertilization by each type are about equal; that is, fertilization is at random.

In a few other animals which have been studied cytologically, it has been found that the *female* has an unlike pair of chromosomes (XY) or only one X (XO), while the male is XX. For such cases a different formulation has often been used: the sex chromosomes have been called Z instead of X, and the other member of this pair W instead of Y. Animals of this type are thus called ZW and ZZ, or, briefly, of the ZW type to distinguish it from the Drosophila or XY type. We adopt here a similar terminology for both types, since the letters are merely symbols and do not indicate homology between X chromosomes in different forms. The two types may be distinguished as male heterogametic and female heterogametic, respectively.

In the domestic fowl, for example, the female lays eggs of two sorts, half with an X chromosome, which when fertilized by any sperm develop into males (XX); and half without an X chromosome, which develop into females. Female heterogamety has been found chiefly in birds and moths. The mechanism is the same as in Drosophila, that is, two types of gametes are formed by one sex and only one by the other sex; and sex is determined at fertilization by the kinds of gametes which unite.

Sex-linked Factors.—The existence of this mechanism was revealed first by cytological methods, but its genetic significance and its wide occurrence have been established through the discovery of genetic factors, which in inheritance have the same peculiar distribution to gametes and offspring as the X chromosomes. Thus in man the appearance of hemophilia chiefly in the sons of "carrier" females was noted nearly a century ago, although it was not until Doncaster in 1908 studied experimentally a case of such "criss-cross" inheritance in the currant moth, Abraxas, that the general mode of inheritance of characters like these became clear. Such characters are called *sex-linked*.

In *Drosophila melanogaster* the discovery of sex-linked inheritance was followed by a study of the distribution of the sex chromosomes, and this correlation of genetical and cytological facts led directly to the proof of the chromosome theory of heredity. In the course of breeding experiments with the normal wild-type fly, which has red eyes, Morgan found one individual in which the eyes were white. This gave rise to a true breeding race of white-eyed flies. When he crossed this new variety with the wild, red-eyed type, the results from a cross of a white male by a red female were quite different from those obtained from the reciprocal cross of red male by white female. The results were found to depend on the sex of the parent in which the trait was introduced into the cross, whereas with other characters, as has been seen, it makes no difference in either the F_1 or F_2 whether a given character is brought in by the male or female parent. The details of these experiments, which have been repeated many times, are shown in Figs. 59 and 60. From the cross of white-eyed male with red female the first-generation flies are red-eyed in both sexes (Fig. 59). When these are bred together, white reappears in a quarter of the F_2 offspring, indicating that red and white eye color are due to an allelic pair of genes of which red acts as the dominant. However, of the F_2 offspring all the females are red, while half of the males are red and half are white. The white male has trans-

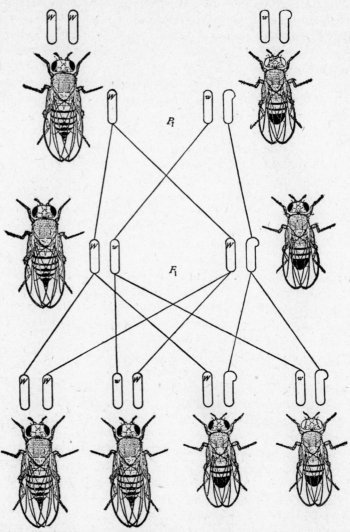

Fig. 59.—Sex-linked inheritance in Drosophila. The cross of red-eyed female by white-eyed male. The course of the sex chromosomes carrying the sex-linked gene W-w is traced from parents to F_2. Females at left, males at right. (*From Morgan, Sturtevant, Muller and Bridges, courtesy of Henry Holt & Company.*)

mitted his eye color only to his grandsons. These F_2 white-eyed males evidently carry no factors for red, since when bred with pure white stock, no red-eyed individuals ever appear among their offspring. The females, however, are apparently of two kinds, genotypically. When bred with pure red males, half of them give nothing but red offspring and are thus pure for red, but the other half must carry some recessive white, for in their offspring *half the males* are white-eyed. When a red male is bred

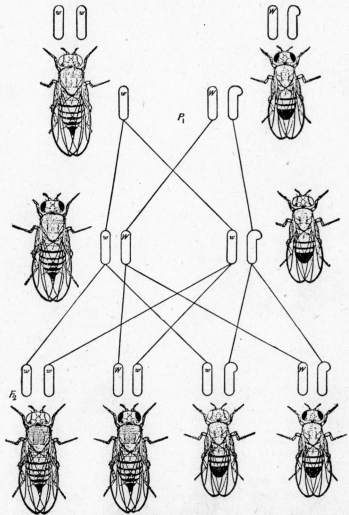

F_{IG}. 60.—Sex-linked inheritance in Drosophila. The cross of white-eyed female by red-eyed male, the reciprocal of the cross shown in Fig. 59. Females at left, males at right. (*From Morgan, Sturtevant, Muller and Bridges, courtesy of Henry Holt & Company.*)

to a white female, however, quite a different result follows (Fig. 60). Among their F_1 offspring all the females are red-eyed and *all the males* are white-eyed. When these are bred together, their offspring (the F_2 consist of red-eyed and white-eyed individuals in about equal numbers in both sexes. All the white-eyed flies are apparently pure, for no red-eyed flies appear in their offspring; and the ꜞꜞꜞ-eyed *males* bred to pure red females also produce only red-eyed descendants. The red-eyed F_1 females, however, must be heterozygous, for when bred to either white or red males, half of their male offspring are always white-eyed.

A typical sex-linked trait in Drosophila, such as white eye color, is found to follow a peculiar type of *crisscross* inheritance. A male trans-

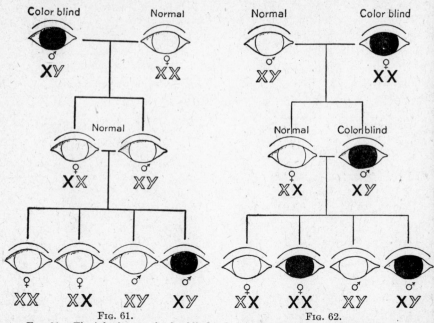

FIG. 61.

FIG. 62.

FIG. 61.—The inheritance of color-blindness. A color-blind man mated with a normal woman. The defect is transmitted only through the daughters and appears in half of their sons, being carried in one of the X chromosomes. Color-blind individuals and chromosomes carrying the gene for this character are shown in black. (*From Dunn, courtesy of the University Society.*)

FIG. 62.—The inheritance of color-blindness. A color-blind woman mated with a normal man. The defect is transmitted to *all* the sons and (in the F_2 mating shown) to both grandsons and granddaughters. (*From Dunn, courtesy of the University Society.*)

mits his sex-linked traits to his grandsons through his daughters. He never transmits them to or through his sons. The trait thus seems to alternate or cross from one sex to the other in its passage from generation to generation. This of course is the mode of transmission followed by the X chromosome, as can be seen in the diagrams. Only the daughters get an X chromosome from the father; whereas both sons and daughters receive an X chromosome from the mother.

In explaining the peculiar inheritance of white eye color in Drosophila, it was assumed that the gene for white eyes *is located in the sex chromo-*

some and that the Y chromosome carries no normal allele for white. On this assumption the ...se became clear, for the white-eyed female crossed with a red male transmitted a gene for white to each offspring and an X chromosome to each offspring. The daughters received also an X chromosome from the father carrying the dominant allele of white and hence were red-eyed. The sons, however, received a Y chromosome from the father and hence no allele of white, and they were thus white-eyed. From the diagrams it is apparent that in all cases the gene for white follows exactly the transmission of the X chromosome.

Over two hundred genes in Drosophila are now known to follow this mode of transmission, and all have been shown to be located in the X chromosome. In man a number of traits including color blindness and hemophilia (bleeder's disease) are inherited in the same crisscross fashion and are thus presumably located in the X chromosome (Figs. 61 and

Non-barred male

Barred female

Fig. 63.—Barring (right) and plain color (left), a sex-linked pair of allelic characters in domestic fowls.

62). Many similar sex-linked characters have been studied in other mammals, insects, and fish. In general the Y chromosome in these forms carries no normal allele of a sex-linked factor, but in a few cases mutant genes have been discovered in the Y chromosome (Drosophila, man, certain fishes). These follow the course of the Y chromosome in inheritance.

In moths and birds a number of sex-linked characters have been found. In these cases, too, the genes for such traits have been shown to follow the known course of transmission of the X chromosome, although sex determination is of the opposite type to that which occurs in Drosophila and mammals. The inheritance of barred plumage in poultry is one of the best-known examples of this type (Fig. 63). The barred pattern, as seen in such breeds as the Barred Plymouth Rock, is dominant over black or red unbarred plumage. Breeding evidence indicates that a male may carry two genes for barring but a female only one; and cytological research has shown that there are two X chromosomes in the cells of the male but only one in those of the female. In the diagrams (Figs. 64 and 65) barred plumage is represented by B and nonbarred by b. The cross between a nonbarred hen and a barred cock produces only barred offspring of both sexes. These inbred produce only barred males in F_2, but approximately half of the F_2 hens are barred and the other half are nonbarred.

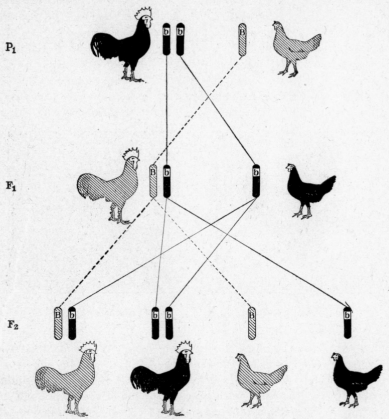

Fig. 64.—Sex-linked inheritance in poultry. The cross of barred ♀ by non-barred ♂. (See Fig. 65.)

The reciprocal cross of barred hen and nonbarred cock gives, as might be expected, a very different result. Here the F_1 males are *all barred*, and the F_1 hens are *nonbarred;* while in F_2 there are equal numbers of barred and nonbarred birds in both sexes. Barring thus follows the same crisscross mode of inheritance as white eyes, except that in the fowl the sex-linked gene goes from mother (XO) to sons only, while the father (XX), transmits it to both sons and daughters. The gene follows the X chromosome in both cases.

In the fowl, pigeon, duck, canary, several species of moths, and one species of fish, sex-linked characters have been studied and found to resemble barring in their inheritance.

An example of sex-linked inheritance in dioecious plants is described on page 274. In the few cases thus far discovered the male is the heterogametic sex.

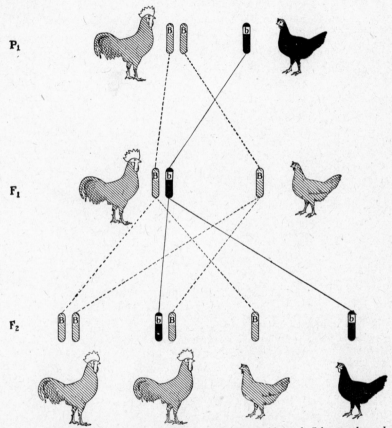

Fig. 65.—Sex-linked inheritance in poultry. The cross of barred ♂ by non-barred ♀. The course of the X chromosomes carrying the sex-linked gene *B* (barring) and its recessive allele *b* is traced from parents to F₂. Chromosomes carrying *B* are cross-hatched; those carrying *b*, solid black. Males at left; females at right.

Nondisjunction of Chromosomes.—The conclusions with regard to the inheritance of both X chromosomes and sex-linked traits remained highly probable inferences from the close parallelism between the behavior of chromosomes and sex-linked genes, until in a specific case it was shown by Bridges that deviations from the usual rules of sex-linked inheritance in Drosophila were directly correlated with irregularities in the transmission of X chromosomes. Ordinarily, as has been noted, white-eyed females bred to red-eyed males produce only red-eyed daughters and white-eyed sons. Bridges found that some females from a strain of white-eyed flies produced, when bred to red-eyed males, not only the expected classes of red daughters and white sons but also a few (about 5 per cent) of *white* daughters and *red* sons. He explained these exceptions by assuming that in the oögenesis of the white-eyed females, both X chromosomes (each with a gene for white) occasionally stayed together at the reduction division, a process which he called *nondisjunction*, so that both went together into the polar body, resulting in some eggs with no X chromosome and in others with two X chromosomes and thus

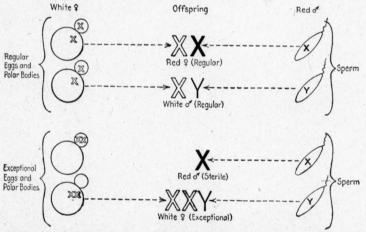

Fig. 66.—Non-disjunction of the X chromosome in *Drosophila melanogaster*. Cross of white ♀ by red ♂. X chromosomes carrying white in outline; those carrying normal allele (red) shown in solid black. (*After Morgan.*)

two genes for white (Fig. 66). The eggs of such a white female would then be not only the usual (X*w*) but the exceptional kinds (X*w*)(X*w*) and (O). When fertilized by the Y sperm of the red male, the (X*w*)(X*w*) egg would produce a fly of genotype (X*w*)(X*w*)Y, which having two X chromosomes would be female and having two white genes would be white-eyed; conversely, when the no-X egg was fertilized by the (X*W*) sperm the resulting offspring would be (X*W*)O and, having but one X, would be a red male. Thus the two exceptional classes of offspring could be accounted for. The white-eyed females produced by nondisjunction should then have two X chromosomes and one Y, and on microscopic examination Bridges found that this was so. Breeding tests of such nondisjunctional females and cytological examination of their progeny have shown conclusively that the visible sex-linked trait has always the same distribution as the sex chromosome, which may be identified under the microscope.

Later L. V. Morgan found females in which the X chromosomes showed 100 per cent nondisjunction. When such a female with the recessive sex-linked character yellow body was bred to a normal gray

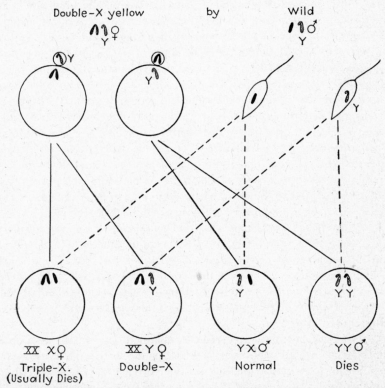

Fig. 67.—Inheritance of "attached-X" chromosomes in Drosophila. The X chromosomes of the mother each carry the gene yellow and these are transmitted together to all viable daughters. The only surviving sons are those which receive the Y chromosome from the *mother* and the X from the father. (*After Morgan.*)

male the daughters were all yellow and the sons were all gray, just the opposite of the expected result of such a mating. It was found that in such females the X chromosomes were attached to each other and thus failed to disjoin, and they also contained a Y chromosome, like the exceptional females found by Bridges. The results of cytological and genetical study of this case are shown in Fig. 67. In all cases the sex-linked genes follow the same course as the X chromosomes. The proofs were thus completed that the sex-linked genes are actually in the X chromosomes and similar evidence is now available for other chromosomes (Chapter IX).

The Parallelism between the Behavior of Chromosomes and Genes.— In this chapter the steps have been described by which certain parts of the nucleus of animal and plant cells, the chromosomes, are distributed among the gametes. This process is not a hypothetical one but a description of fact, since it is founded on actual microscopic evidence. The point which must now be emphasized is that the behavior of the chromosomes, in the history of the formation of gametes and of fertilization, resembles in a very striking way the behavior of the factors of inheritance, the genes, as inferred from the breeding evidence. The truth of the assumptions concerning the behavior of the genes (Mendel's Laws) is convincing, not because these units in the gametes have been seen but because the principles of segregation and independent assortment are the only hypotheses which satisfactorily explain the results of breeding experiments. The parallelism to be noted, then, is that which exists between a concrete set of facts (chromosome behavior) and the hypotheses proposed to explain another set of facts (gene behavior). Aside from the general similarity between these two processes, there are certain specific laws which apparently apply in a similar way to each.

1. Both the chromosomes and the genes behave in inheritance as though they were individual units. The individuality of the chromosomes is a matter of direct observation under the microscope. Each pair of chromosomes can be seen, in favorable preparations, to be different from every other pair. Each gene, likewise, has an individuality which is inferred from its indivisibility in inheritance and its emergence intact and unaltered after a cross.

2. The facts of inheritance can be explained only on the assumption that the genes which make up the genotype of every individual occur in *pairs* (allelic pairs) and that one member of each pair was contributed by one parent of this individual and the other by the other parent. This is precisely the situation observed in the case of the chromosomes, for these are also seen to be definitely associated in pairs, each member of which has been derived from one of the two parents.

3. Each gamete is seen to contain only one member of each pair of chromosomes, and each gamete likewise contains but one member of each pair of allelic genes. That the gametes contain the reduced or haploid number of chromosomes is known from actual chromosome counts, especially at the reduction division. That each gamete contains only one of a pair of genes was found to be a necessary inference from breeding experiments. In fact, the most important of Mendel's principles assumes a process of *segregation* whereby, in the formation of gametes, each factor separates sharply from its alternative or allele, the two

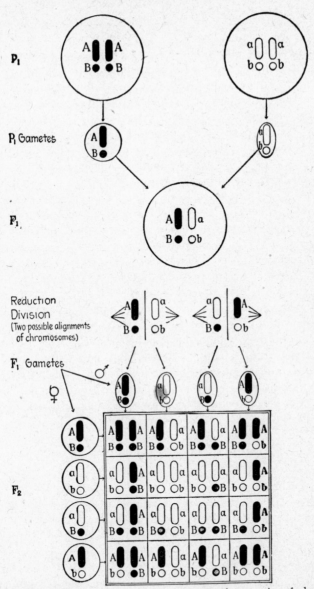

Fig. 68.—Diagram showing independent assortment of two pairs of chromosomes, *A-a* and *B-b*. Note that at the reduction division there are *two* possible alignments of chromosomes producing *four* types of gametes. By random union these produce the sixteen different chromosome combinations shown in the F_2 checkerboard.

members of the pair always entering different gametes so that the gametes are "pure" genetically. Such a separation is actually found to take place between the two members of a pair of chromosomes at the reduction division, resulting in the inclusion of each member of the pair in different daughter cells (gametes). Both genes and chromosomes, then, undergo segregation, and in respect to both each gamete is pure, containing only one member of a pair.

4. The various pairs of chromosomes are assorted or distributed to the gametes independently of each other. A careful study of the diagram in Fig. 68 will show that the principle of independent assortment applies to chromosomes in precisely the same way in which it has been assumed to apply to genes. It seems to be merely a matter of chance to which pole a given member of a chromosome pair goes in the reduction division, so that it is also a matter of chance as to whether a given member of a pair happens to become associated with one or with the other member of another chromosome pair. This is precisely the manner in which genes behave in inheritance, for in the formation of gametes by individuals heterozygous for two or more independent factor pairs, it is purely a matter of chance as to how the members of the various pairs happen to become assorted and associated in the gametes, and segregation in one factor pair is entirely independent of that in every other.

It should be understood, of course, that each chromosome contains many factors and that independent assortment is shown between two factors pairs only if they occur in separate chromosome pairs. If they lie in the same chromosome, they will be *linked* in inheritance, a situation which will be discussed in the following chapter.

REFERENCES

BRIDGES, C. B. 1916. Non-disjunction as proof of the chromosome theory. Genetics **1**.
———. 1938. Revised map of the salivary gland X chromosome of *Drosophila melanogaster*. Jour. Hered. **29**: 11–13.
McCLUNG, C. E. 1902. The accessory chromosome—sex determinant? Biol. Bull. **3**.
MORGAN, L. V. 1922. Non-crisscross inheritance in *Drosophila melanogaster*. Biol. Bull. **42**.
MORGAN, T. H. 1910. Sex-limited inheritance in Drosophila. Science **32**.
———. 1919. The physical basis of heredity. Philadelphia.
———. 1928. The theory of the gene. 2d ed. New Haven.
———, A. H. STURTEVANT, H. J. MULLER, and C. B. BRIDGES. 1923. The mechanism of mendelian heredity. 2d ed. New Haven.
PAINTER, T. S. 1934. Salivary chromosomes and the attack on the gene. Jour. Hered. **25**: 465–476.
SCHRADER, F. 1928. The sex chromosomes. Berlin.
SHARP, L. W. 1926. An introduction to cytology. 2d ed. New York.

SUTTON, W. S. 1902. Chromosomes in heredity. Biol. Bull. **4.**
WILSON, E. B. 1925. The cell in development and heredity. 3d ed. New York.

PROBLEMS

222. Of what advantage do you think it has been for the male and female gametes, in the evolution of sex, to have become so different from each other, the former tending to be small and motile and the latter large and nonmotile?

223. What explanation can you suggest for the presence of polar bodies in the development of the animal egg?

224. Wherever parthenogenesis (the development of a gamete without union with another gamete) occurs among animals, it is always the female gamete which has this power. Why do you suppose this is so?

225. If a character is found to be transmitted only by the mother, in what part of the gamete is it probably transmitted?

226. If the germ cells were formed by direct division of the nucleus without mitosis, how would this affect the character of the gametes and the process of inheritance?

227. What would happen to the chromosomal constitution of the nucleus if the reduction division did not take place?

228. What do you think would happen in the gametogenesis of a species with an *odd* number of chromosomes?

229. Of what advantage in plant reproduction is the complicated system of accessory structures such as the calyx and corolla?

230. Do you think that the characteristics of the fruits of an apple tree will be affected by the source of the pollen which fertilized the flowers? Explain.

231. If half of the chromosomes of an oöcyte pass into the first polar body (which degenerates), why are not some of the chromosomes lost entirely in the process of oögenesis in animals?

232. In some groups of animals and plants the chromosome number of one species is a multiple of that in another. Thus in wheat some species have 14, some 28, and some 42 chromosomes. What does this suggest as to the evolutionary history of these species?

233. In the Drosophilidae (the family to which the vinegar fly belongs) Metz has found that some species have 8 chromosomes while other related species have 6, 8, 10, and 12 chromosomes each. Assuming that all species are descended from an 8-chromosome type, how would you account for the species with more and with fewer chromosomes?

234. In the rather rare cases where two species can be successfully crossed, as the horse and the ass, the hybrids produced are almost always sterile. From what you know of chromosome behavior, what explanation can you suggest for this fact?

235. It is ordinarily impossible to distinguish the sex of young chicks, although it would be very useful to be able to do so. The difference between barred and nonbarred birds, however, can be told at the time of hatching. How could this fact be utilized in certain cases to distinguish the sex of the newly hatched chicks?

236. What effect on the sex ratio would a recessive sex-linked lethal factor have in man?

237. At the time of synapsis preceding the reduction division, the homologous chromosomes align themselves in pairs and one member of each pair passes to each of the daughter nuclei. Assume that in an animal with four pairs of chromosomes, chromosomes A, B, C, and D have come from the father and A′, B′, C′, and D′ have come from the mother. In what proportion of the germ cells of this animal will all of the paternal chromosomes be present together? all of the maternal?

238. If a given character A pertains to the *gametophyte*, and the gametophyte of one plant shows it while that of another plant shows its allele *a*; and if gametes from these two gametophytes unite, what will be the appearance of the succeeding generation of gametophytes with respect to this character?

239. If one gametophyte displays characters A and B and is crossed with another which displays *a* and *b*, what will the next gametophyte generation look like with respect to these two characters?

240. In the honeybee, unfertilized eggs may develop by parthenogenesis, in which case they produce males (drones). The fertilized eggs produce females (workers or queens). In spermatogenesis in bees there is no reduction division. If the females contain 32 chromosomes in the body cells and if oögenesis is the same as in other species, how many chromosomes would you expect to find in the body cells of the males?

241. A queen bee heterozygous for a dominant character mates with a drone which shows the same character. What characters would you expect the male and female offspring to show?

Note.—In all problems involving sex-linked characters, state results for the two sexes separately.

242. In Drosophila, if a white-eyed female is crossed with a red-eyed male, and if an F_1 female from this cross is mated with her father and an F_1 male with his mother, what will be the appearance of the offspring of these last two crosses as to eye color?

243. In Drosophila, if a homozygous red-eyed female is crossed with a white-eyed male, and if an F_1 female from this cross is mated with her father and an F_1 male with his mother, what will be the appearance of the offspring of these last two crosses as to eye color?

244. In Drosophila, if a white-eyed female is crossed with a red-eyed male and the F_2 allowed to interbreed freely, what will be the appearance of the F_3 as to eye color?

245. In Drosophila, if a homozygous red-eyed female is crossed with a white-eyed male and the F_2 allowed to interbreed freely, what will be the appearance of the F_3 as to eye color?

246. In Drosophila, vestigial wings, v, are recessive to the normal long wings, V, and the gene for this trait is not in the sex chromosome. If a homozygous white, long female is crossed with a homozygous red, vestigial male, what will be the appearance of the F_1? Of the F_2? Of the offspring of a cross of the F_1 with each parent type?

247. In Drosophila, what will be the appearance of the offspring of the following crosses: $Ww\ Vv \times w\ vv$; $ww\ Vv \times W\ Vv$?

248. In Drosophila, two red-eyed, long-winged flies when bred together produce the following offspring:

Females: three-fourths red, long; one-fourth red, vestigial.

Males: three-eighths red, long; three-eighths white, long; one-eighth red, vestigial; one-eighth white, vestigial.

What are the genotypes of the parents?

249. In Drosophila, a cross between Bar-eyed females and wild-type (round-eyed) males produces only Bar-eyed males and females in the F_1. Wild-type female × Bar-eyed males produces Bar-eyed females and wild-type males. Explain the inheritance of Bar eye and predict the appearance of the F_2 from each of these crosses.

250. A girl of normal vision whose father was color-blind marries a man of normal vision whose father was also color-blind. What type of vision will be expected in their offspring?

251. A color-blind man marries a woman of normal vision. They have sons and daughters, all of normal vision and all of whom marry normal persons. Where among the grandchildren may color blindness be expected to appear? If there are cousin marriages among these grandchildren, where among *their* offspring may color blindness be expected to appear?

252. A man and woman, both of normal vision have (1) a color-blind son who has a daughter of normal vision; (2) a daughter of normal vision who has one color-blind and one normal son; and (3) another daughter of normal vision who has five sons, all normal. What are the probable genotypes of grandparents, children, and grandchildren?

253. A man's maternal grandmother had normal vision; his maternal grandfather was color-blind; his mother is color-blind; his father is of normal vision. What are the genotypes, as to vision, of the two parents and grandparents mentioned? What type of vision has this man himself? What type have his sisters? If he should marry a woman genotypically like one of his sisters, what type of vision would be expected in the offspring?

Note.—In the following problem assume that right-handedness is dominant over left-handedness and brown eye color over blue.

254. The mother of a right-handed, brown-eyed woman of normal vision is right-handed, blue-eyed, and of normal vision, and her father is left-handed, brown-eyed, and color-blind. This woman marries a man who is left-handed, brown-eyed, and of normal vision, whose father was blue-eyed. What chance will the sons of this couple have of resembling their father phenotypically?

255. In poultry, if a nonbarred cock is crossed with a barred hen and an F_1 female from this cross is mated with her father and an F_1 male with his mother, what will be the appearance of the offspring of these last two crosses, as to barring?

256. In poultry, if a nonbarred cock is crossed with a barred hen and an F_2 from this cross is allowed to interbreed freely, what will be the appearance of the F_3 as to barring?

257. A single-comb, barred cock crossed with a walnut-comb, barred hen produces the following offspring:

4 rose, barred males.
5 walnut, barred males.
2 rose, barred females.
3 rose, nonbarred females.
2 walnut, barred females.
2 walnut, nonbarred females.

What are the genotypes of the parents?

258. In Drosophila vermilion eye color is recessive and sex linked. In exceptional cases vermilion female × normal male produces, in addition to the usual vermilion male and red-eyed female, a few vermilion females and red males. Explain this result and predict what classes of offspring should appear when the vermilion F_1 females from above are crossed with red-eyed males.

259. In the fish Aplocheilus the wild form is brown; other varieties are blue, red, and white. Sex determination is of the XY type (male heterogamety) as in Drosophila. The following results of crossing these varieties were obtained by Aida:[1]

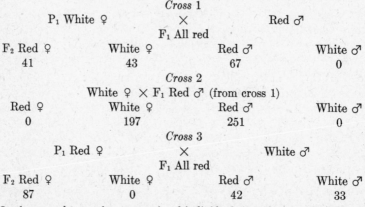

Cross 1

P₁ White ♀   ×   Red ♂
F₁ All red

F₂ Red ♀	White ♀	Red ♂	White ♂
41	43	67	0

Cross 2

White ♀ × F₁ Red ♂ (from cross 1)

Red ♀	White ♀	Red ♂	White ♂
0	197	251	0

Cross 3

P₁ Red ♀   ×   White ♂
F₁ All red

F₂ Red ♀	White ♀	Red ♂	White ♂
87	0	42	33

[1] In the second cross three exceptional individuals have been omitted.

What is the method of inheritance of red and white color? Draw up a factorial chart to make your explanation clear and compare the actual numbers in each class with the numbers to be expected on your hypothesis.

260. In Aplocheilus these further results were obtained by Aida. Sex in these fishes cannot be distinguished until they are a year old, so that sex distribution can be given only for those which live to this age :

$$P_1 \text{ White } ♀ \times \text{ Brown } ♂$$
$$F_1 \text{ All brown}$$

F$_2$...	Brown	Blue	Red	White
Total young...........................	248	57	53	21

Sex of survivors......................	♀	♂	♀	♂	♀	♂	♀	♂
	77	147	56	0	9	37	19	0

Explain the inheritance and the genetic relations of brown, blue, red, and white. Make a factorial chart as in the previous problem, comparing the actual numbers in each class with the numbers expected on your hypothesis.

261. A factor l in Drosophila is recessive, lethal, and sex-linked. If female Ll is crossed with a normal male, what should be the sex ratio of the progeny?

262. In fowls a factor K is recessive and sex linked. All zygotes pure for K die before hatching. A male heterozygous for this factor is crossed with normal females and produces 120 live chickens. How many of these would you expect to be males and how many females?

CHAPTER VIII

LINKAGE AND CROSSING OVER

The Principle of Independent Assortment, which, as has been seen in the preceding chapters, governs the behavior both of genetic factors (genes) and of chromosomes, has been supported by the results of breeding experiments with all sorts of animals and plants during the past third of a century. Soon after the rediscovery of Mendel's Laws some doubt began to be cast on the universal applicability of this principle, since it did not explain certain exceptional results. The increasing frequency with which such exceptions were observed and the more careful study given them led to the formulation of a new principle of inheritance, the principle of *Linkage*. This is the hypothesis which Prof. T. H. Morgan originally devised to explain such exceptions, and its further development has since led to a general revision and clarification of our views as to the physical basis of inheritance, the nature of genes, and even of protoplasm itself.

Coupling and Repulsion.—The first case of what is now called linkage was discovered in 1906 by Bateson and Punnett, in the course of their studies of inheritance in the sweet pea. In one of their experiments two races of sweet peas were crossed, one having purple flowers and forming long pollen grains and the other having red flowers and round pollen. Purple, P, they found to act as a simple dominant to red, p, while long pollen, L, was dominant to round, l. Each trait segregated from its allele in a normal 3:1 ratio in F_2. But instead of finding, as they expected, that these two characters were assorted independently of one another to produce an F_2 ratio of $\frac{9}{16}$ long-pollened, purple; $\frac{3}{16}$ long-pollened, red; $\frac{3}{16}$ round-pollened, purple; and $\frac{1}{16}$ round-pollened, red; they obtained the F_2 ratio below (data from Punnett, 1923):

$$P_1 \qquad \text{Purple, long} \times \text{red, round}$$
$$F_1 \qquad \qquad \text{Purple, long}$$

F_2	Purple, long	Purple, round	Red, long	Red, round	Total
Actual numbers............	4,831	390	393	1,338	6,952
Expected numbers..........	3,910.5	1,303.5	1,303.5	434.5	6,952
Expected ratio............	$\frac{9}{16}$	$\frac{3}{16}$	$\frac{3}{16}$	$\frac{1}{16}$	

192

The numbers obtained were obviously different from those expected on the assumption that flower color and pollen shape assorted independently. The chief peculiarity of the result was that the combinations of traits which occurred in the parents (purple flowers with long pollen and red flowers with round pollen) appeared much *more* frequently than they should have, while the *new* combinations or recombinations of characters different from those introduced by the parents (purple with round and red with long) appeared *less* frequently than expected. If these factors were inherited independently, there should have been 4,345 F$_2$ plants showing the parental combinations; actually there were 6,169; while instead of the 2,607 new combinations expected, there were only 783. It appeared to the experimenters that the genes for purple and long had tended to stay together in inheritance, and they called this phenomenon the "coupling of factors." Later the same characters were involved in a cross similar to the above, except that the genes for flower color and pollen shape were differently associated in the two parents, purple and round entering the cross from one parent, and red and long from the other. The results of such a cross are given below, compared with those which would be expected if *P-p* and *L-l* are inherited independently.

P$_1$ Purple, round $\times$ red, long
F$_1$ Purple, long

F$_2$	Purple, long	Purple, round	Red, long	Red, round
Actual..........................	226	95	97	1
Expected.......................	235.8	78.5	78.5	26.2

Here again it is found that the parental types (purple, round and red, long) are too numerous, for there are 192 of them instead of the 157 expected, while of the new combinations there are only 227 instead of the 262 expected. Apparently, the F$_1$ plants produced more of the parental types of gametes *Pl* and *pL* than of the types *PL* and *pl*, instead of the equality of all four types which should have resulted if the genes assorted independently. From this the investigators inferred that the genes introduced by different parents showed an aversion to entering the same F$_1$ gamete. They called this tendency "repulsion." The two tendencies, coupling and repulsion, were evidently similar in effect, for both resulted in the formation of an excess of the parental combinations of genes and a deficiency of the new type of combinations.

Linkage.—These cases of coupling and repulsion remained for several years as exceptions to Mendel's principle of Independent Assortment. About 1910, however, many additional cases of this type of inheritance were discovered by Morgan in Drosophila. He saw that both coupling and repulsion were examples of a single phenomenon which he termed *linkage*, or the tendency of genes to remain in their original combinations in inheritance. He suggested that such a result would follow if the genes which showed linkage with one another were located *in the same chromosome*, and hence tended to be inherited as a *block*, rather than independently of one another, as Mendel had supposed. This idea soon gathered additional support from the data which Morgan and his coworkers Bridges, Muller, Sturtevant, and others obtained from breeding experiments and cytological study in Drosophila. From such data the chromosome theory of inheritance was formulated, and many of the details of the physical basis of heredity were thus described and explained. The chromosome theory, together with some of the evidence which supports it, will be discussed more fully in the next chapter, while the remainder of this one will present and explain typical cases of linkage in animals and plants.

It has already been shown above by examples from sweet peas that certain factors do not assort independently after a cross but tend to remain in the same combinations in which they entered it. It is not evident from the examples cited what causes this tendency. To make the matter clear, it will be necessary to consider a case of linkage in detail and especially to trace the behavior of the genes during the critical stage of the formation of the gametes of the dihybrid when assortment of genes takes place. From what has been learned of this process in Chapter IV, it would be expected that the combinations of genes in the gametes from a double heterozygote (such as $Aa\ Bb$) would be best determined by backcrossing it to the double recessive, $aa\ bb$. The gametes of the heterozygote, AB, Ab, aB, and ab, unite in this case only with recessive gametes ab; and the appearance of the offspring $Aa\ Bb$, $Aa\ bb$, $aa\ Bb$, and $aa\ bb$ provides an accurate indication of the genetic constitution of the gametes of the heterozygous parent, since each dominant gene in the progeny is directly traceable to the gamete in which it was contained. In an F_2 generation from $Aa\ Bb$, on the other hand, the individuals containing both dominant genes may be traceable to unions either of AB gametes with ab or of Ab with aB, and so on. The assortment of factors in the gametes of the hybrids is obscured by dominance, and the F_2 ratio, therefore, does not give a direct index of the kinds of gametes produced by the F_1. For this reason cases in which linkage is suspected are usually investigated by crossing individuals heterozygous for the genes involved with individuals recessive for these genes.

Linkage in Maize.—A clear case of linkage in maize has been investigated in this way by Hutchison. The difference between colored and colorless seeds in this plant may depend on a single factor pair (C, colored; c, colorless). Colored acts as a simple dominant to colorless. Similarly with regard to the character of the endosperm or the part of the seed which contains the food stored up for the embryo, a single gene has been found to differentiate a type in which the endosperm is full or plump from one in which it is shrunken or indented. Full, S, is dominant to shrunken, s. When a plant with colored, full seeds is crossed with a plant with colorless, shrunken seeds, the F_1 seeds are colored and full. As in the example from sweet peas, an F_2 raised from this F_1 fails to exhibit the $9:3:3:1$ ratio which it is customary to expect from a dihybrid. Instead of such a ratio it is found that nearly all of the F_2 seeds are either colored and full as in one parent or colorless and shrunken as in the other. The new combinations, colored with shrunken and colorless with full, are not found in normal proportions. It is, therefore, evident that the genes for seed color and endosperm character are linked.

In order to test this linkage Hutchison crossed a colored, full-seeded plant with a colorless, shrunken-seeded one. A large number of F_1 colored, full plants ($Cc\ Ss$) were then backcrossed to the double recessive type, colorless, shrunken ($cc\ ss$). It would be expected, on the principle of independent assortment, that the F_1 would form four kinds of gametes *in equal numbers*, CS, Cs, cS, and cs, and that when united with gametes of the type cs, from the double recessive, the following kinds of progeny would be produced *in equal numbers:*

Colored, full.	$Cc\ Ss$
Colored, shrunken	$Cc\ ss$
Colorless, full	$cc\ Ss$
Colorless, shrunken	$cc\ ss$

When the cross was made, however, this expectation was not realized, but the following result was obtained (data from Hutchison, 1922):[1]

P_1 Colored, full $\times$ colorless, shrunken

CS/CS | cs/cs

F_1 Colored, full

F_1 Colored, full $\times$ colorless, shrunken

CS/cs | cs/cs

BACKCROSS PROGENY				
COLORED, FULL	COLORED, SHRUNKEN	COLORLESS, FULL	COLORLESS, SHRUNKEN	TOTAL
CS/cs	Cs/cs	cS/cs	cs/cs	
4,032	149	152	4,035	8,368

[1] In representing the genotype in which the factors are linked, the factor combinations are written as they enter the zygote, those from one parent above a line, those from the other below it.

The parental combinations (colored, full and colorless, shrunken) are *more numerous* than expected, while the recombinations (colorless, full and colored, shrunken) are correspondingly *less numerous* than expected (Fig. 69). This inequality in the progeny of the backcross proves the

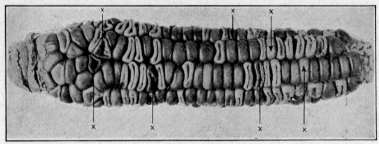

Fig. 69.—The kernels on this ear show linkage of factors for aleurone color and for shrunken endosperm. It resulted from the cross of a heterozygous plant (which had received the factors for *colored and full* from one parent and for *colorless and shrunken* from the other) with a double recessive colorless, shrunken plant. Most of the kernels are colored and full or colorless and shrunken (parental combinations) and a few have the new combinations *colored shrunken* and *colorless full*. Such new combinations are designated by *x*. (*From Hutchinson, in Journal of Heredity.*)

existence of a similar inequality in the gametes of F_1. Instead of being produced in equal numbers, these must have been formed as follows:

Parental combinations....... $\begin{cases} CS & 4,032 \\ cs & 4,035 \end{cases}$

$\qquad\qquad\qquad\qquad\qquad$ 8,067, or about 96.4 per cent of the total gametes tested

New combinations........... $\begin{cases} Cs & 149 \\ cS & 152 \end{cases}$

$\qquad\qquad\qquad\qquad\qquad$ 301, or about 3.6 per cent of the total gametes tested

Under independent assortment these two classes of gametes would each have comprised 50 per cent of the total. It is obvious then that the two factor pairs, C-c and S-s, have not assorted independently, and it may be said that they are *linked* together. The indication of linkage is always some evidence, like the above, of departure from the ratio expected on the theory of independent assortment.

One step, therefore, in the explanation of linkage is the discovery of the fact that the *gametes of a plant or animal which is heterozygous for two linked traits are not formed in equal numbers but that the gametes with the parental combinations of genes are always more numerous than the gametes with the new combinations of genes.* This fact holds good for all pairs of linked characters, no matter in what combination they enter a cross. In the first illustration the factors C-c and S-s entered the cross in the combinations CS from the colored, full parent and cs from the colorless, shrunken parent, and these combinations tended to remain intact; but in another experiment the original parents were colorless, full and colored, shrunken. The F_1 was, of course, the same in appearance as in the previous cross, and this was backcrossed to the double recessive. The

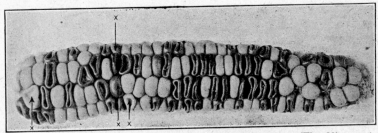

Fig. 70.—An ear of similar ancestry to that on preceding page (Fig. 69) except that the factors entered the F_1 plants in different combinations, *colored and shrunken* coming together from one pure parent and *colorless and full* from the other. The recombinations (*x*) in this case are *colored full and colorless shrunken*. (*From Hutchinson, in Journal of Heredity.*)

progeny of this cross showed (Fig. 70) an excess of colorless, full and colored, shrunken kernels—*the parental combinations*—as shown below:

P_1 Colorless, full × colored, shrunken

cS/cS | Cs/Cs

F_1 Colored, full

F_1 Colored, full × colorless, shrunken

cS/Cs | cs/cs

BACKCROSS PROGENY

COLORED, FULL	COLORED, SHRUNKEN	COLORLESS, FULL	COLORLESS, SHRUNKEN	TOTAL
CS/cs	Cs/cs	cS/cs	cs/cs	
638	21,379	21,906	672	44,595

Whatever the parental combinations may be, linkage tends to keep them intact.

The best explanation of linkage which has been proposed is based on the assumption that linked genes are located *in the same chromosome.* It has been shown above that at the reduction division one member of each pair of chromosomes of the parent goes into each gamete which is formed. If, then, two genes such as *c* and *s* are present in one chromosome of the parental plant, these should be inherited together and should follow the same course as the chromosome which bears them. The history of the chromosomes carrying these two genes is shown in Fig. 71.

Crossing Over.—If two genes are located in the same chromosome, however, and the chromosome remains intact in inheritance, the two factors should remain together in *all* cases, or, in other words, linkage should be complete. This is not what happens, for linkage is generally only partial, the linked genes sometimes separating. In the example cited above, the genes held together in about 97 per cent of the cases but broke apart in about 3 per cent. In other crosses two genes have been found to remain together in nearly all the gametes, as, for instance,

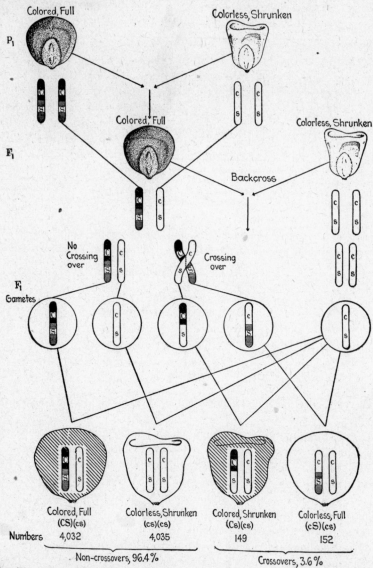

Fig. 71.—Diagram showing the chromosome explanation of linkage and crossing over in maize. The history of the genes for colored-colorless (*C-c*) and full-shrunken (*S-s*) and of the chromosomes in which they are located is traced through a cross between two pure types and the backcross of F₁ with a double recessive. (*Data from Hutchison.*)

in rats, where the gene for albinism and that for yellow coat remain together in over 99 per cent of the F₁ gametes and separate in less than

1 per cent; or the genes may separate in *nearly* 50 per cent of the cases, as in Drosophila, where two genes called "star" and "speck" are associated in 52 per cent and separate in 48 per cent of the gametes. Those cases in which linked factors break apart from their original combinations, that is, in which genes originally separate become united in one gamete or individual, or in which genes originally together become separated, are known as *recombinations,* or *crossovers.* Under independent assortment the parental combinations and the recombinations are approximately equal in number. Under linkage the parental combinations are always *more numerous* than the recombinations. Linkage may vary greatly with different genes, producing all the way from very few to nearly 50 per cent of recombinations.

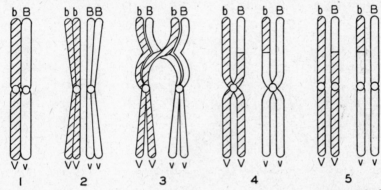

Fig. 72.—Diagram showing the assumed mechanism of crossing over between the loci *b* and *v* in the same chromosome. During meiosis, the chromosome containing *bV* and its homologue containing *Bv* (shown at 1), have each split into two sister chromatids (at 2), held together by the attachment region or centromere which has not divided. In a given proportion of such tetrads, crossing over occurs between nonsister chromatids (at 3). Two composite (crossover) chromatids and two original (non-crossover) chromatids for the *b-v* region, are formed (at 4). When the attachment regions divide (at 5) four different chromatids separate, each chromatid going to a different gamete.

If genes which exhibit linkage do so because they are located in the same chromosome, then it must be assumed that when breaks in this linkage (crossovers) occur, they are caused by an *interchange of parts* between members of a pair of homologous chromosomes, as a result of which the genes are separated and ultimately enter different gametes (Fig. 72). The genes which have crossed over will then appear in different individuals among the progeny.

Evidence as to the mechanism of such *crossing over* and as to the time of its occurrence has been obtained from a study of the chromosomes themselves in the cell divisions immediately preceding gamete formation. It has been pointed out in the preceding chapter that just before meiosis the members of each pair of homologous chromosomes come close together in the process of synapsis and *conjugate,* in most cases extending side by side throughout their length, each portion of one chromosome apparently lying exactly opposite the corresponding portion of the other. There is evidence that this is brought about by the mutual attraction between similar parts of the pair of homologous chromosomes. This clearly affords an opportunity for an interchange of material between the two, and there is some cytological evidence that this does actually take place. Thus Janssens in 1909, before the chromosome theory had been definitely formulated, noted the frequency of apparent crossing or fusion of strands between the two members of chromosome pairs at about this stage. He termed these *chiasmata* (singular chiasma) (Fig. 73) and showed that at a chiasma there is an exchange of segments between the members of the conjugating pair. Since that time, numerous cases in both animals and plants have been described and figured in which

Fig. 73.—Chromosomes of Callisia showing chiasmata.　(*From Sax.*)

two chromatids of a tetrad, at some stage between conjugation and separation, seem to be twisted about one another.

The earlier idea that an exchange comes about by the breaking of the twisted conjugating chromosomes at the point where they cross and that a chiasma thus precedes and may be said to cause a crossover is now generally yielding to the view that the actual exchange of material takes place before chiasma formation and that chiasmata are thus the result rather than the cause of chromosomal interchange in crossing over. There are at present various interpretations of the cytological evidence as to the relationship between chiasmata and crossing over, but there is agreement as to the essential fact that although each pair of chromosomes enters synapsis intact, they may emerge as composite structures, one part (or more), with all its constituent genes, having come from the mother and the other from the father (Fig. 72). It should be emphasized that it is not single genes but blocks of genes (large portions of chromosomes) which are thus presumably exchanged.

The Time of Crossing Over.—It was formerly thought that crossing over occurs between individual whole chromosomes at synapsis. Ample evidence is now at hand, however, that such is not the case but that crossing over does not take place until after the chromosomes have each split into a pair of chromatids, early in prophase, and that it occurs only between chromatids. Thus not two strands are involved in synapsis and crossing over but four—the two chromatids from each of the two conjugating chromosomes (Fig. 72).

This has been proved genetically in a number of cases, especially through the use of races in which there are three chromosomes in a set instead of two (triploids or trisomics, p. 326). In such a case in Drosophila where the genic constitution of each of these homologous chromosomes was known, it was found that all six chromatids might be unlike after crossing over. This result could not take place if crossing over occurred between chromosomes which afterward split into chromatids, for there would then be only three different kinds of chromatids. It is explainable, however, if crossing over does not take place until chromatids have been produced. A somewhat similar proof has been made for maize (Rhoades) where a trisome with two dominant and one recessive allelic genes was found occasionally to bear a gamete with two recessives, which could not occur if crossing over were between whole chromosomes.

Cytological proof that crossing over takes place between chromatids and at the four-strand stage is furnished by cases (among others) where it is possible to identify the two chromosomes involved by some structural difference. Thus in maize Creighton and McClintock found that one of the chromosomes has a terminal knob which is large in some races but small in others. In a plant heterozygous for this knob difference, a large-knobbed chromosome synapses with a small-knobbed one, but at reduction it may be observed that sometimes each of the two pairs of chromatids separating at the first division contains a large-knobbed and a small-knobbed member, thus showing that there has been an interchange of material between two homologous chromatids without involving the entire chromosome. A similar demonstration has been given for Drosophila.

Of course, if crossing over is between chromatids and not chromosomes, the percentage of chiasmata observable in a given region of a chromosome at meiosis must be twice as great as the percentage of genetic crossovers in this region. That this is true is suggested by the fact that where frequency of chiasmata has been measured, this has been found to be about twice the amount of crossing over observed.

The Measurement of Linkage.—Linkage occurs in different degrees and is thus a quantitative phenomenon which may be measured by the amount of crossing over which occurs. If there is but little crossing over between two genes, it is said that the linkage is strong or close; if there is much, it is said that the linkage is weak or loose. The usual method of measuring linkage is therefore to cross an animal or plant which is heterozygous for the linked genes, such as *CS/cs*, with the double recessive *cs/cs* and to count the numbers of individuals in which the two genes remain in their original parental combinations (the noncrossovers) and the individuals in which the two genes have formed new combinations (the crossovers).   The strength of linkage is then expressed as the crossover value, or the percentage of crossovers in the total number of progeny.   Thus in the example used (p. 195) the total number of individuals observed was 8,368, of which the crossovers numbered 301 (149 + 152), or about 3.6 per cent of the total.   The genes for colorless and shrunken or their alleles, colored and full, are therefore said to be linked, with a crossover value of 3.6 per cent.   It should be remembered, of course, that linkage strength varies *inversely* as the crossover value.

The degree of linkage between two given genes is constant for a given set of conditions, and once it is accurately measured, it may be made the basis of prediction for the behavior of these genes in subsequent breeding operations, regardless of the way in which they enter the cross (whether together or apart).   Knowing the character of the gametes formed by an individual heterozygous for two linked genes, it is possible to predict what the offspring of this individual will be, when it is crossed not only with a double recessive but with any other individual.   This can perhaps best be explained by using a somewhat simpler case than that of the maize problem.   Assume, for example, that two genes *A* and *B* are linked with a crossover value of 20 per cent.   If a homozygous *AB* individual is crossed with an *ab* one, the F_1, *AB/ab*, will form the following gametes:

> 40 per cent *AB*
> 40 per cent *ab* } .... 80 per cent noncrossovers
> 10 per cent *Ab*
> 10 per cent *aB* } .... 20 per cent crossovers

Now if it is desired to determine the appearance of the F_2 from the cross *AB/ab* × *AB/ab*, a checkerboard may be constructed in the usual way *except* that the four types of gametes must be weighted by multiplying them by their relative frequencies.   This is necessary because the four types are not now equal in numbers (as in independent assortment); those of the type *AB* are four times as numerous as those of the type *Ab*, for example.   In determining the number of offspring produced by a given gametic combination, therefore, the frequency of one type of gamete must be multiplied by the frequency of the other.   The combinations will thus not be equal in number, but some will be represented by more individuals than others.   The F_2 in the example is worked out in the checkerboard in Fig. 74.   By adding together all the individuals of each visibly similar group, the F_2 will be found to consist of 66 per cent which appear *AB*, 9 per cent *Ab*, 9 per cent *aB*, and 16 per cent *ab*.

A formula for determining crossover percentage from an F_2 ratio is presented at the end of this chapter.

The amount of crossing over, or linkage strength, is also used in determining the location of genes in the chromosomes, since it may be assumed that the frequency of crossing over is proportional to the distance between the genes. Genes which seldom cross over are assumed to be so near together that a break in the chromosome is not likely to occur between them; while those which cross over more frequently are assumed to be farther apart. This is explained at greater length in the next chapter.

	4 AB (40%)	1 Ab (10%)	1 aB (10%)	4 ab (40%)
4 AB (40%)	16 (AB) (AB)	4 (AB) (Ab)	4 (AB) (aB)	16 (AB)(ab)
1Ab (10%)	4 (AB) (Ab)	1 (Ab) (Ab)	1 (Ab) (aB)	4 (Ab) (ab)
1 aB (10%)	4 (AB) (aB)	1 (Ab) (aB)	1 (aB) (aB)	4 (aB) (ab)
4 ab (40%)	16 (AB) (ab)	4 (Ab) (ab)	4 (aB) (ab)	16 (ab) (ab)

Fig. 74.—Checkerboard showing the expected composition of the F_2 from a cross between individuals differing in two linked genes *Aa* and *Bb*, which show 20 per cent of crossing over.

Complete Linkage.—The examples used have all been drawn from cases of partial or incomplete linkage, in which crossing over occurs with measurable frequency. There are a number of cases, however, in which linkage appears to be complete, so that the genes always remain in their original combinations. This may be due to the absence of crossing over under special conditions, or it may mean that the genes are so near together in the chromosome that a break never occurs between them.

Examples of the first type are very common in experiments with Drosophila, since in this fly it has been found that crossing over rarely or never takes place in the germ cells of the *male*. Thus if a gray-bodied, vestigial-winged fly is crossed with a black-bodied, long-winged one, the F_1 generation is found to consist entirely of gray-bodied, long-winged flies. If one of the F_1 *males* is crossed to the double recessive type (a black-bodied, vestigial-winged female), only two kinds of offspring are produced—gray, vestigial and black, long (Fig. 75). The expected types of crossovers—gray, long and black, vestigial—do not appear at all. If, however, an F_1 *female* fly is crossed with a black, vestigial male, the four

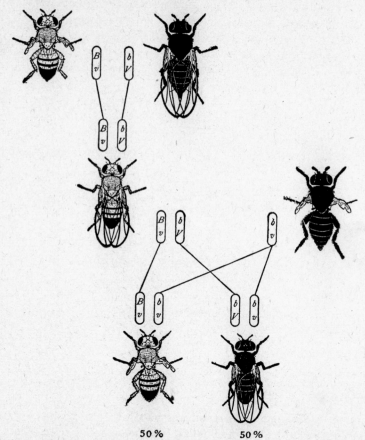

50 %   50 %

Fig. 75.—Complete linkage (no crossing over) in the male of Drosophila. Results of a cross between a gray, vestigial male and a black, long female; and of a backcross of the F_1 *male* with a black, vestigial female. Note that the offspring of this backcross are all like the original parents and that there are no crossovers. (*From Morgan, Sturtevant, Muller and Bridges, courtesy of Henry Holt & Company.*)

expected types (Fig. 76) are produced in the following proportions (data from Morgan, 1919):

NONCROSSOVERS		CROSSOVERS	
Gray, vestigial	Black, long	Black, vestigial	Gray, long
41.5 per cent	41.5 per cent	8.5 per cent	8.5 per cent
83 per cent		17 per cent	

Crossing over is evident in about 17 per cent of the gametes. The second experiment shows that a perceptible distance separates the genes for black and vestigial and that absence of crossovers in the gametes of

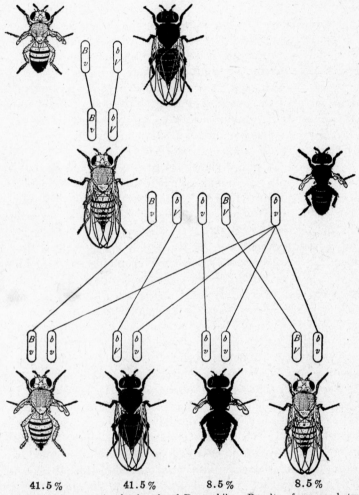

41.5 %   41.5 %   8.5 %   8.5 %

Fig. 76.—Crossing over in the female of Drosophila. Results of a cross between a gray, vestigial male and a black, long female; and of a backcross of the F₁ *female* with a black, vestigial male. (*From Morgan, Sturtevant, Muller and Bridges, courtesy of Henry Holt & Company.*)

the male is not due to the extreme closeness of the genes in the chromosome. It must be due, then, to conditions peculiar to the male, such as the nonoccurrence of chiasmata in spermatogenesis. Only a few cases are known in which linkage is always complete in one sex; in the several species of Drosophila it is so in the male, and in the silkworm moth, in the female. In other animals and plants for which there is sufficient evidence, crossing over is found to occur in both sexes, although the frequency may differ somewhat in males and females.

Theoretically, cases of complete linkage should be possible in which genes do not separate because they are so close together in the chromosome that a break cannot occur between them. Actual instances which might be explained in this way are rare or may not occur at all.

Factors Affecting the Strength of Linkage.—The amount of crossing over between two given genes has been shown in some cases to be affected by various internal and external factors. Allowance should be made for these if careful measurements of linkage are to be made. Sexual differences in crossing over have already been mentioned. The other potent internal factor is modification of the normal structure of the chromosomes. Thus it was found that in hybrids between certain races of Drosophila there was practically no crossing over between some of the genes. Such results, at first thought to be due to genes for the suppression or reduction of crossing over, have now been shown to follow from the *inversion* of portions of a chromosome (p. 234). In individuals heterozygous for such an inversion, homologous genes do not lie opposite each other, a condition that apparently reduces normal recombination. It is a curious fact that, if a pair of Drosophila chromosomes is heterozygous for an inversion, crossing over is increased in the other pairs. In maize also, chromosome rearrangements such as inversions and translocations, (p. 239) may interfere with normal pairing within the affected chromosome pair. In Drosophila mutations are known which tend to decrease the amount of crossing over in particular regions of a chromosome, in an entire chromosome, or in the entire chromosome complement. Moreover Bridges has shown that with increasing age of the female in *Drosophila melanogaster* the amount of crossing over in her gametes tends to be reduced. This effect is nearly negligible in the X chromosome and for large parts of II and III but is particularly marked in the middle regions, that is, the regions near the spindle-fiber attachment, in these last two. There is evidence from several other directions that the amount of crossing over in any region depends on the distance of that point from the spindle-fiber attachment, probably because the coiling and association of the strands begin at such attachment points.

External factors also affect the frequency of crossing over. Females of *D. melanogaster* were reared by Plough at low, intermediate, and high temperatures. He found that at both extremes the percentage of crossing over was greater than at the intermediate temperature. By transferring female flies from the extremes to room temperature and observing the length of time before the crossover percentage dropped, he was able to determine the stage in egg development at which temperature was effective in altering the percentage and found that the initial effect appeared at about the time of chromosome conjugation.

In addition to heat, treatment with X rays or with certain chemicals may profoundly affect crossing over, the general result being to increase the frequency. Under the influence of X rays, for example, crossing over may be induced to occur in the autosomes of Drosophila males.

Although the strength of linkage is thus shown to depend on several variables, knowledge of these has made it possible to control them and thus under carefully standardized conditions to obtain repeatedly the same linkage relations between the same genes, indicating that an orderly process underlies these phenomena.

Somatic Crossing Over.—Although linkage and crossing over were first demonstrated during the meiotic cycle they have been shown to occur also in somatic cells, at least in certain animals. Stern has demonstrated this for *Drosophila melanogaster*. When two linked genes affecting characters that can be seen in most areas of the body, such as yellow body and singed bristles, have entered the zygote separately (from different parents), $y\ Sn/Y\ sn$, the heterozygote normally shows the effect of the dominant alleles, that is, gray body and normal bristles. But under certain conditions (presence of a type of mutation which is known as "Minute") the heterozygous fly shows spots of tissue in which each of the recessives has become homozygous (yy and $sn\ sn$), that is, some spots show yellow and others show singed. This could occur only if crossing over between y and sn had taken place at a four-strand stage, when a $y\ sn$ (crossover) chromatid had been segregated into the same daughter cell with a $y\ Sn$ (noncrossover) chromatid in one case ($y\ sn/y\ Sn$) and with a $Y\ sn$ (noncrossover) chromatid in the other ($y\ sn/Y\ sn$). These two types of spots were found in large numbers; other assumptions lead to types of spots which were not found. The assumed exchange that occurs between chromatids in somatic crossing over is facilitated by the "somatic pairing" that occurs in Diptera in which the homologous chromosomes lie side by side in somatic cells. Somatic crossing over has not been demonstrated in other organisms, although in maize Jones has found neighboring spots of different genetic constitution in the aleurone and endosperm. Some of these appear to be due to exchanges between homologous chromosomes; but whether these occur by crossing over or by some other mechanism is not certain.

Measurement of Linkage from F_2 Data.—There are a number of methods for determining crossover values from F_2 data. One of these (from Immer) is presented below. Here a, b, c and d are the numbers of individuals in the phenotypic classes AB, Ab, aB, and ab, respectively. The crossover value when A and B come into the cross separately ("repulsion") is designated by p and when they come in together ("coupling") by $1 - p$. The value of p is determined from the equation

$$p = \sqrt{\frac{-(bc + ad) + \sqrt{(bc + ad)^2 + ad(bc - ad)}}{(bc - ad)}}$$

The standard error of both p and $1 - p$, when n is the total number of individuals, is then

$$\sigma_p \text{ and } \sigma_{1-p} = \sqrt{\frac{(1 - p^2)(2 + p^2)}{2n(1 + 2p^2)}}$$

The application of this formula to the data on linkage between purple, long and red, round in sweet peas, given on page 192 is made as follows:

$$p = \sqrt{\frac{-(bc + ad) + \sqrt{(bc + ad)^2 + ad(bc - ad)}}{(bc - ad)}}$$

a = 4,831	bc = 153,270
b = 390	ad = 6,463,878
c = 393	bc + ad = 6,617,148
d = 1,338	bc − ad = − 6,310,608
n = 6,952	

$$p = \sqrt{\frac{-6,617,148 + \sqrt{(6,617,148)^2 + 6,463,878(-6,310,608)}}{-6,310,608}}$$

$$= 0.8799$$

$$\sigma_p = \sqrt{\frac{(1 - p^2)(2 + p^2)}{2n(1 + 2p^2)}} = \sqrt{\frac{(1 - 0.8799^2)(2 + 0.8799^2)}{2 \times 6,952(1 + 2 \times 0.8799^2)}}$$

$$= 0.0042$$

Since this is a coupling cross, the crossover value is $(1 - p)$ or 0.1201 ± 0.0042.

The χ^2 test shows the data to give a close fit to expectation for an F_2 with 12 per cent crossing over.

This formula is used when both genes show 3 : 1 segregation. When one shows 3 : 1 and the other 1 : 1, or in cases of complementary gene action, other formulas are to be employed (see Immer).

REFERENCES

BRIDGES, C. B. 1929. Variation in crossing over in relation to age of female in *Drosophila melanogaster*. Carnegie Inst. Wash. Publ. **391**.

────── and E. G. ANDERSON. 1925. Crossing over in the X-chromosomes of triploid females of *Drosophila melanogaster*. Genetics **10**: 418–441.

CREIGHTON, HARRIET B., and BARBARA McCLINTOCK. 1931. A correlation of cytological and genetical crossing over in *Zea mays*. Proc. Nat. Acad. Sci. **17**.

HUTCHISON, C. B. 1922. The linkage of certain aleurone and endosperm factors in maize, and their relation to other linkage groups. Cornell Agr. Exp. Sta. Memoir **60**.

IMMER, F. R. 1930. Formulae and tables for calculating linkage intensities. Genetics **15**.

JANSSENS, F. A. 1928. La théorie de la chiasmatypie. Nouvelle interpretation des cenèses de maturation. La Cellule **25**.

JONES, D. F. 1937. Somatic segregation and its relation to atypical growth. Genetics **22**.

MORGAN, T. H. 1928. The theory of the gene. 2d ed. New Haven.

———, A. H. STURTEVANT, H. J. MULLER, and C. B. BRIDGES. 1923. The mechanism of mendelian heredity. 2d ed. New York.

———, C. B. BRIDGES, and A. H. STURTEVANT. 1925. The genetics of Drosophila. Bibliographia Genetica **2**.

PLOUGH, H. H. 1917. The effect of temperature on crossing over in Drosophila. Jour. Exp. Zool. **24**.

PUNNETT, R. C. 1923. Linkage in the sweet pea (*Lathyrus odoratus*). Jour. Genetics **13**.

RHOADES, M. M., and B. McCLINTOCK. 1935. The cytogenetics of maize. Bot. Rev. **1**: 292–325.

STERN, C. 1936. Somatic crossing over and segregation in *Drosophila melanogaster*. Genetics **21**: 625–730.

PROBLEMS

263. Why should it be true that if crossing over is between chromatids, the percentage of chiasmata in a given region will be twice as great as the percentage of genetic crossovers there?

264. If two loci *a* and *b* are 10 map units apart, in what percentage of the gametes should a chiasma have been formed in this region?

265. If the average number of chiasmata per tetrad is two, what should be the maximum length of the genetic map of this chromosome?

266. Why should spindle-fiber attachment influence the amount of crossing over between chromatids?

267. How would you prove that purple flower color and dark stem color in Datura, which occur together, are due to a single gene rather than to two linked genes?

268. How would you determine whether characters which show no crossing over were due to alleles or to closely linked genes?

269. In Drosophila the genes for red, eosin, and white eye color are alleles. The gene for yellow body is linked with white eye with a crossover value of 1.5 per cent. What is the probable crossover value between eosin and yellow?

270. From what you have learned of the chromosome mechanism of crossing over would you expect to find chiasmata in spermatogenesis in Drosophila?

271. If a factor for high egg production and one for barring are both sex-linked traits, of what practical importance would this be to the poultry breeder?

Note.—In problems involving linkage it is customary to designate the normal alleles of mutant genes by + (wild type). The genes in each member of a pair of chromosomes are written separately above and below a line (p. 226).

272. Assume that genes a and b are linked and show 40 per cent of crossing over. If a $\frac{++}{++}$ individual is crossed with one which is $\frac{a\,b}{a\,b}$, what will be the genotype of the F_1? What gametes will the F_1 produce and in what proportions? If the F_1 is crossed with a double recessive $\frac{a\,b}{a\,b}$, what will be the appearance and genotypes of the offspring?

273. If the original cross is $\frac{+b}{+b} \times \frac{a+}{a+}$, what will be the genotype of the F_1? What gametes will it produce? If the F_1 is crossed back with a double recessive, what will be the appearance of the offspring?

274. What will be the appearance of the F_2 ($F_1 \times F_1$) of the crosses described in the two preceding questions?

275. An individual homozygous for genes cd is crossed with wild type and the F_1 crossed back to the double recessive. The appearance of the offspring is as follows:

$$
\begin{array}{ll}
903 & ++ \\
898 & c\ d \\
98 & +\ d \\
102 & c\ +
\end{array}
$$

Explain this result, giving the strength of the linkage between c and d. If assortment between c and d were independent, what would be the result of this cross?

276. If the cross in the preceding question had been between a homozygous $+d$ individual and a homozygous $c+$ one, what would be the result of the cross of $F_1 \times$ the double recessive?

277. Calculate the percentage of crossing over between the factors for colorless aleurone and shrunken endosperm in corn from the combined data from both coupling (p. 196) and repulsion (p. 197) experiments.

Note.—In Drosophila the mutant known as "black," b, has a black body in contrast to the wild type, which has a gray body; and the mutant "arc," a, has wings which are somewhat curved and bent downward, in contrast to the straight wings of the wild type.

278. In the two following crosses the parents are given (homozygous in each case) together with the counts of the offspring of F_1 females bred to black, arc males (data from Bridges and Morgan):

I. Black, arc $\times$ wild type (gray, straight)
   F_1 females $\times$ black, arc males give:

Gray, straight	1,641
Gray, arc	1,251
Black, straight	1,180
Black, arc	1,532

II. Black, straight × gray, arc
    F_1 females × black, arc males give:

Gray, straight... 281
Gray, arc.. 335
Black, straight.. 335
Black, arc... 239

From these data calculate the crossover value between black and arc.

Note.—In Drosophila the mutant known as "vestigial," v, has wings which are very much reduced as compared with the long wings of the wild type.

279. In the two following crosses the parents are given, as in the previous question, together with the counts of offspring of F_1 females × black, vestigial males (data from Bridges and Morgan):

  I. Black, vestigial × wild type (gray, long)
     F_1 females × black, vestigial males give:

Gray, long... 822
Gray, vestigial.. 130
Black, long.. 161
Black, vestigial... 652

  II. Black, long × gray, vestigial
     F_1 females × black vestigial males give:

Gray, long... 283
Gray, vestigial.. 1,294
Black, long... 1,418
Black, vestigial... 241

From these data calculate the cross over value between black and vestigial.

Note.—In tomatoes Jones has found that tall vine is dominant over dwarf, and spherical fruit shape over pear. Vine height and fruit shape are linked, with a crossover percentage of 20 per cent.

280. If a homozygous tall, pear-fruited tomato is crossed with a homozygous dwarf, spherical-fruited one, what will be the appearance of the F_1? of the F_1 crossed with a dwarf, pear? of the F_2?

281. What *genotypically different* types will there be in the F_2 of the preceding cross? What offspring will each of these produce if selfed?

282. A certain tall, spherical-fruited tomato plant crossed with a dwarf, pear-fruited one produces 81 tall, spherical; 79 dwarf, pear; 22 tall, pear; and 17 dwarf, spherical. Another tall spherical plant crossed with a dwarf pear produces 21 tall, pear; 18 dwarf, spherical; 5 tall, spherical; and 4 dwarf, pear. What are the genotypes of these two tall, spherical plants? If they were crossed what would their offspring be?

Note.—The inheritance of grain color in wheat is described on page 107.

283. What would be the F_2 ratio of red and white grains from a cross of red by white if two duplicate factors for red were linked, with a crossover value of 10 per cent?

Note.—In rats dark eyes are due to the interaction of two genes R and P, the recessive allele of either producing light eyes. These genes are in the same chromosome.

284. When homozygous dark-eyed rats $\dfrac{+\ +}{+\ +}$ were crossed with double recessive ones $\dfrac{r\ p}{r\ p}$ and the F_1 crossed back with the double recessive, the following offspring were obtained (data from Castle):

Dark-eyed.. 1,255
Light-eyed.. 1,777

When $\dfrac{+p}{+p}$ animals were crossed with $\dfrac{r+}{r+}$ ones and the F_1 crossed back with the double recessive, the following offspring were obtained:

Dark-eyed... 174
Light-eyed... 1,540

Calculate the linkage between r and p.

285. In Drosophila white eye color and club wing are both sex-linked with a crossover value of about 15 per cent. If a wild-type female (red, long) is crossed with a white, club male, what will be the appearance of the offspring? If both males and females of the F_1 are crossed back to pure white, club stock, what will be the offspring in each case?

286. In the fowl assume that e (early feathering) and B (barring) are sex-linked and show 20 per cent of crossing over (in the male only). If a male from a cross of late-feathered barred male × early, black female is mated with an early, black female, what will be the appearance of their offspring, as to feathering and barring?

287. Assume that genes a and b are linked, with a crossover percentage of 20 per cent; and that c and d are also linked, with a crossover percentage of 10 per cent but are in another chromosome. Cross a plant homozygous for $ABCD$ with one which is $abcd$ and cross the F_1 back on $abcd$. What will be the appearance of the offspring of this cross?

Note.—In tomatoes red fruit color is dominant over yellow and is independent of the factors for height and fruit shape (for other data see Problem 280).

288. Cross a homozygous tall, spherical-fruited, red-fruited plant with a dwarf, pear-fruited, yellow-fruited one and then cross the F_1 back with a dwarf, pear, yellow. What will be the appearance of the offspring?

289. In sweet peas a cross of a homozygous, procumbent, hairy, white-flowered plant with a bush, glabrous, colored-flowered one, produces an F_1 which is all procumbent, hairy, and colored-flowered. If this F_1 is crossed on a bush, glabrous, white-flowered plant, the offspring would be expected to show approximately the following distribution (data adapted from Punnett):

	Per Cent
Procumbent, hairy, colored	6
Procumbent, hairy, white	19
Procumbent, glabrous, colored	6
Procumbent, glabrous, white	19
Bush, hairy, colored	19
Bush, hairy, white	6
Bush, glabrous, colored	19
Bush, glabrous, white	6

Explain these results, determining the strength of such linkages as may be observed.

290. In Drosophila yellow body is sex-linked and recessive to the gray body of the wild fly. Vermilion eye is also sex-linked and recessive to the wild red eye. The genes for yellow and vermilion show about 28 per cent of crossing over. The gene for vestigial wings is in one of the autosomes. If a homozygous yellow-bodied, red-eyed, long-winged female is crossed with a homozygous gray-bodied, vermilion-eyed, vestigial-winged male; and if an F_1 female is crossed with a yellow, vermilion, vestigial male, what will be the appearance of the offspring of this last cross?

291. Assume that an individual homozygous for $++$ is crossed with one homozygous for ab and that the F_2 from this cross is as follows:

$$334 ++, 37+b, 38\ a+, \text{ and } 87\ ab$$

How different is this result from that which you would expect if assortment between a and b were independent? What is the linkage between a and b? Test your result by determining χ^2.

292. Using the data given in your text for the F_2 of a cross in sweet peas between purple-flowered, round-pollened plants and red-flowered, long-pollened ones, determine the strength of the linkage between flower color and pollen shape.

293. In sweet peas a cross between a homozygous bright-flowered, tendril-leaved plant and a dull-flowered, acacia-leaved (tendrilless) plant produced an F_1 which was all bright, tendril. The F_2 from this cross was as follows (data from Punnett);

424 bright, tendril
99 dull, tendril
102 bright, acacia
91 dull, acacia

The cross of bright, acacia on dull, tendril also gave an F_1 which was all bright, tendril, but the F_2 in this case was as follows:

847 bright, tendril
298 dull, tendril
300 bright, acacia
49 dull, acacia

What is the percentage of crossing over between these genes?

294. $AABB \times aabb$ gives the following segregation in F_2:

AB	Ab	aB	ab
582	172	169	77

Do you think that a and b are linked or independent? Give evidence for your answer. Compare the actual distribution with the theoretical expectation on the basis of (1) independent assortment of a and b: (2) 40 per cent crossing over between a and b, using the χ^2 test.

CHAPTER IX

GENES AND CHROMOSOMES

The facts presented in the preceding chapter have led to the conclusion that linkage, instead of being a sporadic exception to Mendelian inheritance, is actually a widespread, orderly occurrence, subject to laws which are not only of the same cogency as those dealing with the segregation of factors but which also give a reasonable explanation of the *mechanism* of segregation and assortment. The facts of linkage are best explained by assuming that linked genes are located in the same chromosome and that breaks in the linkage, or crossovers, are due to an actual interchange of parts between homologous chromosomes.

Further research, in which the results of experimental breeding have been continually verified by direct examination of the chromosomes, have led to the development of a general theory—the chromosome theory of inheritance—which maintains that the genes are located in the chromosomes. This was not an entirely new idea, for Weismann, beginning in 1883, built up a theory of inheritance which regarded the chromosomes as the bearers of the elements of heredity, which he called *ids*. Investigators in the field of experimental embryology had also shown, even before the rediscovery of Mendel's laws, that the nucleus rather than the cytoplasm of the gametes provided the physical basis of inheritance. Fragments of eggs without nuclei, for example, could be fertilized by sperm of another species, and the embryos so produced showed the characters brought in by the sperm. Elimination of the paternal chromosomes from an early embryo, on the other hand, was followed by the development of the maternal characters only.

By 1903 W. S. Sutton in the United States and Theodor Boveri in Germany had proposed a theory of the localization of Mendelian factors in the chromosomes and Sutton by pointing out in detail the parallelism between the behavior of the chromosomes and the Mendelian units foreshadowed the general theory that was to develop.

The present theory, however, is based chiefly on the proofs, provided by *breeding experiments*, that the transmission of specific genes can be explained by and predicted from the operation of the chromosome mechanism as disclosed by cytological studies. The chromosome theory assumes that genes are parts of chromosomes. This is a very broad statement with many suggestive implications. It means that each gene

TABLE XVIII.—PARTIAL LIST OF THE FOUR GROUPS OF LINKED MUTANT
GENES IN *Drosophila melanogaster*, INCLUDING ONLY THOSE MOST USEFUL
FOR EXPERIMENTS (*After Bridges* 1937)

For locations see Fig. 82

CHROMOSOME I OR X	CHROMOSOME II	CHROMOSOME III	CHROMOSOME IV
Bar eye (*B*)	abrupt bristles (*ab*)	anarista (*aa*)	abdomen-rotatum (*ar*)
Beadex wing (*Bx*)	apterous (*ap*)	approximated veins	bent wings (*bt*)
bifid veins (*bi*)	arc wings (*a*)	(*app*)	cubitus interruptus
bobbed bristles (*bb*)	aristaless (*al*)	bithorax (*bx*)	(veins)(*ci*)
carmine eye (*cm*)	black body (*b*)	blistery wings (*by*)	eyeless (*ey*)
carnation eye (*car*)	blistered wings (*bs*)	cardinal eye (*cd*)	grooveless scutellum
crossveinless wing	bloated wing (*blo*)	claret eye (*ca*)	(*gvl*)
(*cv*)	Bristle (*Bl*)	crossveinless-c wings	Scutenick scutellum
cut wing (*ct*)	brown eye (*bw*)	(*cvc*)	(*Scn*)
dusky wing (*dy*)	chaetelle bristles (*chl*)	crumpled wings	shaven bristles (*sv*)
echinus eye (*ec*)	cinnabar eye (*cn*)	(*cmp*)	
facet eye (*fa*)	clot eye (*cl*)	curled wings (*cu*)	
folded wings (*fo*)	comb-gap sex combs	curvoid wings (*cur*)	
forked bristles (*f*)	(*cg*)	Deformed eye (*Dfd*)	
furrowed eye (*fw*)	curved wings (*c*)	Delta veins (*Dl*)	
fused veins (*fu*)	dachs legs (*d*)	Dichaete wings (*D*)	
garnet eye (*g*)	dachsous wings (*ds*)	divergent wings (*dv*)	
Hairy wing (*Hw*)	dumpy wings (*dp*)	ebony body (*e*)	
lozenge eye (*lz*)	echinoid eye (*ed*)	fluted wings (*fl*)	
microchaete hairs	engrailed scutellum	glass eye (*gl*)	
(*mc*)	(*en*)	Glued eye (*Gl*)	
miniature wing (*m*)	expanded wings (*ex*)	Hairless (*H*)	
ocelliless (*oc*)	fat body (*ft*)	hairy body (*h*)	
prune eye (*pn*)	four-jointed legs (*fj*)	Henna eye (*Hn*)	
raspberry eye (*ras*)	Gull wings (*G*)	inturned bristles (*in*)	
roughex eye (*rux*)	hook bristles (*hk*)	javelin bristles (*jv*)	
ruby eye (*rb*)	humpy thorax (*hy*)	karmoisin eye (*kar*)	
rugose eye (*ru*)	Jammed wings (*J*)	Lyra wing (*Ly*)	
sable body (*s*)	jaunty wings (*j*)	maroon eye (*ma*)	
scute bristles (*sc*)	knot veins (*kn*)	Minute bristles (*M*)	
scalloped wing (*sd*)	lanceolate wings (*ll*)	Minute-g bristles	
silver body (*svr*)	light eye (*lt*)	(*Mg*)	
singed bristles (*sn*)	Lobe eye (*L*)	Minute-w bristles	
tan body (*t*)	minus bristles (*mi*)	(*Mw*)	
uneven eye (*un*)	morula eyes (*mr*)	pink eye (*p*)	
vermilion eye (*v*)	narrow wings (*nw*)	Prickly bristles (*Pr*)	
wavy wing (*wy*)	net veins (*nt*)	radius incompletus	
white eye (*w*)	plexus veins (*px*)	(veins) (*ri*)	
yellow body (*y*)	purple eye (*pr*)	rase bristles (*ra*)	
	reduced bristles (*rd*)	rotated abdomen (*rt*)	
	rolled wings (*rl*)	rough eye (*ro*)	
	roughish eye (*rh*)	Roughened eye (*R*)	
	scabrous eye (*sca*)	roughoid eye (*ru*)	
	speck wings (*sp*)	scarlet eye (*st*)	
	Star eye (*S*)	sepia eye (*se*)	
	staroid eye (*std*)	sepiaoid eye (*sed*)	
	sternopleurals (*Sp*)	spineless bristles (*ss*)	
	straw body (*stw*)	stripe body (*sr*)	
	Streak thorax (*Sk*)	Stubble bristles (*Sb*)	
	thick legs (*tk*)	taxi wings (*tx*)	
	vestigial wing (*vg*)	thread aristae (*th*)	
	welt eye (*wt*)	tilt wings (*tt*)	
		veinlet (*ve*)	
		white-ocelli (*wo*)	

occupies a measurable portion of space and that many hundreds of genes must be packed into the small compass of a tiny thread of chromatin, which can be seen only with high powers of the microscope. The nucleus of each cell is, on this view, to be regarded as a complex aggregation of units which are arranged and guided through the processes of inheritance and development by those laws which in the end are the physical and chemical laws of living matter.

Genes of Drosophila.—Most of the evidence upon which the chromosome theory was first based was derived from one animal, *Drosophila melanogaster*, although in recent years the principles have been confirmed and extended by experimental analysis of other species of Drosophila and other animals; and especially of the maize plant which has provided

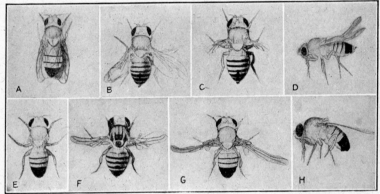

Fig. 77.—Some of the variations, chiefly affecting the wings, which have arisen by mutation in Drosophila. *A*, "truncate;" *B*, "balloon;" *C*, "vestigial;" *D*, "jaunty;" *E*, "apterous;" *F*, "strap;" *G*, "antlered;" *H*, "dachs." (*After Bridges and Morgan.*)

excellent material for cytogenetic study. Drosophila has been carefully studied by both geneticists and cytologists for over twenty-five years and has proved to be the best material yet found for experiments in genetics. It breeds readily in captivity and is extremely prolific, a single pair of flies producing upward of two hundred progeny within two weeks after mating.[1] One of its chief advantages for genetic studies is its great variability, for the wild-type fly has produced spontaneously under domestication hundreds of mutations, which have given rise to true-breeding varieties. Moreover it responds to treatment with radiations by producing great numbers of hereditary variations of all kinds. Many of the variations are well marked and easily distinguished with or without the microscope. Examples of some of the mutant types are shown in Fig. 77 and drawings of the chief external details of the wild-type fly are shown in Fig. 78. The inheritance of over five hundred distinct characters

[1] See Appendix (p. 397) for culture methods used in breeding Drosophila.

has been traced to genes that are inherited according to the Mendelian
principle of segregation.

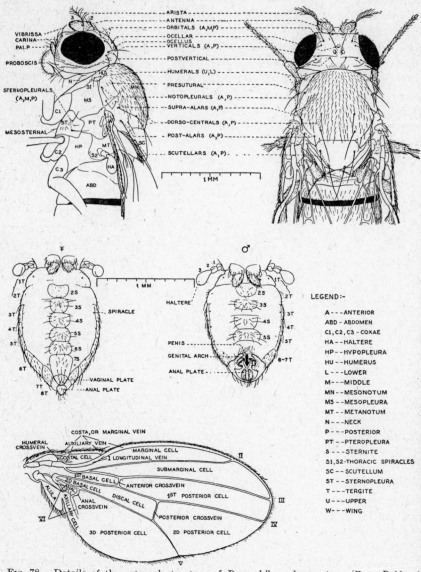

Fig. 78.—Details of the external structure of *Drosophila melanogaster.* (*From Bridges.*)

The Limitation of the Linkage Groups.—It has been discovered that
the characters of Drosophila occur in four groups (Table XVIII), the genes
in each group being linked with one another but inherited independently

of those in every other group. It is also known that there are four pairs of chromosomes in Drosophila (Fig. 79). One large chromosome has been found to be of major importance in the determination of sex, and one large group of genes (over 150) is inherited in a *sex-linked* fashion as explained in Chapter VII. There are two other large groups of genes and two other large chromosomes. Only a few genes belonging to the fourth group have been found, and the fourth chromosome is very small, being only about one-twelfth the size of the large ones. The correspondence between the groups of genes and the chromosomes, when considered together with the other evidence, is obvious. *There are as many groups of linked genes as chromosomes*, and each group represents the genes that are located in one chromosome. Morgan has called this the principle of Limitation of the Linkage Groups and has assumed that in animals and

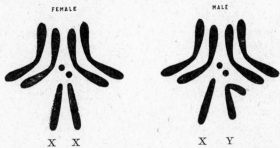

FEMALE   MALE

X X   X Y

FIG. 79.—Diagram showing the four pairs of chromosomes in Drosophila. The X chromosomes are I, the two other large pairs II and III, and the small pair IV. (*After Bridges.*)

plants generally the number of groups of linked genes is limited by the number of pairs of chromosomes. The evidence from Drosophila on this point is convincing, for several species of Drosophila have been studied and in all of these the number of linked groups corresponds with the number of chromosome pairs, as follows:

Species	Linkage groups	Chromosome pairs
D. virilis	6	6
D. pseudoobscura	5	5
D. melanogaster	4	4
D. willistoni	3	3

Sufficient evidence from maize (*Zea mays*) has been obtained to show that the 400 or more genes now known fall into 10 linkage groups, corresponding to the 10 haploid chromosomes, while in peas (*Pisum sativum*) there are 7 linkage groups and 7 chromosomes. In other animals and plants in which several linkage groups are known, the number of linkage groups has nowhere been found to exceed the number of chromosomes. In the tomato, genes are known in 10 out of the 12 chromosomes; in the morning-glory, in 12 out of 15; in the mouse, in 15 out of the 20; and in the rabbit in 11 out of the 22.

Cytological Evidence.—Evidence such as the above, while cogent, is of a negative character. Positive and conclusive evidence of the association of particular genes with particular chromosomes has been provided by combined cytological and genetical study of cases of nondisjunction (p. 182) and of other changes in the number of chromosomes.

In Drosophila, individuals were found which had but *one* of the small fourth chromosomes. These were less viable than normal and could be distinguished by certain characteristic differences from the normal flies (p. 325). When such haplo-IV individuals were crossed with flies with the recessive character eyeless, both normal and eyeless flies were found among the progeny. The eyeless progeny were found to have only one IV chromosome, while the normal progeny had two. It was obvious that the eyeless progeny had received no IV chromosome from the haplo-IV parent and *no* normal allele of eyeless, providing good evidence that the eyeless gene and its normal allele *are located in the IV chromosome*. This is confirmed by the breeding behavior of flies with three IV chromosomes. Such triplo-IV flies are triploid instead of diploid for all IV chromosome genes (p. 325).

In maize and Datura also, where an individual has *three* instead of two members of one chromosome, its progeny show segregation of one mutant gene or one linked group of genes in unusual but typical *trisomic* ratios, as explained in detail on page 326. The correspondence of breeding behavior and cytological appearance shows that this group of genes is located in the particular chromosome set which has an extra member, and a simple and immediate method of determining the specific chromosome that carries each linkage group is thus available.

Cytological Demonstration of Crossing Over.—Convincing evidence of the association of genes with chromosomes is further provided by the proof that, where there is an interchange of material between two homologous chromosomes, there is also an interchange of genes by crossing over. This has been shown in a number of cases, but Stern's demonstration in Drosophila is simple and complete. The essential feature of this demonstration is the use of strains in which it is possible to distinguish the two members of a pair of chromosomes from each other and from normal chromosomes of the same set. This is sometimes possible when as a result of *translocation* (p. 231) a portion of one chromosome has broken away and become attached to another, thus constituting a visibly different configuration. By this means Stern was able to obtain a race of Drosophila in which a portion of a Y chromosome had through translocation become attached to the end of one of the X chromosomes, forming a somewhat L-shaped body, easily distinguished from a normal X. In another race one of the X chromosomes had been broken into two approximately equal parts. The terminal portion (to which the spindle fiber was attached) remained in its normal position. The other portion was translocated to one of the small IV chromosomes. The race was viable, since the entire material of the X chromosome was present although in two separate pieces. By crossing these strains and producing females in which one X chromosome showed one of these translocations and the other X the other, it was possible to distinguish both the X chromosomes in the same individual from each other and from the autosomes.

Stern now succeeded in obtaining such females which were heterozygous for two sex-linked mutations located in the upper end of the X chromosome; carnation (*cr*), an eye-color mutant, and Bar (*B*) causing a narrowing of the eye. (The method of determining the location of genes in a chromosome will be described later in this chapter.) Carnation is recessive and Bar dominant. Such a fly therefore has eyes of normal (red) color and Bar shape, with a genotype (*cr B*) (*Cr b*), or $\dfrac{cr\ B}{+\ +}$. It was known from the way in which the stock had been made up that the *cr* and *B* genes were in the upper half of the broken X chromosome and that their two normal alleles were in the X bearing the translocated Y portion. Such a female was bred to a male having both the recessive genes (*cr* and the wild-type allele of Bar) in its X chromosome. The offspring of such a cross of double heterozygote by double recessive could be classified by inspection into four groups, as in any case of linkage. The females alone were studied. Of these there were two noncrossover classes (carnation Bar and normal) and two crossover classes (carnation with normal shape and Bar with normal color). These may be represented as follows:

NONCROSSOVERS		CROSSOVERS	
$\dfrac{cr\quad B}{cr\quad +}$ $\dfrac{+\quad +}{cr\quad +}$		$\dfrac{cr\quad +}{cr\quad +}$ $\dfrac{+\quad B}{cr\quad +}$	

The X chromosomes of these four classes of females were then studied. One of each pair, coming from the male parent, should evidently be normal. Its mate, coming from the female, should be distinguishable by its abnormal character and might be expected to show the effect of any cytological crossing over which had occurred in the maturation of the eggs. The genetic and cytological results are shown in Fig. 80. It is evident that in the two classes of genetical noncrossovers the maternal X is as it was in the mother, either broken into two or entire and provided with the translocated fragment. In the genetical crossovers, however, the maternal X has evidently resulted from crossing over, since in the Bar, normal flies the fragment of the Y is now attached to the upper half of the divided X, and in the carnation, normal flies an apparently normal

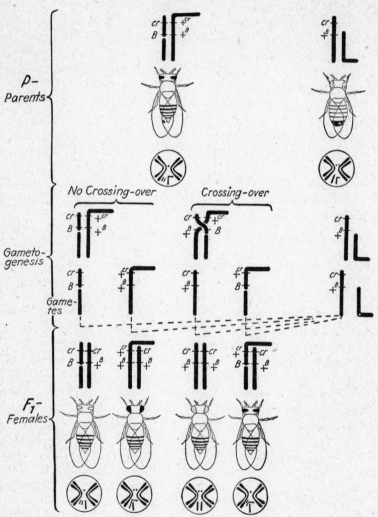

Fig. 80.—Diagram of Stern's experiment demonstrating crossing over cytologically. See text for details. (*From Stern.*)

chromosome is present. These are the results which should obtain if there had been an interchange between the two X chromosomes of the mother at a point near the upper end of the X and between the locations of the *cr* and *B* genes. Of the F_1 female flies, 364 were tested, in all but five (and these presumably the result of experimental error) there was a complete correspondence between the genetic and the cytological facts. In other words, genetic crossing over was proved to be accompanied by cytological crossing over, an actual exchange of material between homologous chromosomes.

Linear Arrangement of Genes in the Chromosome.—Breeding experiments with Drosophila and with maize have not only established the prime fact that the genes are located in the chromosomes, but they have also shown how they are *arranged* in the chromosomes. It has been shown that genes in the same linkage group (and thus presumably in the same chromosome) differ markedly in the strength with which they are linked. Now if it is assumed that the genes are distributed in a *single line* along the chromosome and that, in *general, the distance between two genes in a chromosome is proportional to the amount of crossing over between them,* a gene map of each chromosome for which there are sufficient data may be constructed, and each gene may be assigned to a definite position in the chromosome. This assumption (with some qualifications to be discussed later) has been tested by experience and is now generally accepted as an additional principle of heredity which Morgan has called the Linear Order of the Genes.

If two genes A and B, for example, cross over very infrequently (say, in 5 per cent of the cases), they are assumed to be very *near* to each other on the chromosome, so that the chance that a break in the chromosome will occur in the short distance between them is very small. On the other hand, if two genes A and C appear to be very loosely linked and show crossing over in a large percentage of the cases (say, in 35 per cent), they are assumed to lie relatively *far* apart on the chromosome, since the chance of a break occurring within the long distance that separates them is presumably relatively large. If these assumptions are sound ones, then by measuring the amount of crossing over between A and B and, independently, that between B and C, it should be possible to predict the amount of crossing over between A and C, for if the linked genes are *on the same line* and the amount of crossing over between genes is proportional to the distance between them, then the distance AB plus the distance BC should equal the distance AC. In many cases this relationship is found to hold true. Thus in crosses between red-eyed, yellow-bodied flies and white-eyed, gray-bodied flies it has been found that crossing over between yellow and white occurs in only about 1.5 per cent of the cases. In other crosses between white-eyed, normal-winged flies and red-eyed, bifid-winged flies, crossing over between white and bifid occurs in about 5.5. per cent of the cases. It may be assumed, then, that yellow and white are about 1.5 units apart, while white and bifid are 5.5 units apart. If the gene for white lies on a line with and between the genes for yellow and bifid, one would expect to find that yellow-white (1.5) plus white-bifid, (5.5) equals yellow-bifid (7.0). Such is the case, for in independent experiments yellow and bifid show about 7 per cent of crossing over. These three genes might be placed on a map which would show accurately the relations of the three genes as follows:

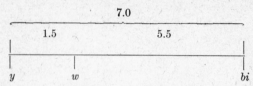

This relation does hold with genes that display relatively little recombination and which are probably near together in the chromosome. It does not hold, however, with genes that are relatively far apart, so that the statement that the distance between genes is proportional to the amount of crossing over between them must be qualified by specifying that the genes must be near together. Moreover, these relations are deduced only from breeding data (frequency of recombination) and "distance" must therefore be understood as crossover distance. Whether this corresponds exactly to physical distance will depend on whether the unit of crossover distance, that within which 1 per cent of crossing over takes place, corresponds everywhere to the same unit of physical distance in the chromosome. As we shall see, this is not always true (p. 232).

Double Crossing Over.—In many experiments with genes that show much crossing over, it has been found that the amount of crossing over appears to be lessened and the apparent distance between the distant genes appears to be shortened by the occurrence of *double crossing over*, or a break in two parts of the chromosome at once. Thus if three genes, *a*, *b*, and *c*, are located in one chromosome, crossing over might take place between *a* and *b* and between *b* and *c* at the same time. If the cross $ABC/abc \times abc/abc$ were made, the following type of gametes formed by the heterozygote might be found:

Noncrossovers	$\dfrac{ABC}{abc}$	genes in their original combinations
Single crossovers	$\dfrac{A-bc}{a-BC}$	a break between A and B
	$\dfrac{AB-c}{ab-C}$	a break between B and C
Double crossovers	$\dfrac{A-b-C}{a-B-c}$	breaks between A and B and between B and C at once

The zygotes formed by the last two types of gametes resemble in one respect the noncrossover type, since the parental combinations of factors AC and ac have been reconstituted by double crossing over, so that in these gametes *a* and *c* have the same relation as in the parents.

If these were the only two factors involved in such a case, these *AC* and
ac combinations from double crossing over would be indistinguishable
from the noncrossover classes, *AC* and *ac*, and would be added to them,

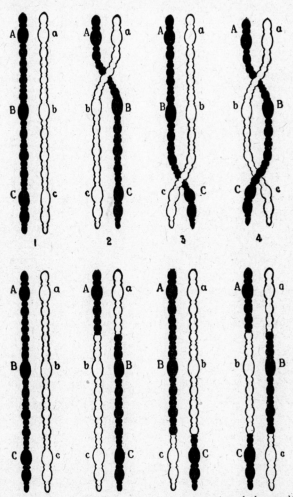

Fig. 81.—Diagram showing the mechanism (upper row) and the results (lower row)
of crossing over in a pair of chromatids. 1, no crossing over; 2, crossing over between
A and *B*; 3, crossing over between *B* and *C*; and 4, double crossing over between *A* and *B*
and between *B* and *C*. The lower row shows the resulting chromatids which pass into
the gametes.

so that the percentage of crossing over would seem to be less than the
actual distance of *ac* as determined by adding the distances *ab* and *bc*.
The diagram in Fig. 81 and the legend accompanying it show the assumed
chromosome mechanism of double crossing over.

The hypothesis of double crossing over explains those experimental results that are at variance with the theoretical expectation based on simple crossing over.

Thus when a fly with the three sex-linked genes *rb* (ruby eye color), *ct* (cut wings), and *v* (vermilion eye color) is crossed with a wild-type fly and the F_1 heterozygous females are crossed with the triply recessive type, the results shown in Table XIX are obtained.

TABLE XIX.—RESULTS OF A "THREE-POINT" CROSS IN DROSOPHILA (*After Morgan, Bridges, and Sturtevant*, 1925)

$$P_1 \; \female \; \frac{rb \; ct \; v}{rb \; ct \; v} \times \male \; + + + \text{(wild type)}^*$$

$$F_1 \; \female \; \frac{rb \; ct \; v}{+++} \times \male \; rb \; ct \; v$$

CLASSES OF PROGENY FROM ABOVE CROSS

NONCROSSOVERS	SINGLE CROSSOVERS	DOUBLE CROSSOVERS
rb ct v 539	rb | + + 137	rb | + | v 11
+ + + 590	+ | ct v 120	+ | ct | + 4
	rb ct | + 114	
	+ + | v 107	

| Totals..... 1,129 | 478 | 15 |

* In Table XIX the nomenclature now in general use in linkage experiments is employed. The wild-type allele of each gene is represented by + instead of by the corresponding large (or small) letter, as in previous chapters. Where it is necessary to designate the wild-type alleles at different loci, they may be written $+^{rb}$, $+^{ct}$, etc. The symbols +, *rb*, etc., designate either genes, when the whole genotype is written, or phenotypic appearance, as in the backcross progeny in the table. Loci are represented in the same line in the order (if known) in which they occur in the chromosome; the genes in the two chromosomes of a pair are written above and below a line, and in heterozygotes they are so written as to show in what combinations the genes entered the cross. Thus ruby, cut female × vermilion male would be written: $\frac{rb \; ct \; +}{rb \; ct \; +} \times + + v$, and the F_1 female: $\frac{rb \; ct \; +}{+ + \; v}$. Positions of crossing over are indicated by vertical lines: thus *rb* | + + is an individual which must have arisen from a gamete in which crossing over occurred in the region between *rb* and the next locus to the right, etc. For further use of this system of notation see Bridges and Morgan (1923).

If we consider only ruby and vermilion, there were 478 flies, or 29.4 per cent of the total (1,622), showing separation or crossing over between these genes. There were, however, 15 flies, or 0.9 per cent of the total, showing double crossing over. This could be disclosed only by the presence of a third gene, *ct*, lying between *rb* and *v*. Those progeny in which *ct* has changed its relationship with both *rb* and *v* (*rb* + *v*) must contain a chromosome resulting from *two* breaks, one between *rb* and + and one between + and *v*. These cases of crossing over would be concealed in an experiment involving only *rb* and *v*, as *rb v* and + + flies would be counted as noncrossovers. Since each of the double crossover flies represents *two* cases of crossing over, we must add two times 0.9 per cent, or 1.8, to 29.4 to give the total percentage of crossing over between *rb* and *v*, making this value 31.2 per cent. Thus where only two distant genes are followed, the apparent percentage of crossing over is always less than the actual percentage, because of the reunion of these two genes into their original combinations through double crossing over.

In estimating the spatial relations between the genes in the illustration used, it would be necessary to know also that no double crossing occurred between *rb* and *ct* or between *ct* and *v*. By the use of other intermediate genes this has been established in this case. It is therefore possible to calculate the total true percentage of crossing over between the single loci involved. Ruby and cut crossed over in 272 cases (137 + 120 + 11 + 4) out of the total of 1,622 gametes tested, or in about 16.7 per cent. Cut and vermilion crossed over in 236 cases (114 + 107 + 11 + 4), or in 14.5 per cent. Assuming that distance is proportional to crossover percentage, these three genes may be represented as lying on a straight line as follows:

The "distance" from *rb* to *v* is equal to the sum of the "distances" *rb–ct* and *ct–v*; but as has been shown, the *apparent* crossing over between *rb* and *v*, when only these two points are followed, is only 29.4 per cent. The lower value of the last figure is due to double crossing over.[1]

In representing the spacing of genes along the chromosome, it is best to obtain the longer "distances" by adding together the shorter "distances," since the latter are less affected by double crossing over.

Interference and Coincidence.—In the above case, breaks between *rb* and *ct* occur in 16.7 per cent of the cases and between *ct* and *v* in 14.5 per cent of the cases. If a break occurring between *rb* and *ct* does not influence the chance of a break occurring between *ct* and *v*, that is, if crossing over in one region is entirely independent of crossing over in the other, then the chance of breaks occurring in both regions at the same time should be equal to 16.7×14.5 per cent, or 2.4 per cent. Actually there were only 0.9 per cent of simultaneous breaks (double crossovers). This discrepancy between the actual percentage of double crossing over and the percentage expected on the assumption that each crossing over is an independent event has been found so frequently as to require explanation. The most striking discrepancy is in the case of genes that are very near together such as yellow, white, and bifid (p. 224). Here a crossover

---

[1] It is also possible to predict roughly the amount of crossing over to be expected between two genes when the "distance" between them is known and when the amount of double crossing over in this region has been ascertained in other experiments. Thus "distance," 31.2, minus twice the percentage of double crossing over (0.9×2) or 1.8 = 29.4 per cent.

in one region (*y–w*) entirely prevents or interferes with crossing over in the next region (*w–bi*), for no double crossing over occurs in the region from *y* to *bi*. This might be explained on mechanical grounds by assuming that at synapsis the chromosomes do not coil tightly about one another but are somewhat rigid, so that if bent or coiled between *y* and *w*, they will be unable to cross again between *w* and *bi*. Such complete interference obtains within short distances (about 12 crossover units in the X chromosome) and completely inhibits double crossing over. Within longer areas the effect of interference decreases as the distance from the first crossover increases, until in the X chromosome there is no interference between two crossovers separated by about 45 units.

The effect of interference is measured by calculating the ratio of the number of actual double breaks found to the number of double breaks which should occur if there were no interference. This ratio

$$\frac{\text{actual number of doubles}}{\text{expected number of doubles}}$$

is termed *coincidence*. Thus in the case of *rb–ct–v*, the actual percentage of doubles was 0.9, but the expected was 2.4; the coincidence is 0.9/2.4 or .37. In this region of the X chromosome, therefore, only about a third as many double crossovers are found as would occur if one crossover did not interfere with another.

Weinstein, Muller, Bridges, and others have measured the coincidence for the three large chromosomes of Drosophila and have shown that it is not uniform throughout the same chromosome or in different chromosomes. For each region of each chromosome there is a certain minimal length within which there is never any double crossing over. This probably represents the minimal length of the pieces of chromosome exchanged when crossing over occurs. At a certain distance the effect of one crossing over on another disappears (coincidence = 1.00) and then reappears beyond this point, showing that the piece of chromosome between the breaks tends to be of a certain average or modal length (about 45 units in the X chromosome).

The significance of interference and coincidence is twofold: First, it shows that what takes place at crossing over is an exchange of *blocks of genes*, arranged in a linear order and of certain characteristic lengths depending on the chromosome and the particular region. Second, it provides information essential to the accurate placing of genes in the chromosome map, since where crossing-over data on distant genes must be used, the figures must be corrected for double crossing over and for coincidence before they can fairly represent "distance."

Chromosome Maps.—In Fig. 82 are shown some recent crossover maps prepared for Drosophila. Each of the genes listed on the maps has

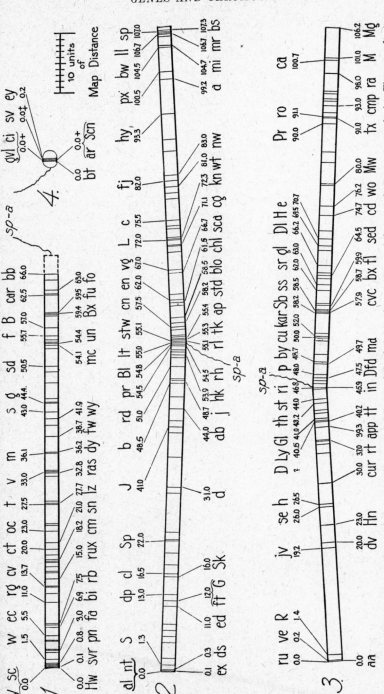

FIG. 82.—Genetical map of the four chromosomes of Drosophila showing the positions of the more important gene loci. Figures refer to distances from the "left" end of the chromosome as determined from percentage of recombination as observed in linkage experiments. Symbols refer to loci listed and described in Table XVIII. Loci above the chromosome are those most useful in genetic experiments. Spindle attachment points are indicated by *sp-a*. (*After Bridges*.)

been traced to one of the four chromosomes, by testing its linkage relations with each of the four groups. It has been located on the map by measuring its crossover value with the genes that appeared to be nearest to it (assuming that 1 per cent of crossing over equals one unit of distance) or in case of long distances by applying the necessary corrections for double crossing over, coincidence, and other special conditions in the chromosome or region that is being mapped. It will be asked how distances in excess of 50 units can be possible, since crossing over may vary only from nearly zero (no crossing over) to nearly 50 per cent (independent assortment). It is true that the *amount of recombination* between two genes never exceeds 50 per cent, but, because of double crossing over, it is necessary to measure long distances by adding together the sums of the recombination values for intermediate genes as explained above. These sums frequently exceed 50 in the long chromosomes. In the second chromosome, for instance, the genes for "star" and "speck" appear on the map as 105 units apart. When star and speck are crossed, they show less than 50 per cent of crossing over (actually about 48.7 per cent), but this is known to be due to the reduction caused by double crossing over. When the intermediate percentages are added, the sum is in excess of 100, which expresses the true distance between these two genes.

"Map distance," therefore, does not always correspond to crossover percentages as measured directly, and consequently the amount of crossing over between two genes cannot be read directly from the maps, except with genes so near together that no double crossing over occurs in the distance between them.

Comparison of Cytological and Genetical Maps.—The evidence that has been obtained from the intensive genetical and cytological study of Drosophila shows that the known genes of this species may be arranged in an orderly system of four linear groups, corresponding to the four pairs of chromosomes. The question now arises, do the relations between the genes in a linkage group, as derived from the data of crossing over, actually represent the spatial relations of these genes in the physical structure of the chromosome?

Opportunities for testing this question have been given by correlated genetical and cytological studies of departures from the normal relations between groups of linked genes or between the genes of the same linkage group. These rearrangements are found as rare spontaneous "mutations" or may be induced to occur by treatment of the flies with X rays or radium (p. 308). Bridges discovered that occasionally a number of genes, which normally belong to one linkage group, may suddenly acquire a new linkage relation with genes belonging to another linkage group. Thus a group of genes at one end of the II chromosome of *D. melanogaster*, comprising those from arc to the end, was found in one stock to show linkage with III chromosome genes. This occurrence was termed "translocation" and explained by the assumption that a piece of the II chromosome had broken off and become attached to the III chromosome near the locus of rough. Many other cases of translocation have been studied, and this interpretation has been confirmed by cytological evidence (p. 333). Where the translocation involves a large piece of chromosome, the chromosome from which it has been broken is visibly shorter, and the piece may sometimes be seen attached to another chromosome.

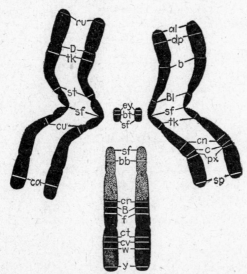

Fig. 83.—Cytological maps of the chromosomes of *Drosophila melanogaster*, showing the approximate location of various genes and of the spindle fibers (*sf*). The inert region of the X-chromosome is represented by the stippled portion of the rod-shaped chromosomes. The longer V-shaped chromosomes (left) are the third chromosomes; the shorter V-shaped chromosomes (right) are the second chromosomes; the smallest pair, the fourth chromosomes. (*From Dobzhansky.*)

Dobzhansky has taken advantage of the large numbers of breaks induced by X rays and has compared the "genetic length" of the translocated piece, as derived from crossover map data, with the actual length of the translocated piece as measured in cytological preparations of the chromosomes at metaphase. By studying a number of different translocations in this way, it has been possible to construct another type of map, the metaphase chromosome map, showing the approximate location of a number of gene loci in all of the chromosomes (Fig. 83) and to identify the second linkage group of genes with the shorter of the two V-shaped autosomes, and the third group with the longest of the autosomes.

These metaphase maps may now be compared with the crossover maps (Fig. 84). The order of the genes in the metaphase maps corresponds exactly with their order as previously determined from crossover data, thus providing cytological confirmation of this important principle. The relative distances between the same gene loci on the two maps, however, do not correspond in all regions. The discrepancies are greatest at the centers of the two large autosomes and at the right or "bobbed" end of the X chromosome. In these regions one crossover unit corresponds to a relatively much greater distance on the physical chromosome than in other regions. It happens that these are the regions of spindle-fiber attachment, and it is evident that in these places the frequency of crossing over per unit of chromosome length is low. Moreover it appears that no less than one-third of the whole length of the X chromosome, at the spindle-fiber end, is inert in the sense of containing practically no

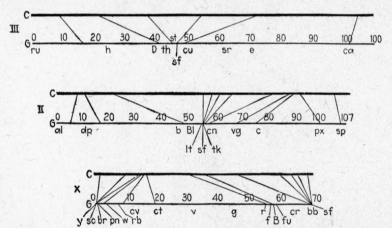

Fig. 84.—Comparison of the genetic and cytological maps of the third (III), Second (II), and X chromosomes (X) of *Drosophila melanogaster*. *C*, the cytological map; *G*, the genetic map. Figures indicate the genetic distances in map units. (*From Dobzhansky.*)

known gene loci (only bobbed near the end) and very little crossing over occurs in it. The crossover distance from the locus of carnation (*cr*) to the end is only about 7 units (10 per cent of the genetic length), yet this region comprises over 30 per cent of the metaphase chromosome. Near the spindle-fiber attachments of the II and III chromosomes there are also inert regions. It seems clear then that the unit of measure in the crossover maps is a variable one and that the amount of crossing over in any region is related to its proximity to the spindle-fiber attachment and to other regional peculiarities in the chromosomes.

Salivary Maps.—By studying various inversions, translocations, deficiencies, and duplications in the salivary chromosomes of flies with known mutant genes, Painter, Bridges, Demerec, and others have been able to specify the physical location of a number of genes. A recent salivary map of the X chromosome, compared with the crossover map is shown in the frontispiece. The gene order is the same in both maps, and the relations between crossover values and physical distance vary as they do when the metaphase map is used. The inert region of the X appears in the salivary chromosome only as a few faint bands at the spindle fiber end; and probably consists, as does the Y chromosome, chiefly of heterochromatin, that is, chromatin which does not respond to the chromatin stains used. Thus those portions that contain few or no mutant genes are also structurally different from the gene-bearing portions.

In a few cases individual gene loci have been identified with individual bands, suggesting that these are or contain the actual genes.

Deficiency.—By use of the crossover maps it has been possible to interpret many of the types of mutant changes that have occurred in

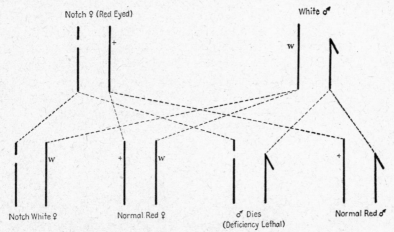

FIG. 85.—The inheritance of Notch deficiency in *Drosophila melanogaster*.

Drosophila and other organisms and later to confirm the interpretation by examination of the chromosomes themselves. Thus a mutation known as Notch wing in *Drosophila melanogaster*, found only in females, behaves as though it were due to a sex-linked dominant, lethal in males, located at about 3 in the crossover map of the X chromosome. Notch[1] females crossed with normal males regularly give ⅓ Notch females, ⅓ normal females, ⅓ normal males. A Notch female from a red-eyed stock crossed with a white male gives Notch and normal offspring as expected, but all the Notch flies show the recessive *white* eye (which is located at 1.5), as though the Notch female contained no wild-type allele of white (Fig. 85). The normal-winged flies are all red eyed. Similarly, the gene facet, at 3.0, showed this peculiar pseudodominance when crossed

---

[1] The Notch mutation has occurred several times. In the example used, based on work by Mohr, the mutation known as Notch[8] was studied.

with Notch, and the gene Abnormal at 4.5 was also affected. Bridges and Mohr, who studied this condition, assumed that Notch was due to the absence of a piece of chromosome in this case bearing the loci from white through Abnormal. This was called a *deficiency*, and in conformity with the assumption, the map of the X in Notch is about four units shorter than normal. Much later the actual absence of this section of the chromosome in Notch females was proved by examination of the salivary gland chromosome.

FIG. 86.—Portions of salivary chromosome II of Drosophila heterozygous for Notopleural, a deficiency for a series of bands (44E-45E). It is evident that in the deficient strand (above), the bands between the arrows on the normal one (below) are missing. (*From Bridges.*)

Evidence from the Salivary Gland Chromosomes of Drosophila.—Our conceptions of the relations between genes and chromosomes have been strikingly confirmed and extended through recent studies of the so-called giant chromosomes of Drosophila (Fig. 52) by Painter, Bridges, and others. These chromosomes show a structural differentiation of crossbands of heavily stained material by which individual parts of each chromosome can be recognized. By studying these chromosomes in flies containing deficiencies (Fig. 86) or rearrangements of the linkage

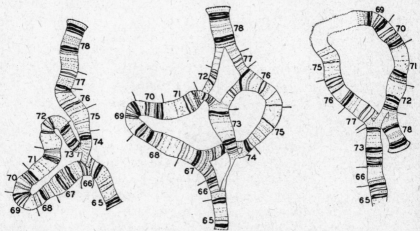

FIG. 87.—Inversions in salivary chromosome B¹ of *Drosophila azteca* as revealed by loop formation. (*From Dobzhansky.*)

groups induced by X rays, it has been possible to determine the order and the position in the chromosome of many of the gene loci.

Sturtevant, for example, noted in 1913 the first case of *inversion* or a change in the usual order of the genes. This was disclosed first by the suppression of crossing over in flies heterozygous for a mutant chromosome, and Sturtevant assumed that this effect was due to an inversion of the normal order of gene loci, for example from *a b c d e f g* to an order such as *a b e d c f g* in the mutant. It was assumed that crossing over was suppressed because the genes in the inverted section were no longer opposite to their homologous or allelic genes, so that opposite loci did not attract each other normally and normal synapsis and crossing over could thus not occur. Although the interpretation was made highly probable by the crossing over and mapping experiments, conclusive cytological evidence was not obtained for Drosophila until the salivary chromosomes of inversion heterozygotes were examined. Then it was found, as had been predicted, that the section of the chromosome associated with a genetic inversion showed an inverted order of the bands resulting in the formation of loops (Fig. 87) by which homologous bands are brought together.

Balanced Lethals.—A recognition of the fact that crossing over may be suppressed (now interpreted as the effect of inversion) led to the discovery by Muller of the first case of balanced lethals. This has been of great importance, both in the practical maintenance of stocks containing lethals and in the interpretation of complex breeding behavior such as that found in Oenothera. The case observed by Muller may serve as an example of the whole group. Muller studied a stock of Drosophila with deformed wings known as Beaded. Beaded flies mated together first produced about $\frac{2}{3}$ Beaded to $\frac{1}{3}$ normal offspring, as though Beaded were due to a single dominant gene which was lethal when homozygous. By selection he obtained from this stock one which bred practically true to Beaded but which rarely produced a normal fly. Beaded flies from this latter stock crossed with normals, however, produced 50 per cent Beaded and 50 per cent normal, showing that they were still heterozygous for Beaded. It required an extended analysis to discover how the Beaded stock which gave ratios of 2 Beaded to 1 normal differed from the Beaded stock which bred true. The first stock was found to contain in the third chromosome a dominant mutation, Beaded, which was lethal when homozygous. Such Beaded flies were thus always heterozygous *Bd*. The true-breeding Beaded flies were also of this same composition *Bd/+*, but in addition they were found to contain another lethal *l*, also in the third chromosome and linked to Beaded. The lethal had apparently arisen by mutation during the selection experiment. In addition, the true-breeding Beaded flies contained a factor that almost completely prevented crossing over between Beaded and the new lethal, probably an inversion. Thus crosses between true-breeding Beaded flies were of this sort:

$$\text{♀} \frac{Bd\ +}{+\ l} \times \text{♂} \frac{Bd\ +}{+\ l}$$

F₁ gametes (no crossing over) $\quad \begin{matrix} Bd\ + \\ +\ l \end{matrix} \qquad \begin{matrix} Bd\ + \\ +\ l \end{matrix}$

$$\text{F}_1 \text{ zygotes} \begin{cases} \dfrac{Bd\ +}{Bd\ +} \text{ dies, } BdBd \text{ lethal} \\[2mm] \dfrac{+\ l}{+\ l} \text{ dies, } ll \text{ lethal} \\[2mm] \dfrac{Bd\ +}{+\ l} \text{ viable, Beaded} \\[2mm] \dfrac{+\ l}{Bd\ +} \text{ viable, Beaded} \end{cases}$$

Thus nearly all flies which survived were Beaded, but a half of the total progeny dies, and the Beaded stock "bred true" only in the sense that almost no nonbeaded flies survived. The rare normals which survived were due to crossing over by which the wild-type allele of Beaded was released from its association with the lethal.

This balanced system obviously provided for the maintenance of heterozygosity. Its application to the perpetual hybrids of Oenothera and to the "mutations" which arise from these was pointed out by Muller.

Bar Duplication.—An understanding of the way in which genes are located in chromosomes, and especially a study of the salivary chromosomes, have led to an interpretation of the curious behavior of the mutant Bar eye in Drosophila. This has long been known as a dominant located at 57.0 on the crossover map of the chromosome. Zeleny found that in cultures of homozygous Bar, normal-eyed flies appear with very low but regular frequency; about 1 out of 1,500 offspring shows this reversion to wild type. Even less frequently a mutant form known as Ultrabar appears with eyes much smaller than Bar. Both Ultrabar and the reverted wild type breed true.

Sturtevant and Morgan found that the rare changes from Bar to wild type were always accompanied by a peculiar unequal crossing over in the Bar region. This was detected by using Bar females in which two other mutant genes very near to the Bar region were present. It was then found that as a result of this rare unequal crossing over the two Bar genes that had entered the cross in the two parental chromosomes emerged side by side in one chromosome and produced the Ultrabar, or as it is now called, the Double-bar effect, while the other chromosome had lost the Bar locus by crossing over and was thus wild type. Since the latter chromosome showed no effect of deficiency, the Bar gene which it had contained must have been due to a duplication. A unique situation appeared in that when two Bar genes were present in one chromosome of heterozygous Double Bar ($BB/+$) the eyes of the fly were much smaller, that is, Double Bar, than when the two Bar genes were present in opposite chromosomes B/B (Bar). This was the first demonstration of what Sturtevant called "position effect," that is, that the effects of a gene may be influenced by its position in the chromosome and by its neighboring genes (p. 336).

Proof that the "mutation" to Bar consisted of a duplication of a small section of chromosome was provided by Bridges from a study of the salivary gland chromosomes. He found that this section was repre-

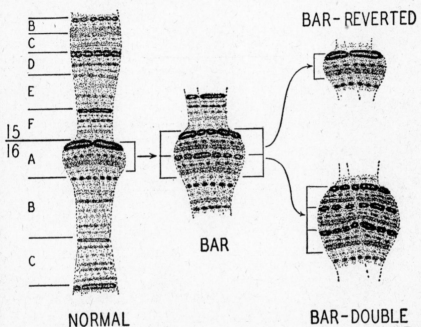

FIG. 88.—The Bar region in salivary chromosome I, showing duplication of bands in Bar and Double-bar. (*From Bridges.*)

sented but once in wild-type stock and in wild type obtained by reversion from Bar; but it was present twice in Bar and three times in Double Bar (Fig. 88). Thus the actual physical basis of the Bar mutation was fixed in the chromosome, and it was shown to be due to the repetition of normal constituents of the wild-type chromosome. Bridges had previously found that certain recognizable sequences of bands in the salivary chromosomes were found in more than one place. He called these "repeats" and supposed that one method by which chromosomes might evolve from simpler conditions was by such duplication of materials.

The Cytogenetics of Maize.—As so frequently happens in genetics, principles discovered by an intensive analysis of one form, either plant or animal, are confirmed and extended by an equally intensive study of

I

0 sr striate leaves
22 P pericarp color
47 as asynapsis
74 br brachytic plant
79 f1 fine striped leaves
96 an anther ear
123 gs green striped leaves
150 bm2 brown midrib

II

0 ws3 white sheath
11 lg1 liguleless leaf
30 gl2 glossy seedling
49 B anthocyanin intensifier
56 sk silkless ear
68 fl floury endosperm
74 ts1 tassel seed
82 v4 virescent seedling

III

0 a1 anthocyanin color
28 na nana plant
39 ba1 barren stalk
56 ts4 tassel seed
63 Rg ragged leaf
85 d1 dwarf plant
103 cr crinkly leaf

IV

0 de1 defective endosperm
35 Ga gametophyte
56 Ts5 tassel seed
66 sp1 small pollen
69 lo lethal ovule
71 su sugary endosperm
74 de16 defective endosperm
100 Tu tunicate ear
105 j2 japonica striping
111 gl3 glossy seedling

V

0 a2 anthocyanin color
6 bm1 brown midrib
7 sa spindle attachment
8 bt brittle endosperm
12 bv brevis height
31 pr red aleurone
40 ys yellow stripe
72 v2 virescent seedling

VI

0 po polymitotic
13 Y1 yellow endosperm
41 Pl purple plant color
51 sm salmon silks
61 py pigmy plant

VII

0 v5 virescent seedling
14 ra ramosa ear
18 gl1 glossy seedling
28 Tp teopod
34 ij iojap striping
52 Bn brown aleurone

VIII

0 ji japonica striping
11 ms8 male sterile
30 v16 virescent seedling

IX

0 terminal knob
2 yg2 yellow green
21 C aleurone color
24 sh shrunken endosperm
39 bp brown pericarp
54 wx waxy endosperm
58 sa spindle attachment

X

0 Rp rust-resistance
28 li lineate striping
38 sp2 small pollen
43 gl golden plant color
57 R aleurone and plant color
84 dz dwarf plant

FIG. 89.—A genetical map for maize (Zea mays). (Courtesy of Dr. M. M. Rhoades.)

another form. Among plants the study of the relations between genes and chromosomes has been carried farthest by investigators working with Indian corn, *Zea mays*. In this species 10 groups of linked genes have been discovered and each group has been mapped and identified with one of the 10 chromosomes of the haploid or monoploid group (Fig. 89). This has been facilitated by the fact that each chromosome is morphologically different, by the discovery of some 400 mutant genes affecting not only all parts of the plant but also the behavior of the chromosomes, and by the close cooperation of many investigators under the leadership of R. A. Emerson of Cornell University. In many cases a linkage group could be identified with a specific chromosome by the so-called trisomic method (p. 326). The localization of genes at specific points in the chromosome was accomplished by the study of deficiencies and translocations, either spontaneous, induced by X rays, or brought about by the action of specific genes, such as the gene sticky (*st*) which causes the chromosomes to stick together at meiotic metaphase and thus increases the frequency of nondisjunction, translocation, deficiency, and fragmentation of chromosomes.

Fig. 90.—Drawing of the end regions of a pair of maize chromosomes, one of which shows a deficiency; four chromomeres are lacking from right end of lower chromosome. × 4500. (*From McClintock.*)

McClintock, for example, examined the chromosomes of certain plants that had been shown by breeding experiments to be deficient for several adjacent linked genes. The chromosome that had been identified with the linkage group containing these genes was shown to lack several chromomeres (Fig. 90). Thus the cytological basis of deficiency was established and the physical location of these genes was disclosed.

In locating genes in chromosomes much use has been made of reciprocal translocations or segmental interchanges in which nonhomologous chromosomes have exchanged parts. This results in ring formation at synapsis (p. 331), and the actual chromosomes involved can be identified by their structural peculiarities. Such plants also show linkage between genes which normally belong to two different linkage groups, and it is possible, by measuring the amount of crossing over, to specify the region in which each linkage group was broken (p. 333). Thus if the genes in a chromosome have been placed on the crossover map in order *a b c d e f g*, a mutual translocation between this group and another may break the group between *c* and *d*. In one of the interchange chromosomes the order should be *a b c*-break and in the other *g f e d*-break. If a second translocation between this chromosome and another broke the linkage group between d and e, then d must be located between the first break and the second.   By comparing the genetical and cytological findings in a number of such cases, it has been possible to specify the locations of many genes in the chromosomes and to show that the linear order of the genes is not only a necessary inference from the data of linkage and crossing over but a fundamental fact about the structure of chromosomes.

REFERENCES

BRIDGES, C. B., 1936.   The Bar "gene" a duplication.   Science **83**: 210–211.

————. 1937.   Correspondences between linkage maps and salivary chromosome structure as illustrated in the tip of chromosome   II R of *Drosophila melanogaster*.   Cytologia, Fujii Jubilee Volume: 745–755.

————. 1937.   Revised data on culture media and mutant loci of *Drosophila melanogaster*.   Tabulae Biologicae **14**: 343–353.

————, and T. H. MORGAN. 1919.   The second-chromosome group of mutant characters.   Carnegie Inst. Wash. Publ. **278**.

———— and ————.   1923.   The third-chromosome group of mutant characters of *Drosophila melanogaster*.   Carnegie Inst. Wash. Publ. **327**.

————, E. N. SKOOG, and LU-CHI LI.   1936.   Genetical and cytological studies of a deficiency (notopleural) in the second chromosome of *Drosophila melanogaster*.   Genetics **21**: 788–795.

DOBZHANSKY, T. 1929.   Genetical and cytological proof of translocations involving the third and the fourth chromosomes of *Drosophila melanogaster*.   Biol. Cent. **49**.

————. 1936.   Induced chromosomal aberrations in animals, in Biological Effects of Radiation.   (Edited by Duggar.)   New York.

EMERSON, R. A., G. W. BEADLE, and A. C. FRASER.   1935.   A summary of linkage studies with Maize.   Cornell Univ. Agr. Exp. Sta. Memoir.   **180**.

MCCLINTOCK, BARBARA. 1931.   Cytological observations of deficiencies involving known genes, translocation, and an inversion in *Zea mays*.   Univ. Missouri Res. Bull. **163**.

MORGAN, T. H. 1919.   The physical basis of heredity.   Philadelphia.

————. 1928.   The theory of the gene.   2d ed.   New Haven.

————, C. B. BRIDGES, and A. H. STURTEVANT.   1925.   The genetics of Drosophila.   Bibliographia Genetica **2**.

————, A. H. STURTEVANT, H. J. MULLER, and C. B. BRIDGES.   1923.   The mechanism of Mendelian heredity.   2d ed.   New York.

MULLER, H. S. 1918.   Genetic variability, twin hybrids, and constant hybrids in a case of balanced lethal factors.   Genetics **3**: 422–499.

RHOADES, M. M., and BARBARA MCCLINTOCK.   1935.   The cytogenetics of maize.   Bot. Rev. **1**: 292–325.

PROBLEMS

295. In Drosophila white eyes (w), miniature wings (m), and forked bristles (f) are sex-linked and recessive to the wild-type characters red eyes, long wings, and straight bristles.   In a cross of $\dfrac{w\,f\,m}{w\,f\,m} \times +++$ the F$_1$ females crossed with $w\,f\,m$ males gave the following:

	PER CENT
White, forked, miniature........................	26.8
Red, straight, long.............................	26.8
White, straight, long............................	13.2
Red, forked, miniature..........................	13.2
White, straight, miniature.......................	6.7
Red, forked, long..............................	6.7
White, forked, long.............................	3.3
Red, straight, miniature........................	3.3

a. Designate noncrossover, single-crossover, and double-crossover classes.

b. Determine the percentage of crossing over between white and forked, white and miniature, and miniature and forked, and from this determine the order of these genes in the chromosome.

296. From the data in Problem 295 compare the percentage of crossing over between the two most distant genes with the sum of the percentages of crossing over between the two end genes and the center gene. Explain this difference. Construct a chromosome map of these genes.

297. If a homozygous red, forked, long fly is crossed with a homozygous white, straight, miniature and an F_1 female is crossed with a white, forked, miniature male, predict the phenotypic proportions of the progeny.

298. In Chinese primroses short style is dominant over long, magenta flower over red, and green stigma over red. When from the cross of homozygous short, magenta flower, green stigma by long, red flower, red stigma, the F_1 was crossed with long, red flower, red stigma, the following offspring were obtained (data from Altenburg):

Style	Flower	Stigma	
Short	Magenta	Green	1,063
Long	Red	Red	1,032
Short	Magenta	Red	634
Long	Red	Green	526
Short	Red	Red	156
Long	Magenta	Green	180
Short	Red	Green	39
Long	Magenta	Red	54

Map the chromosome in which these genes lie.

299. Using the two single crossover values from Problem 295, calculate the expected percentage of double crossing over assuming no interference, and compare this with the actual percentage of doubles. Calculate the coincidence for this region of the chromosome.

300. Calculate the coincidence in Problem 298 and compare with that in Problem 295.

301. In maize, F_1 plants from the cross of colored, shrunken, starchy × colorless, full, waxy were crossed with colorless, shrunken, waxy plants, and the following progeny observed (data from Hutchison):

Colored, shrunken, starchy.............................. 2,538
Colorless, full, waxy.................................... 2,708
Colored, full, waxy...................................... 116
Colorless, shrunken, starchy............................. 113
Colored, shrunken, waxy.................................. 601
Colorless, full, starchy................................. 626
Colored, full, starchy................................... 4
Colorless, shrunken, waxy................................ 2

Map the positions of c, s, and w and determine the coincidence.

302. In Drosophila the mutant "morula," m, has a peculiar eye modification in which the facets are more irregular in size, shape, and color than are those of the normal eye. (For descriptions of mutants "black" and "arc," see Problem 278.)

In the four following crosses the genes for arc, black, and morula entered the crosses in all four possible combinations, as stated. The counts in each case are the results of mating F_1 females with arc, black, morula males. Only the recessive alleles are named, the normal dominant alleles being assumed to be present unless the recessive is mentioned. Thus "black" flies are $b++$, possessing the dominant alleles of arc and morula. The four crosses are as follows:

I. Arc, black, morula × wild type; F_1 female × arc, black, morula male.
II. Arc, black × morula; F_1 female × arc, black, morula male.
III. Black, morula × arc; F_1 female × arc, black, morula male.
IV. Black × arc, morula; F_1 female × arc, black, morula male.

The results of these four back crosses are given below (data from Bridges and Morgan):

	Cross I	Cross II	Cross III	Cross IV
Wild type....................	613	95	3	164
Black.........................	445	40	13	187
Arc...........................	38	713	113	21
Morula.......................	82	851	107	7
Arc, black...................	55	884	96	8
Black, morula................	29	666	120	15
Arc, morula..................	467	33	14	187
Arc, black, morula...........	514	79	2	133

Determine the crossover percentage between black and arc, arc and morula, and black and morula. Map the chromosome for these three points.

303. Below are the data from Bridges and Morgan for the crossovers between the genes black, curved, purple, speck, star, and vestigial in chromosome II of Drosophila. On the basis of the data, map the chromosome for these five genes

as accurately as possible. Remember that determinations for short distances
are more accurate than those for long ones.

Genes	Total flies	Crossovers
Black-curved.............................	62,679	14,237
Black-purple.............................	48,931	3,026
Black-speck.............................	685	326
Black-star..............................	16,507	6,250
Black-vestigial..........................	20,153	3,578
Curved-purple...........................	51,136	10,205
Curved-speck...........................	10,042	3,037
Curved-star.............................	19,870	9,123
Curved-vestigial.........................	1,720	141
Purple-speck............................	11,985	5,474
Purple-star.............................	8,155	3,561
Purple-vestigial.........................	13,601	1,609
Speck-star..............................	7,135	3,448
Speck-vestigial..........................	2,054	738
Star-vestigial...........................	450	195

Locate also on this map the genes for arc and morula, studied in Problem 302.
(Arc and morula are on the opposite side of black from star.)

304. A breeder of Chinese primroses has three plants, each of which has short
styles, magenta flowers, and green stigmas. The offspring of each, when crossed
on a triple recessive plant, are presented below, symbols being used instead of
words (*L* short style, *l* long, *R* magenta flower, *r* red, *S* green stigma, *s* red).

Plant 1 × *lrs*	Plant 2 × *lrs*	Plant 3 × *lrs*
290 *LRs*	40 *LRs*	221 *LRS*
151 *LRS*	19 *LRS*	218 *lrS*
288 *lrS*	37 *lrS*	57 *LrS*
147 *lrs*	21 *lrs*	60 *lRS*
37 *LrS*	289 *LrS*	
20 *Lrs*	150 *Lrs*	
39 *lRs*	291 *lRs*	
21 *lRS*	148 *lRS*	

What are the genotypes of these three plants?

305. In chromosome II of Drosophila (data from Bridges and Morgan) occurs
the gene for "curved" wings, *c*. In this chromosome occurs a lethal gene *l*,
which when homozygous causes the death of the individual. *LL* and *Ll* animals
live, *ll* ones die. The gene for "curved" shows a crossover value of 8.7 per cent

with this lethal gene. Cross two flies of the genotype $+ +/c\ l$ together; cross two others of the genotype $+ l/c +$. What will be the appearance of the offspring in each case?

306. In rats two genes r and p (referred to in Problem 284) are linked. *RRpp* animals have pink eyes and light-colored coats; *rrPP* animals have red eyes and light-colored coats. *RRPP* animals have dark eyes and dark coats. Albinism, *cc* (pink eyes and white coat), is also linked with r and p. Design an experiment to measure this linkage and to map the chromosome containing r, p, and c, giving all necessary steps and crosses.

307. State how you would determine how extensive the deficiency is which produces the mutant Notch.

308. How can the approximate position of such a deficiency as Notch be determined without finding the actual genes which are missing?

309. How can it be determined whether a given variation is due to a gene mutation or to a small deficiency (as in Notch)?

310. If a small deficiency, producing a trait like Notch, were to occur in an autosome, how different would its genetic behavior be from that described for Notch?

311. Notch female, red-eyed, by wild-type (normal winged), white-eyed male gives white-eyed Notch and red-eyed normal offspring. If one of their white-eyed Notch offspring is mated with a red-eyed male, what will be the appearance of their offspring?

312. Explain just how it is possible, by studying the behavior of two genes close to the Bar locus, to prove that as a result of crossing over there may be two Bar "genes" in one chromosome and none in the other.

313. Why is a deficiency more likely to be lethal in males than in females in such an organism as Drosophila?

314. What other factors, aside from the position of the spindle-fiber attachment, can you suggest as possible causes of difference between various parts of a chromosome in amount of crossing over per unit of cytological length?

315. Crossover suppressors were at first regarded as genes whose specific effect was to prevent crossing over. It was found, however, that they produced this effect only when *heterozygous*. Show how the modern conception of inversion as a cause of crossover suppression explains this fact.

316. How is it possible to identify a given gene locus with a given band on the salivary chromosome?

CHAPTER X

CYTOPLASMIC INHERITANCE

The theory that the *genes* constitute the fundamental physical basis of inheritance is now supported by such a body of evidence that it may be regarded as thoroughly established. The implications of this theory are profound not only for the problems of genetics, but for those of development and evolution as well. One should remember, however, that despite this predominance of the gene, the actual protoplasmic link between an individual and its two parents is more than a complement of genes or chromosomes, or even a pair of nuclei, for the egg contributes a mass of cytoplasm far larger than either gamete nucleus. It is evidently essential to determine what function, if any, this gametic cytoplasm may have in heredity.

In discussing this problem it is important to distinguish two possible roles that the cytoplasm may play. One concerns the *transmission* of hereditary materials which determine the character of the zygote; the other relates to the manner in which these and other agencies control the process of *development* itself. For our present purposes we shall be concerned primarily with the former question and shall try to discover whether there is in the cytoplasm a transmission system analogous to (though independent of) that which is known to exist in the nucleus, and what part such a system may play in inheritance.

This problem is still far from a satisfactory solution. Many geneticists regard the genes, located in the chromosomes, as the only carriers of an organism's heritage and attribute whatever influence the cytoplasm may appear to have on development to differences induced in it very early by the action of the genes of the mother. Others, notable among whom is von Wettstein, believe that there is sufficient evidence for the existence in the cytoplasm of a somewhat similar but independent vehicle of inheritance. For the system of genes in the nucleus von Wettstein has proposed the term *genome* and for the system of analogous entities in the cytoplasm the term *plasmon*. Our problem thus resolves itself into the question of whether a plasmon really exists or not.

Evidence for and against it has been derived from a number of sources. The very common fact that the offspring of reciprocal crosses (female A × male B and female B × male A) are usually identical indicates that for most hereditary characters the influence of male and of female gametes

245

is equivalent; and since the nuclei of sperm and egg are equivalent, whereas their cytoplasmic contents differ (being practically absent in the sperm), this has served as a convincing argument that genetic similarities and hereditary variations are in general due to nuclear factors. The plasmon, if it exists at all, evidently plays a relatively minor part in heredity. There are a number of characters, however, for which reciprocal crosses produce unlike results and these are inherited entirely or almost entirely through the female parent alone. Since the possession of cytoplasm is the only important respect in which female gametes differ from male ones, these cases of "maternal" inheritance constitute important evidence for the existence of a plasmon.

Particularly important among these are certain traits in plants involving chloroplast development and constituting the so-called "albomaculatus" types of leaf variegation, in which the normal green tissue is irregularly spotted with patches of paler green or white, a type of variation intensively studied by Correns and others. These may be small or may include entire leaves or branches. This character occurs in a wide variety of plants, and its inheritance has been determined in more than 20 genera. Flowers in wholly green branches produce seed which grow into normal plants; flowers on variegated branches yield offspring which have variegated foliage, and flowers from branches wholly white give progeny without chlorophyll; but in every case the source of the pollen has no influence on the offspring. Inheritance is wholly maternal. Variegation seems clearly to be determined by agencies localized in the cytoplasm rather than in the chromosomes. A satisfactory explanation of the mechanism of inheritance for such a trait is available, however, since variegation is evidently the result of differences in chloroplast development and since the primordia of these bodies, from which the plastids of the whole plant are ultimately derived, are present in the cytoplasm of the egg. For this system Renner has proposed the term *plastome*. Such plastid differences should thus be expected to show maternal inheritance. It is still a matter of doubt whether there are two kinds of plastid primordia, irregularly distributed at the growing point, or whether there is a "diseased" condition of the plastids. In a few cases, as in *Pelargonium zonale*, the variegation, which appears as a colorless margin to the leaf, may be transmitted through both parents (though in an irregular fashion) perhaps because a little cytoplasm enters with the male nucleus. The situation is complicated by the fact that such plants are periclinal chimeras, with one or two layers of colorless cells surrounding a core of green.

In all these cases, variegation is concerned with plastid development and is determined by conditions in the cytoplasm independent of the nucleus. They admittedly constitute a notable instance of non-Mendelian inheritance. One should remember, however, that in contrast to these cases, only about 40 of which are known, there are several hundred other instances of chlorophyll or plastid modifications, resulting in albinism or various grades of plastid abnormality, where the trait is undoubtedly controlled by genes. Genes thus may influence plastids as they do all other structures; but in a few cases these bodies may be affected by nongenic agencies.

Cytoplasmic inheritance of plastid traits is easy to understand because of the obvious mechanism involved. There are a few cases where maternal inheritance occurs in traits which are not concerned with plastids, and these provide a more difficult problem. Among these is the case of male sterility in maize described by Rhoades. This character, which consists in the abortion of much or all of the pollen (though not the ovules) is transmitted solely through the mother and never by the pollen. Since gene markers are now known for all the 10 chromosomes of maize, Rhoades was able to replace each of the chromosomes of the male-sterile race with one from normal stock. Male sterility was found not to belong to any of the 10 linkage groups thus tested, and seems to be controlled by some agency in the cytoplasm independent of the chromosomes.

A somewhat more complex situation occurs in the genus Epilobium, a member of the Onagraceae closely related to Oenothera, which has been studied intensively by Lehmann, Michaelis, Renner, and others. Reciprocal crosses between *E. hirsutum* and the markedly different *E. roseum* are very dissimilar. Where *hirsutum* is the female parent, the offspring are nearly sterile and have anthers and petals which are much reduced in size. Where *roseum* is the female parent, there is little sterility, and the floral parts are well developed. There are also reciprocal differences in the size of the plant and of its vegetative organs. By repeated back-crossing of the F_1 (*roseum* ♀ × *hirsutum* ♂) with *hirsutum* male, Michaelis produced a type in which the cytoplasm was derived from *roseum* but the chromosomal complement was presumably now entirely from *hirsutum*. When this was crossed reciprocally with pure *hirsutum*, similar differences were observed as when pure *roseum* and pure *hirsutum* were crossed, indicating that these differences were due to the cytoplasm, since the genes were now presumably identical. Renner and Michaelis regard the evidence from Epilobium as strongly indicative of an hereditary vehicle in the cytoplasm. Lehmann and his students explain the differences in reciprocal crosses in this genus as due to the production of specific changes in the cytoplasm by different gene combinations or to differences in reaction of a given nucleus in different cytoplasms.

Somewhat different in type are the extensive studies of von Wettstein on mosses of the family Funariaceae. He observed no differences in reciprocal crosses between *varieties* of *Funaria hygrometrica*, the characters segregating in normal Mendelian fashion. When the two *species F. hygrometrica* and *F. mediterranea* were crossed, however, marked differences between the reciprocal crosses appeared. For most traits the segregating gametophyte offspring tended to resemble the maternal parent, the paternal types often failing to appear. A few characters showed normal segregation. When the two *genera* Funaria and Physcomitrium were crossed, the offspring were all similar to or identical with the female parent. Many of the spores were sterile. Von Wettstein interprets these results as due to the failure of genomes similar to that of the male parent to survive and function in cytoplasm derived from a different source. This conclusion is supported by evidence from polyploid races produced by regeneration of gametophytes from sporophyte tissue. By this means it was possible to introduce as many as three sets of paternal chromosomes from one genus into the eggs of the other genus, but even with this preponderance of the male genomes, inheritance was still entirely maternal. Although these facts show convincingly that there are marked developmental incompatibilities between genes and cytoplasm and that, when the two are derived from different sources, the cytoplasm may prevent the genes from acting, this is still hardly an absolute proof of the existence of a plasmon.

Goldschmidt's theory of sex determination in Lymantria (p. 259) provides still another example. Here (according to the present explanation) the tendency toward maleness is carried in the sex chromosome and that toward femaleness in the cytoplasm, with the result that reciprocal crosses between different races may be very different in their sex expression. Several cases of maternal inheritance have been reported in mammals, but here it is usually impossible to determine whether cytoplasmic transmission or early effects of the maternal genotype are responsible.

Evidence as to cytoplasmic inheritance, however, can be derived from quite another source, through the study of cases of *merogony*, where the egg cytoplasm comes from one parent and the nucleus (sperm) from the other so that their effects can be compared. The classic experiments in this field were performed by Boveri, who fertilized enucleated eggs of one species of sea urchin with sperm from a markedly different one. Although development did not persist beyond the pluteus stage, the merogonous embryos seemed to resemble the species from which the sperm was derived, indicating that the nucleus controlled development even when surrounded by cytoplasm from a very different source. Boveri's results are open to serious question, however, since there is evidence that the nuclear material was not entirely removed from the egg, and since the resemblance to the male parent might well be explained on simple genetic grounds.   In other cases, undoubted merogonous embryos did not develop far enough to establish whether nucleus or cytoplasm is in control.   The recent work of Hadorn, however, indicates that for certain traits the male nucleus may be without effect in some merogonous tissues.   Two species of Triton (*T. palmatus* and *T. cristatus*) differ clearly in the character of the epidermis.   Hadorn fertilized the egg of *palmatus* with the sperm of *cristatus* and succeeded in removing the *palmatus* nucleus before nuclear fusion.   The embryo (thus haploid) develops only to the blastula stage; but a portion of the presumptive epidermis, if grafted to a normal larva of another species, *T. alpestris*, maintains its identity and develops to the adult state.   Here it resembles the epidermis of the parent *palmatus* which contributed the cytoplasm rather than the parent *cristatus* which contributed the nucleus.   For this trait, at least, the cytoplasm rather than the nucleus seems to have the decisive effect, a result quite the opposite from Boveri's.

A number of cases of merogony have been found in plants.   One of the best was reported by Kostoff, in which a triploid plant of *Nicotiana Tabacum* with 72 chromosomes was pollinated by the widely different *N. Langsdorfii*, with a diploid number of 18.   Most of the offspring were hybrids and short-lived.   The only one that developed to maturity resembled *N. Langsdorfii* (the male parent) exactly, save for its smaller size, and was found to have 9 chromosomes, closely resembling those of this species.   It had evidently arisen from an egg of *Tabacum* where the nucleus had been inactivated or destroyed and in which the complement of *Langsdorfii* chromosomes alone had persisted.   Here the cytoplasm seems to have had no effect at all upon the character of the offspring.

There are a number of other instances among seed plants where, from a cross between widely different species, or even genera, offspring have arisen which exactly resemble the male parent and which have transmitted their traits to their offspring.   However, in a cross between two genera of the higher fungi as reported by Harder, there is evidence of some cytoplasmic effect.   Here "male" and "female" gametes both contribute nucleus and cytoplasm.   From a conjugant cell, before nuclear fusion, Harder removed the female nucleus by micromanipulation and then effected another sexual fusion with a male gamete.   Thus nuclei from only one genus developed in cytoplasm furnished by both.   Certain characters of the resulting plant seemed to show some influence of the cytoplasm, but sex, the most definite trait, was clearly controlled by the nucleus.

The evidence, both from reciprocal crosses and from merogony, as to the existence of a definite hereditary mechanism in the cytoplasm, is therefore conflicting.   As to certain plastid characters in plants, the occurrence of cytoplasmic inheritance and the mechanism for its operation

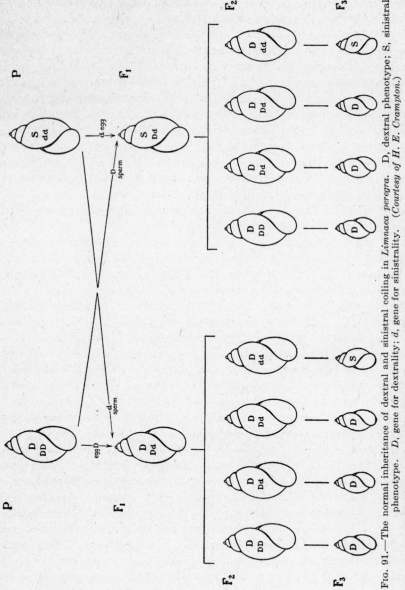

Fig. 91.—The normal inheritance of dextral and sinistral coiling in *Limnaea peregra*. D, dextral phenotype; S, sinistral phenotype. D, gene for dextrality; d, gene for sinistrality. (*Courtesy of H. E. Crampton.*)

seem clearly established. In other cases the situation is not clear, though in several the evidence for cytoplasmic transmission is strong.

The fact that the vast majority of traits thus far studied are clearly controlled by genes suggests the possibility that these apparent exceptions are merely cases where the genic control is masked in some way. Incompatibilities between genes and cytoplasm, as in von Wettstein's mosses, may explain some cases. Selective elimination of gametes or selective fertilization, both of which are known to occur occasionally, may explain others. More important than either, probably, are the instances where admitted differences in the egg cytoplasm, which markedly affect the development of the offspring, can be shown to be due to the influence upon the egg cytoplasm, before reduction, of the genes of the mother.

Early Effects of Maternal Genes.—A notable instance of this is the inheritance of direction of coiling in the shells of snails. Many species of snails are known in which the shell always coils to the right (dextral) and many others in which it coils to the left (sinistral). In a few species both dextral and sinistral individuals occur. In one (*Limnaea peregra*) dextrality appears to behave as a simple dominant to sinistrality, as shown by the breeding experiments of Boycott, Diver, and Garstang, as interpreted by Sturtevant. The character of the coiling, however, is determined not by the individual's own genes but by those of its mother. Some of these snails which are themselves phenotypical dextrals produce all sinistral offspring; and such individuals by appropriate genetic tests may be shown to be homozygous for the recessive sinistral gene. Their dextral character must have been determined by the presence of a dextral gene in *their* mothers (Fig. 91). This shows that it is not the "character" of the mother but her genes which impress upon the cytoplasm of all her eggs before maturation a certain type of pattern which finds expression during the early cleavage divisions of the egg. The direction of coiling in snail's shells had previously been shown by Crampton, Conklin, and others to be determined by the orientation of the spindle at the second (possibly at the first) cleavage division. In the sinistral type the spindle is tipped toward the left of the median line; in the dextral type, toward the right (Fig. 92). This is in turn determined by some relationship of the egg to the mother before maturation. This gene thus acts on the eggs in the ovary, influencing the direction of an early cell division and thus the type of asymmetry and the pattern of the future individual. It is expressed in the cytoplasm and has no relation to the particular genes that may be carried either in the egg nucleus or in that of the sperm.

In snails it is also known that another character of the shell which appears later in development is determined by the genetic constitution of the embryo itself as in ordinary inheritance. Colored striping or banding of the shell acts as a simple recessive to plain or unbanded shell, and reciprocal crosses between these types give the same result in F_1. This character is apparently determined after the early cleavages have taken place, and the genes brought in by the sperm exert their full influence at this time.

Such cases as the inheritance of coiling in snails show how maternal inheritance and the dissimilarity of reciprocal crosses may be due to an effect of maternal genes in the egg cytoplasm which simulates true cytoplasmic inheritance. Such effects doubtless occur in many other instances

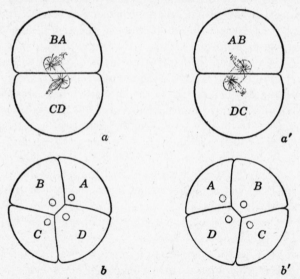

FIG. 92.—Above, the first cleavage stage in a snail, showing position of spindles for next cleavage division in left-handed (sinistral) cleavage (a) and right-handed (dextral) cleavage (a'). Below, same after cleavage; b, sinistral type, b', dextral type. (*After Morgan.*)

where they are more transient and do not become embodied in a permanent structure like the shell. Cytoplasmic differentiation in the egg is known to have an important influence on development, and the localization of different materials in various regions is clearly related to the pattern of embryonic differentiation which later follows. The polarity and symmetry shown by the young embryo are evidently determined in the cytoplasm of the egg from which it grows, as are also such physiological characters as the rate of cleavage; and in these early traits the influence of the male gamete which fertilizes the egg is negligible. It seems rather unlikely that such traits as these are controlled by a specific mechanism carried in the cytoplasm when they can be explained equally well as early induction effects of maternal genes brought about before the reduction division. Such an hypothesis may explain some of the cases of cytoplasmic inheritance which have been described above.

The problem of the extent and importance of cytoplasmic inheritance is evidently still far from solution. If the plasmon is held to govern the development of only those characters that have their physical basis in the cytoplasm, like the plastids, there can be no doubt of its existence. Whether there are independent determiners for other characters in the cytoplasm must still be regarded as an open question. At any rate, nucleus and cytoplasm are intimately associated and cannot be thought of as strictly independent systems. The nucleus doubtless affects the chemical and physical character of the cytoplasm in many ways, and the cytoplasm constitutes the most immediate and intimate part of the environment in which the genes operate. The very important role of the cytoplasm in the origin of differentiation and in development is universally recognized. That it plays a part in hereditary transmission is also clear; but that this part is a relatively minor one and clearly subsidiary to the dominant genic mechanism in the nucleus seems to be the safest conclusion from the evidence at present available.

REFERENCES

BOVERI, T. 1918. Zwei Fehlerquellen bei Merogonieversuchen und die Entwicklungsfähigkeit merogonischer und partiell-merogonischer Seeigelbastarde. Arch. Entw.-Mech. **44.**

BOYCOTT, A. E., C. DIVER, and S. L. GARSTANG. 1929. Inheritance of sinistrality in *Limnaea peregra*. Phil. Trans. Roy. Soc. London *B*, **219.**

CORRENS, C. 1928. Über nichtmendelnde Vererbung. Zeitschr. Ind. Abst. Vererb. Suppl. Bd. **1.**

EAST, E. M. 1934. The nucleus-plasma problem. Amer. Nat. **68.**

HADORN, E. 1937. Die entwicklungsphysiologische Auswirkung der disharmonischen Kern-Plasmakombination beim Bastardmerogon *Triton palmatus* (♀) × *Triton cristatus* ♂. Arch. Entw-Mech. **136.**

HARDER, R. 1927. Zur Frage nach der Rolle von Kern und Protoplasma im Zellgeschehen und bei der Übertragung von Eigenschaften. Zeitschr. Botanik **19.**

KOSTOFF, D. 1929. An androgenic Nicotiana haploid. Zeitschr. Zellforsch. **9.**

LEHMANN, E., and J. SCHWEMMLE. 1927. Genetische Untersuchungen in der Gattung Epilobium. Bibliotheca Botanica **95.**

MICHAELIS, P. 1933. Entwicklungsgeschichtlich-genetische Untersuchungen an Epilobium. Zeitschr. Ind. Abst. Vererb. **65.**

RENNER, O., and W. KUPPER. 1921. Artkreuzungen in der Gattung Epilobium. Ber. Deutsch. Bot. Ges. **39.**

RHOADES, M. M. 1933. The cytoplasmic inheritance of male sterility in *Zea mays*. Jour. Genetics **27.**

STURTEVANT, A. H. 1933. Inheritance of direction of coiling in Limnaea. Science **58.**

VON WETTSTEIN, F. 1924. Morphologie und Physiologie des Formwechsels der Moose auf genetischer Grundlage. Zeitschr. Ind. Abst. Vererb. **33.**

PROBLEMS

317. How would you distinguish between "maternal" and "cytoplasmic" inheritance?

318. Cases like that of variegation in *Pelargonium zonale*, which are determined by the cytoplasm but inherited through both parents, show no clear segregation as in Mendelian inheritance. Explain.

319. How would it be possible to determine whether the chloroplast differences in cases of variegation are due to two types of chloroplasts or to a diseased condition of some of the plastids?

320. In what respects do cases of cytoplasmic inheritance resemble those of sex-linked inheritance? In what respects do they differ?

321. How could you explain Hadorn's results with Triton without assuming cytoplasmic inheritance?

322. If an infectious disease were to be transmitted from mother to offspring through the egg, how would you distinguish this from cytoplasmic inheritance?

323. Castle has maintained that body size in mice is due in part to factors not in the chromosomes. State two sources of evidence which could be used to test the truth of this hypothesis.

324. How might it be possible to distinguish between true cytoplasmic inheritance and the induction of a cytoplasmic change by a gene before reduction?

325. In the case of a plant which is a true-breeding heterozygote because of balanced lethals (as are many races of Oenothera and other plants), what indication of this condition could be easily recognized without performing a breeding experiment?

326. From the cross of a homozygous banded, dextral-shelled female snail by an unbanded, sinistral male (p. 251) describe the F_1, F_2, and F_3 generations from self fertilization, giving genotypes and phenotypes.

327. What progeny should be expected from (a) a cross of F_1 female from Problem 326 by a banded, dextral male; (b) a cross of F_1 female from Problem 326 by an unbanded, sinistral male?

CHAPTER XI

THE DETERMINATION OF SEX

The essential feature of sexual reproduction is the union of two *different* gametes. In animals and the higher plants the two types of gametes are markedly different in morphology and behavior, the male gametes being relatively small and ordinarily motile; the female, larger and less active. In many of the lower plants, however, the two types of gametes do not differ in form or size but show clearly defined *physiological* differences. Sexual union occurs only between gametes belonging to unlike physiological types.

Sex in Animals.—In most of the species of higher animals a given individual produces either male or female gametes, but not both, so that a sharp distinction appears between male and female individuals. Furthermore, sexual reproduction, as one of the major functions of the organism, involves not only the specialized sexual structures themselves but the coordination of all the parts. The fundamental sexual difference is, therefore, usually accompanied by a marked diversity between male and female in size, general metabolism, instincts, and structures involved in mating or fertilization; and in such characters as combs, horns, hair, and plumage in vertebrate animals, the development of which is influenced by the presence of functioning sexual glands. The distinction between male and female in animals is thus usually far more profound than that between two individuals differing in one of the comparatively minor traits which, because of ease of observation, have been the subject of breeding experiments. Hermaphroditism, or the production of both male and female gametes by the same individual, occurs regularly in a few animal species and as an anomaly in some others, but the separation of the sexes is an outstanding feature of higher animals.

In the protozoa it has not been possible to speak of differentiated sexes in the same terms as those used for the metazoa, but the recent work of Sonneborn shows that in certain races of Paramecium two physiologically different types of individuals occur; and that these differences are inherited and sex determined in a manner analogous to that found in the higher animals.

Sex in Plants.—In plants the situation is more complex owing to the occurrence in the life cycle of two distinct generations: a haploid *gametophyte* bearing sex organs, alternating with a diploid nonsexual *sporophyte* which produces spores. This type of life history has now been demonstrated in all but the very simplest plants (p. 269). In most of the higher seed plants both types of gametophytes are borne on the same sporophyte and even in the same flower, so that the sporophytic individual is bisexual or hermaphroditic. In some species, however, male and female gametophytes are borne on separate plants, and such dioecious forms may thus be said to be sexually distinct. Even here, the differences between male and female individuals extend usually only to the character of the floral parts, although recent evidence indicates that there may be physiological or chemical differences between the sexes as well.

The sex difference in plants, at least in sporophytes, is thus less sharply marked than in animals. The tendency of most higher plants to be hermaphroditic, the numerous intergradations between this condition and a unisexual one, the frequent irregularities in male and female parts, and their susceptibility to change under altered environmental conditions make the problem of sex determination and differentiation in plants a difficult and complex one. Although the fundamental mechanisms involved are probably similar to those in animals, we shall, in what follows, first define the problems and discuss the theories of sex determination derived from studies of animals and later relate these as far as is possible to sex determination in plants.

Problems.—The first problem is to explain the occurrence in animals of two different types of individuals: males and females. The sexual differences are, in general, sharp and discontinuous; they indicate profound differences between members of the same species, even between brothers and sisters whose heredity must in nearly all other respects be very similar. What determines the fact that one of these individuals will be a male and produce sperms, while another develops as a female and produces eggs? These two kinds of individuals among the higher animals are usually produced in approximately equal numbers and fall into distinct alternative classes. These facts suggest the operation of some exact mechanism in inheritance. The problem of finding the mechanism by which this primary difference between the sexes originates we shall call the problem of *sex determination*.

The second problem arises from the first. Granted that there is an exact process in reproduction which accounts for the *origin* of two sexually different types of zygotes, how does this primary difference lead to the profound and widespread divergence between the mature male and female individuals? This—the problem of *sex differentiation*—is chiefly concerned with what happens during development. Since, however, our information concerning sexual differences has been drawn chiefly from observation of adult or developed characters, as is the case with most of the differences on which the theories of genetics rest, variations in the sexual "characters" may give us new and valuable information concerning the primary sex difference itself.

The Chromosome Mechanism of Sex Determination.—Two discoveries of prime importance for the problem of sex determination have already been mentioned (p. 173). One of these was the disclosure of a difference in chromosome constitution between male and female animals, and this has recently been extended to several species of dioecious plants. The other was the proof that *sex-linked* genes are located in the sex chromosome and that they thus identify the offspring receiving this chromosome so that its distribution to the gametes and progeny may be inferred from genetic evidence. These discoveries showed that the pri-

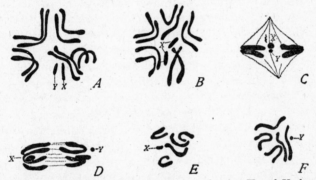

Fig. 93.—The chromosomes of a fly (Calliphora) showing X and Y chromosomes in *A*, spermatogonia; *B*, oogonia; *C*, and *D*, first spermatocyte (reduction) division; *E*, and *F*, X and Y spermatocytes after reduction. (*From The Cell in Development and Heredity, by E. B. Wilson, 3d ed., copyright 1925 by the Macmillan Company. Reprinted by permission.*)

mary sexual difference is inherited like other Mendelian traits and brought the problem definitely into the field of genetics.

Sex Chromosomes.—About the time of the rediscovery of Mendel's laws it was shown that in certain insects there are two kinds of sperms, produced in equal numbers, one of which has an extra or *accessory* chromosome that is lacking in the other. The suggestion was made by McClung (1902) that this chromosomal difference in the male gametes is in some way related to the determination of sex and that eggs fertilized by one type of sperm produced males and by the other type produced females. Such accessory chromosomes came to be known as the *sex chromosomes*, as distinguished from the others or *autosomes*, which are present equally in both sexes (Fig. 93).

The chromosomal constitution of the body cells and gametes in many species of animals at once became the subject of investigation. A considerable number of cases in insects and mammals were found in which there are two types of sperm, only one possessing the accessory chromosome; and this chromosome, often single and unpaired and usually distinguishable from the others, was recognized in the body cells of male individuals.

In many species of insects (such as Drosophila), in all of the mammals which have been investigated, in many fish and amphibia, and in several dioecious plants (such as Melandrium), the females have two X chromosomes, the males but one. In most of these species, the males have another peculiar chromosome, the so-called Y chromosome, which acts as a mate to the X, although it is probably not exactly equivalent or homologous to it. The females may therefore be described as XX individuals; the males, as XO or more commonly XY. At the reduction division in the female the two X chromosomes pair and disjoin, one going to each pole, so that all the eggs are alike, each containing an X chromosome. In the male the reduction division separates the two members of the XY pair, one member going to each pole, so that two kinds of sperms (male heterogamety) are formed in equal numbers, half with X, and half with Y. In males with an X but no Y the X passes at random to one pole or the other, so that half the sperm have an X and half have none. Fertilization of an X egg by an X sperm produces an XX individual which ordinarily develops into a female; fertilization of an X egg by a Y sperm (or an O sperm) produces an XY (or XO) individual which becomes a male. The sex of the offspring in these species thus seems to be determined at fertilization by the kind of sperm which fertilizes the egg, and since the two kinds of sperm are produced (by chance assortment of the single X at the reduction division) in equal numbers and fertilization takes place at random, equal numbers of male and female zygotes are generally produced. The following scheme summarizes this type of sex determination:

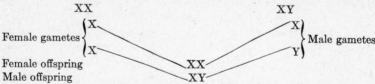

BODY CELLS OF THE FEMALE PARENT   BODY CELLS OF THE MALE PARENT
                XX   XY

Female gametes { X   X } Male gametes
               { X   Y }
Female offspring   XX
Male offspring   XY

In several other animals, including a few species of moths, birds, and fish, the *females* are XY or XO, and *males* XX. Here two kinds of eggs are produced in equal numbers, half with X and half without, while the sperms are all alike, each containing X. The X eggs fertilized by X sperm produce XX individuals or males; the Y or O eggs produce XY or XO individuals or females. Sex is thus ordinarily determined by the type of egg from which the new individual arises.

In both cases the sex of the offspring is determined by the chromosomal constitution of the uniting gametes.

Thus in many instances the sexual difference seems to depend on the presence of one or of two sex chromosomes. In a few other cases the sexes appear to differ by a whole set of chromosomes, the females being diploid and arising from fertilized eggs, the males being haploid and arising from parthenogenetic eggs. Apart from these facts little is known about this mode of sex determination. It will be discussed briefly later in this chapter (p. 268.)

The Balance Theory of Sex.—Although the simple, diagrammatic method of sex determination described above seems to explain adequately the ordinarily sharp segregation of the two sexes, their production in equal numbers, and the numerous differences between them (since they differ in a whole chromosome), it proved quite inadequate to explain certain cases in which these usual accompaniments of the sex difference were present in modified form. In a number of species of animals there have appeared, in addition to normal males and females, peculiar individuals which are neither typical males nor typical females but have some male and some female characters which may be so intimately mixed as to give their possessors the appearance of being true intermediates between maleness and femaleness. Goldschmidt, who has studied the laws governing the appearance of such individuals in the gypsy moth, *Lymantria dispar*, has called them "intersexes" (Fig. 94). Such forms, which have been found in many species of insects (especially in species hybrids) and in worms, Crustacea, and several classes of vertebrates, have all degrees of mixture of male and female characteristics, both in the external characters and genitalia as well as in the sexual organs themselves. Near one extreme, in the Lymantria series, are nearly female individuals with traces of male characteristics in one or a few parts; near the opposite end are nearly normal males with a slight admixture of female traits. At the ultimate extremes are females which are known from other evidence to have begun their existence as genetic males (XX individuals in this case), that is, their sex has been reversed; and at the other extreme end are sex-reversed males which began as genetic females (XY). How can the occurrence of such individuals be reconciled with the theory that sex is determined at fertilization by the chance distribution of X and Y chromosomes to different gametes and different individuals? This theory provides for only two alternatives, that is, XX or XY, whereas in cases of intersexuality there appear to be several additional and intermediate possibilities.

In Lymantria.—The first of these series of intersexes to be thoroughly studied was that which occurs in the gypsy moth. Goldschmidt found that when certain European races of this insect were crossed with other races from Japan, intersexes always appeared among the descendants, even though each race when bred pure produced only normal males and females. The production and appearance of intersexes followed certain

Fig. 94.—Series of female intersexes in *Lymantria dispar*, from normal female (above) through increasing grades of maleness to sex reversed male (lower right). (*From Goldschmidt.*)

regular rules depending on the male and female parents used in the cross. The main features of his results can best be shown in tabular form as follows:

Cross	Parents	Sons	Daughters
1	European "weak" ♀ × Japanese "strong" ♂..................	Normal	Intersexual
2	Japanese "strong" ♀ × European "weak" ♂.................	Normal	Normal
3	F₂ from cross 1...................	Normal	½ normal, ½ intersexual
4	F₂ from cross 2...................	½ normal, ½ intersex.	Normal

These and other crosses leave no doubt that the tendency to form intersexes is inherited in a regular manner. In moths, in general, the males are XX, the females XY; and within pure races this sex chromosome constitution is decisive. In crosses between races which produce intersexes, however, two further variables have to be taken into account; one is a factor for maleness in the sex chromosome which has different strengths, that is, presumably occurs in different allelic forms, in different races; the other is an influence tending in the opposite direction toward femaleness, also varying in different races, and this seems to be inherited through the cytoplasm of the eggs, that is, all the eggs of an individual are alike with respect to the strength of this tendency. The sexual condition of the offspring of crosses is decided by the relative strengths or *balance* existing between these two opposed tendencies. This interpretation is supported by extensive evidence from many interracial crosses.

Goldschmidt and his coworkers have also proposed a mechanism by which these sex genes influence the development of the sexual characters. The essential assumptions here, as found first in the worm Bonellia, established by a careful study of the embryological development of Lymantria and later extended to Drosophila, are that intersexes in these forms begin their development as males (or females) and develop as such up to a certain critical point, the so-called "turning point," after which their development is of the opposite sexual type. The mixture of male and female parts is thus explained as due to the supersession of one type of sex tendency by the other. Sex development is conceived as essentially a competition between opposed tendencies in which the race is eventually won by that type of process (either male or female) which proceeds most rapidly at the critical period of determination of each organ or part involved.

Intersexes and Supersexes in Drosophila.—A similar indication that sex is the result of a ratio or balance between male-determining and female-determining agencies has been found by Bridges in *Drosophila melanogaster.* He discovered a strain which produced, in addition to normal males and females, a large percentage of intersexes. These, like the Lymantria intersexes, consist of mixtures of male and female characters both in the external genitalia and secondary sex characters and in the primary sex organs themselves (Figs. 95 and 96). They are extremely variable, ranging from male-like to female-like, although nearly all of them have the sex comb on the forelegs, which is characteristic of males. All of them are entirely sterile. When examined cytologically, they were found to have *three* of each autosome (II, III, and IV) but only *two* X chromosomes. The mothers which produced such flies were found to be complete triploids, that is, they had *three* X's and *three* of each autosome, or twelve in all. Their sexual characters were completely female, although they could be identified by certain somatic traits such as large, coarse eyes and large body size.

Bridges' interpretation of these facts follows:

The intersexes and $3n$ (triploid) types lead to the conclusion that sex in *Drosophila melanogaster* is determined by the autosomes as well as by the X chromosomes, the ratio of autosomes to X's being the significant relation. The old formulation of $2X = ♀$ is at once seen to be inadequate; for here we have individuals with two X chromosomes and yet [they] are not females. They are shifted out of the female class by the presence of an extra set of autosomes, and thereby the autosomes are proved to play a positive role in the production of sex. Since the intersexes differ from females by the assumption of certain male characters, this effect of the autosomes is due to an internal preponderance

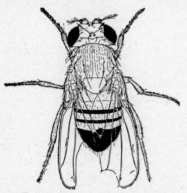 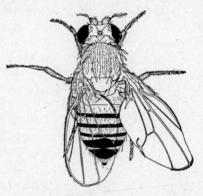

Fig. 95.—Male-type intersex (2X:3A) in *Drosophila melanogaster*. (*From Bridges.*)

Fig. 96.—Female-type intersex (2X:3A) in *Drosophila melanogaster*. (*From Bridges.*)

of "male-tendency" genes. We may now reformulate the sex relation as follows: Both sexes are due to the simultaneous action of two opposed sets of genes, one set tending to produce the characters called female and the other to produce the characters called male. These two sets of genes are not equally effective, for in the (chromosome) complement as a whole the female tendency genes outweigh the male and the diploid (or triploid) form is female. The male-tendency genes in the autosomes are more numerous or more effective than those in the X chromosome, while the net effect of genes in the X chromosome is a tendency to the production of female characters. When in a diploid zygote the relative effectiveness of the female-tendency genes is lowered by the absence of one X, the male-tendency genes outweigh the female, and the result is the normal male. When the two sets of genes are acting in a ratio between these two extremes, as in the case in the ratio of 2X:3 sets of autosomes (2X:3A), the result is a sex intermediate—the intersex.

Further breeding of the triploid females produces an array of sex types, in which the grade of development of male and female characters was found to be correlated with the ratio between the number of X chromosomes and the number of autosomes present (Fig. 97).

Thus a sterile female type has been recognized, with abnormally developed ovaries and female characters modified. This has been

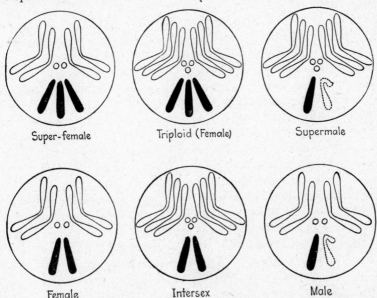

FIG. 97.—Effect on sex of the balance between X-chromosomes (solid) and autosomes (outlined) in *Drosophila melanogaster*.

called "superfemale" and has been shown to have three X chromosomes and two sets of autosomes (3X:2A); the preponderance of female genes in the three X's over the male genes in the autosomes is more marked

TABLE XX.—SEXUAL TYPES IN *Drosophila melanogaster* (*After Bridges*)

Sex	X chromosomes	Sets of autosomes (A)	Sex index (ratio X/A)
Superfemale..........................	3	2	1.5
Normal female {tetraploid.............	4	4	1.0
triploid...............	3	3	1.0
diploid...............	2	2	1.0
haploid[1].............	1	1	1.0
Intersex............................	2	3	0.67
Normal male.......................	1	2	0.50
Supermale.........................	1	3	0.33

[1] A whole individual of this type has not yet been obtained, but patches of tissue with one X and one of each autosome have been found in diploid flies. These patches show female characters.

than in the normal female with two X's, and this is reflected in a modification of the female characters. Conversely sterile "supermales," with male characters exaggerated, have been found to have one X and three sets of autosomes. A summary of the various sexual types is given in Table XX.

In this table it is clear that the ratio between the number of X chromosomes and the number of autosomes determines the sexual character. All types with a ratio of 1X:1A are females, regardless of the actual number of chromosomes; those with a ratio of 1X:2A are males; an intermediate ratio produces intersexes; a lower one, supermales; and ratios above 1 result in superfemales.

Intersexuality thus results from disturbances in the normal number of chromosomes, whereas in Lymantria it occurs in what are probably normal diploid individuals. The *Drosophila melanogaster* type may then be called *triploid* intersexuality.

In the case of *melanogaster* it is probable that the genes affecting sexual characters are multiple. Their distribution in all four chromosomes is evidence of this fact, although it might be objected that a single differentiator of sex might still be present in the X. This possibility has been tested by Dobzhansky and Schultz, who have studied the effect of the addition of fragments of X chromosome of various lengths (obtained from translocations, p. 231) to the usual 2X:3A chromosome group of intersexes. The results showed that the intersexes containing an additional fragment of the X chromosome are more female-like than those without the fragment and that the longer the fragment of the X added the greater the shift in the type of the intersexes toward the female. Female effect is therefore proportional to *amount* of X chromosome, which must mean that female-tendency genes are present in all parts of the X studied, that is, that they are multiple genes. This makes it probable that the balance which determines sex in Drosophila is reached through the action of many sex genes and not through two genes only which vary in strength or valency, as supposed by Goldschmidt.

In spite of this difference in interpretation of the genetic basis of sex as between Lymantria and Drosophila, the manner in which the balance or ratio affects development of sexual characters is remarkably similar in the two species. It has been shown by Dobzhansky and Bridges that the triploid intersexes begin as males and develop as such up to a certain point, after which they develop as females. When this turning point comes early in development, both the earlier and later appearing sexual parts are converted into the female type, so that an individual very like a normal female, except for fertility, results.[1] When the turn-

[1] In fact one intersex with an additional fragment of X chromosome (about 2½X/3A) was fertile; complete functional sex reversal had occurred presumably very early in development.

ing point comes later in development, only those characters which differentiate last are affected, and a male-type intersex with traces of female characters is produced.

If the location of the turning point in time determines the degree of development of sex characters, then any agency which makes this turning point occur earlier in development should make Drosophila intersexes more female-like. High temperature probably has this effect, as Dobzhansky has shown.

Thus it appears that in both the case of Lymantria and of Drosophila (the most adequately analyzed cases) sex is determined to start in either a male or female direction by the genetic nature of the gametes which unite at fertilization. The final outcome as judged by the *characters* of the adult individual, however, is affected by many conditions and interactions during development. One important condition is the relative excess of one type of gene over the other; the greater the excess the earlier are the developmental processes affected. Other important influences doubtless come from the external environment, such as differences in temperature. The appearance in most species of animals of two sharply defined sexes means that there are probably two relatively stable points of equilibrium, one centering around maleness, the other around femaleness, and that in such cases the excess of one type of gene over the other is considerable and decisive in the earliest stages of development. The decision is usually given by the presence of two sex chromosomes in one set of individuals and by but one in the other. The role of a sex chromosome in determining sex is therefore like that of a weight added to either one side or the other of a scale; it tips the balance and only thus decides the outcome, and it probably does this by virtue of the specific genes which it carries.

Intersexes have also been studied in *Drosophila virilis* by Lebedeff but here the situation differs from that in Lymantria and from *D. melanogaster*. In *virilis* as in *melanogaster* the sex chromosome mechanism is XX = female, XY = male. A single gene in chromosome III appears to have no phenotypic effect in males but when homozygous in females causes them to develop into sterile males. When other modifying genes are present in such females, sex reversal is incomplete and both male and female parts are produced, resulting in hermaphrodites.

In the common aquarium fish, *Lebistes reticulatus*, Winge has also found sex reversal and intersexuality due to mutant genes acting within the normal chromosome constitution. Here the sex chromosome mechanism is as in Drosophila, XX = female, XY = male. A few exceptional males were found which were XX, that is, they were sex-reversed females. They were fertile and when crossed with normal females (XX) produced only daughters. By continued back crossing of these and their descendants to the XX males a race was obtained in which all individuals were

XX; nevertheless both sexes were produced because one pair of autosomes in the female was heterozygous for a sex-determining factor of major importance. This autosome, therefore, had become effectively a new sex chromosome, and in this race the many color and pattern genes in the former sex chromosome, X, no longer showed sex-linkage but ordinary autosomal inheritance. Sex reversal in the opposite direction has also occurred in Lebistes; that is, XY females have been found. These when crossed with normal XY males give ratios of 3 males (XY, XY, YY):1 female. Here, unlike Drosophila, YY males are viable.

Winge's interpretation is that the X chromosome in Lebistes has predominantly female-tendency genes, the Y has predominantly male tendency, while certain autosomes have female, others male, influence. The balance is usually tipped by the X chromosomes, XX being female, XY male. However, in cases like the above, mutations in autosomes can be decisive for sex and thus an autosome may assume the role of the X chromosome.

Genetic Control of Sex Ratio.—Not only may the degree of development of the sexual characters be altered by gene mutations, as in the above cases, but the ratio in which the sexes are produced is also under genic control. The effect of sex-linked lethals on the sex ratio has already been mentioned. Still another way in which the ratio may be altered has been demonstrated recently by Sturtevant and Dobzhansky. Certain males of *Drosophila pseudoobscura* have been found to give offspring consisting almost entirely of daughters, regardless of the nature of the female to which they have been mated. Such males have been found to contain a mutation "sex ratio," *sr*, in the X chromosome, the effect of which is to cause the X chromosome to undergo an equational division at meiosis and the Y chromosome to degenerate, so that only X-containing sperm are produced. The gene is without effect in females. The distribution of this gene in a population is obviously an important factor in determining the relative frequency of males and females.

Gynanders.—Occasionally two types of tissue, male and female, may coexist in the same individual, each type developing according to its own genetic constitution, resulting in a sexual mosaic or gynander. These are often male on one side and female on the other (bilateral gynanders). In many of these the autosomal characters known to have been transmitted to the fly appear in all parts of the gynander. On the male side appear the sex-linked characters received from *either* the mother *or* the father; while the characters of the female parts show the presence in these parts of both the maternal and paternal X chromosomes, as though one of the X chromosomes had been eliminated from the male parts, leaving them XO (which is known to produce maleness, p. 173) while the female parts are XX. Such a gynander appears to have begun development as a female (XX) and at some early cell division to have lost one of the X chromosomes from part of the tissues.

In silkworms gynandromorphism has appeared as an inherited condition which segregates as though due to a single gene, which also determines the production of somatic mosaics (Fig. 98). The gynanders arise from eggs with *two* nuclei, one XX from which the male parts descend; the other XY, which gives rise to the female parts. Somatic mosaics result when one nucleus is, for example, *Aa*, and the other, *aa*. These two diploid nuclei arise from the retention of one polar-body nucleus and fertilization of both this and the egg nucleus by different

FIG. 98.—Mosaic silkworm larvæ. (*From Goldschmidt and Katsuki.*)

sperms; and this peculiarity, determined by the action of one gene, may result in individuals mosaic for sexual or somatic characters or both. Aside from the intrinsic interest attaching to the successful analysis of so complex a case (carried out by Goldschmidt, Katsuki, Tanaka, and others) it shows clearly that in some animals, at least, the balance which determines sex is decided within the individual tissues, which develop thereafter each according to its own genetic constitution. In vertebrates, where correlating mechanisms such as hormones prevent the isolation of tissues, so clear-cut a case is hardly to be expected. In such forms as Habrobracon and the honeybee in which males are haploid, females diploid, gynanders develop from binucleate eggs. One nucleus is fertilized and gives rise to female parts, the other unfertilized gives rise to male parts. The female parts therefore inherit from both parents, the male parts inherit from the mother alone.

Sex Determination in Hymenoptera.—In ants, bees, and wasps parthenogenesis is widespread. Males have never been known in nature to develop from fertilized eggs. Females usually arise from fertilized eggs, but in some species alternation of generations occurs, a bisexual generation from unfertilized eggs alternating with a female generation from fertilized eggs. In other species no males are known and females produce females indefinitely by parthenogenesis. Females are always diploid, even though they develop parthenogenetically. Males are haploid, and all sperms from any one male are alike, no matter how mixed the race from which he comes.

In the parasitic wasp *Habrobracon juglandis*, Whiting has shown by means of many mutant genes that its heredity resembles that of the honeybee. A recessive female crossed with a dominant male produces recessive males and dominant females; but in this case the males are from unfertilized eggs, and there is no constant sex ratio to be expected. An old mated female that has used up her supply of sperm or an unmated female produces only males.

If the parents are closely related, a few sons appear which, unlike their normal haploid brothers, have fathers, for they show the dominant traits of both parents. These biparental males have 20 chromosomes like their sisters instead of 10 like their haploid brothers. They are highly inviable and fraternities in which they occur have very low egg hatchability.

Whiting has shown by means of the sex-linked factor for fused antennae that females are XY with two sets of autosomes and that normal males are either X or Y with one set of autosomes. The biparental diploid males are correspondingly XX or YY with two sets of autosomes. They are thus homozygous for sex genes rather than heterozygous, like females. Thus the problem of sex determination in this group is brought in line with ideas of genic balance.

A female heterozygous for fused (Fu X/fu Y) crossed with a fused male, fu X, for example, produces haploid wild type males (Fu X and Fu Y), fused males (fu Y and fu X), and biparental offspring as follows:

Males................ 9 wild type (Fu X/fu X); 1 fused (fu X/fu X)
Females.............. 1 wild type (Fu Y/fu X); 9 fused (fu Y/fu X)

About 10 per cent of crossing over occurs between fused and the sex-determining part of the chromosome pair, X and Y.

If the parents come from different stocks unrelated to each other, no biparental males occur, and all fertilized eggs are female producing. There is much better egg hatchability in this case as the poorly viable diploid males are replaced by females.   How this replacement is brought about is not yet understood.   Theories of selective fertilization, differential maturation, sex reversal, multiple alleles, and multiple factors have been suggested; but this part of the problem remains unsolved.

The Effects of Hormones.—The general theory of sex as the result of a balance between opposed tendencies has been successfully applied to the conditions found in many animals.   In the higher animals and especially in vertebrates the secondary products of the sex glands—the sex hormones—may very considerably alter the final characters.   In the fowl, for example, early removal of the ovary from a "determined" female may reverse some of the normal processes and result in the development of male comb, plumage, and behavior and even in the appearance of a testis.   An extreme case of sex reversal of this sort has been reported by Crew.   A hen, said to have laid fertile eggs, ceased laying, developed male comb and plumage, crowed, finally functioned as a male, and became the father of two chickens.   Its ovary had apparently been destroyed by disease and replaced by two testes.   A similar case has been reported in pigeons, and such reversals of sex are known to occur normally in certain amphibia, fish, and lower forms in which an individual may begin life as a functional female and later become a functional male.

The effect of early hormonal influence on sexual characters in cattle has been studied by Lillie and others, who have shown that where twins of *opposite* sex are born, one is a normal male while the other is usually a sterile female with many male-like traits—the so-called "freemartin." The evidence from early development shows that through anastomosis of blood vessels, the blood of one embryo, with its hormones, may enter the blood stream of the other.   In this case the male hormones seem to influence the development of the female embryo in a male direction.

Sex Determination in Plants.—The problem of sex in plants, as has been pointed out, is somewhat more complicated than in animals because of the occurrence of gametophytic and sporophytic generations, in each of which there may be varying degrees of sexual differentiation.   In general, differences associated with sex are less marked in plants than in animals and in many cases are entirely physiological in character.   Furthermore, many plants are clearly bisexual or hermaphroditic, and, at least among sporophytes, there may be every intergradation between this condition and strict unisexuality.   A study of sex in plants may therefore be expected to provide evidence as to the beginnings of both sex determination and sex differentiation in general.

Thallophytes.—Sexual reproduction is known to occur in all plants of this group above the blue-green algae and bacteria, but in many of the simpler forms the two sexes, as well as the gametes which they produce, are morphologically similar.   Blakeslee first showed that in such forms there may be a physiological differentiation of two types. In the bread molds (Mucor and its allies, the Mucorales) he found that zygospores (resulting from sexual fusion between hyphae) are sometimes produced by the union of hyphae from the same mycelium or individual. Such forms he termed *homothallic*. In most cases, however, zygospores are formed only when two distinct individuals (mycelia) come together; and in such cases the mycelia must be physiologically different as to sex, or *heterothallic*. Within a given heterothallic species it is possible to assign every individual to one of two types, arbitrarily designated as "plus" and "minus." Two plus individuals will not unite sexually, nor will two minus individuals, but when a plus and a minus mycelium are in contact, zygospores are produced by fusions between them. It is thus easily possible to determine the type of any unknown individual by growing it in contact with a known plus race and a known minus one. That there is a fundamental difference between these two types is also shown by recent biochemical studies involving the so-called Manoilov reaction, a very delicate test whereby it has been found possible to distinguish the blood of male from that of female animals and the tissues of staminate plants from those of pistillate ones. The plus and minus mucors react differently to this test, the former behaving like females and the latter like males, indicating a rather fundamental chemical difference between the two types.

The separation of the sexes following germination of the zygospore is not well understood. In some cases the sporangium which immediately develops is all of one sex, indicating that differentiation has taken place in the germinating zygospore itself; in others, both plus and minus spores are found in this sporangium.

Heterothallism is now known to occur in many other thallophytes, both algae and fungi. Thus in the unicellular alga Chlamydomonas, gametes must belong to different types if they are to unite. The filaments of Ulothrix and the gametes produced in them, although morphologically similar, have recently been shown by Gross to be sexually distinct, some being plus, some minus.

Many of the basidiomycetes have plus and minus uninucleate mycelia. Anastomoses between these give rise to a binucleate mycelium, which ultimately produces the sporophore. The two strains are probably separated again in the cell divisions immediately preceding the formation of the basidiospores, from which new uninucleate plus and minus mycelia again arise. More than two distinct types have been reported in a number of basidiomycetes.

The actual point in the life cycle at which sex determination takes place has been located much more definitely in some of the ascomycetes through the work of Dodge. In several species of Neurospora (the pink bread mold) the mycelia are uninucleate and thus presumably haploid and have been clearly shown to be heterothallic. Through fusion between two mycelia of opposite type, a diploid perithecium develops, and in this the asci or spore cases are produced. Each ascus is originally uninucleate, but in most species, by three successive divisions of this nucleus eight spores are ultimately produced. Since these spores

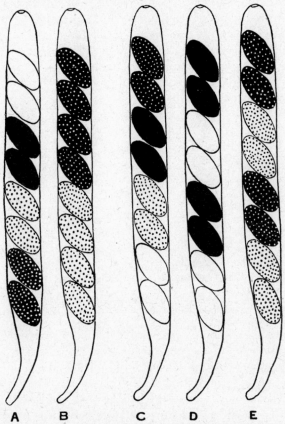

Fig. 99.—Segregation in asci of *Neurospora sitophila.* Black and white spores indicate segregation for sex; dotted and plain, that for presence or absence of conidia. Thus in *C*, segregation for sex occurred at the first division and for conidia formation at the second division. (*From Dodge.*)

retain their original order in the ascus, it is possible from their positions to determine the lineage of each and thus to distinguish the groups separated at the first, the second, and the third cell divisions in the ascus. By a delicate technique Dodge has been able to isolate each of the eight spores of an ascus and to grow from each a mycelium. When this is done, it is found that sometimes the first four spores (1, 2, 3, and 4 numbered from the bottom) give one sexual reaction (plus, let us say) and the other four (5, 6, 7, and 8) an opposite one, indicating that the segregation of the two sexual types was accomplished at the *first division* (Fig. 99, *B, C*). In other cases, however, spores 1, 2, 5, and 6 are plus, and 3, 4, 7, and 8 are minus, indicating that the products of the first division still possess both sexual potentialities and that these are not segregated until the *second division* (Fig. 99, *A, D, E*). Such a separation rarely occurs in the third division, apparently. It is interesting to note that a vegetative character, the production of conidia, may also segregate at the first or the second division and that it does so independently of the segregation for sex (Fig. 99). The chromosomal situation in these plants is unknown, but the genetic data would thus seem to indicate that hereditary potentialities are here sometimes segregated at the first division, sometimes at the second, and sometimes *at both.*

Fig. 100.—Chromosomes of Sphaerocarpos; from female gametophyte, above, and from male, below. Sex chromosomes indicated by X and Y. (*From Allen.*)

Bryophytes.—In some of the bryophytes both male and female sex organs are produced on the same plant (the gametophyte), and all the spores carry the potentialities of both sexes. Many other species, however, are clearly heterothallic, the plants all being either strictly male or strictly female. The Marchals have shown that in these cases about half the spores in a sporogonium (which arises from a fertilized egg) develop into male plants and about half into female ones, thus indicating that the segregation for sex takes place at spore formation. Regeneration experiments carried on by the Marchals and by Fritz von Wettstein have also shown that protonemata arising from any cell of a male plant will produce nothing but male plants, and from a female nothing but female ones; but that those regenerating from the tissue of the sporogonium (which is diploid) give rise to *bisexual plants.* Determiners for sex are thus sharply separated in the unisexual gametophytes, come together in the diploid sporophytes, and are again separated at sporogenesis, presumably by the meiotic divisions.

The first clear case of a chromosomal mechanism associated with sex determination in plants was also found in this group. In the heterothallic liverwort Sphaerocarpos, both Douin and Allen showed that the four spores resulting from the division of a single spore mother cell give rise to two female and two male gametophytes. Allen later found that in every cell of the female gametophyte there are seven chromosomes, evidently homologous with seven in the cells of the male gametophyte, and in addition one large X chromosome, the homologue of which, in the male, seemed to be a very much smaller Y chromosome (Fig. 100). The diploid sporophyte is thus $14A + X + Y$, the female gametophyte $7A + X$, and the male $7A + Y$. Here the segregation of the XY pair at meiosis parallels that of the sexes, suggesting that femaleness is associated with the X and maleness with the Y. These chromosomes evidently carry other determiners than those for sex, however, since Allen has found that the character of separate spores (as opposed to their persisting union in tetrads) is inherited only through the female parent and is thus presumably determined by a gene in the X chromosome, a condition comparable to that of a sex-linked trait in animals. Other examples of heterochromosomes associated with sex differences, though in a somewhat more complicated fashion, have been found among other liverworts.

Spermatophytes.—The great majority of seed plants have heterothallic gametophytes arising from two types of spores produced on the same sporophyte. The spore-bearing structures are now termed flowers, the microsporangia (bearing microspores or pollen grains) being borne on stamens and the megasporangia (bearing megaspores) on carpels. Among most species both these structures occur in the same flower, which is thus bisexual or hermaphroditic. In many cases, however, stamens and carpels are borne on different flowers but on the same plant, which is then termed *monoecious*. Numerous intermediate conditions between hermaphroditism and monoecism are known. It is significant that the sporophytic plant is capable of producing both microspores and megaspores, however these may be distributed among individual flowers; and that the primary sexual difference thus seems to be without a genetic basis but to arise in genetically identical material during the development of the sporogenous tissues.

Among a few of the seed plants the two types of spores are borne not only in different flowers but on different plants, the primary sexual difference, actually manifest in the gametophyte, thus being pushed back into the sporophyte, where it has a definite genetic basis. In such *dioecious* species it is possible to speak of "male" and "female" plants in the sense that they bear spores which will develop into male or female gametophytes, respectively.

The genetic difference between these two types was first studied by Correns in the early years of this century. In the genus Bryonia he found that if a female of *B. dioica*, which is dioecious, was pollinated by the monoecious species *B. alba*, all the offspring were female plants. If *B. alba*, on the contrary, was pollinated by *B. dioica*, about half the offspring were male and half were female. From this Correns inferred that in the dioecious species the eggs are of one sort as far as sex determination is concerned but that the male gametes are of two kinds, half male in tendency and half female. In other words, the male plant seems to be heterozygous for sex (XY) and the female homozygous (XX).

Fig. 101.—Adult rosettes of *Lychnis dioica;* on the left a plant of the normal form, *typica;* on the right a plant of the narrow-leaved form, *angustifolia.* (*From Shull.*)

Studies by Baur, Shull, Winge, and others on dioecious species of the genus Melandrium (Lychnis), a member of the pink family, still further strengthened this hypothesis by demonstrating several cases of sex-linked inheritance of the male-heterogametic type. Thus in the dioecious *Melandrium album* (*Lychnis dioica*) there is a broad-leaved form and a narrow-leaved one (Fig. 101). This difference is apparently due to a pair of genes (*Bb*) in the X chromosome. The narrow type is recessive and is lethal in pollen grains, the X*b* grains dying. Thus a female plant homozygous for broad leaves crossed with a narrow-leaved male will produce all broad-leaved male offspring:

$$(XB)(XB) \times (Xb)Y$$
$$(XB)Y \text{ broad-leaved male}$$
$$(XB)(Xb) \text{ not formed}$$

If the female parent is heterozygous, the offspring will likewise all be male, but half will be broad-leaved and half narrow-leaved. Thus:

$$(XB)(Xb) \times (Xb)Y$$
$(XB)(Xb)$ not formed
$(XB)Y$ broad-leaved male
$(Xb)(Xb)$ not formed
$(Xb)Y$ narrow-leaved male

A heterozygous female crossed with a broad-leaved male, on the contrary, produces both male and female offspring, the latter all broad-leaved, and the former half broad and half narrow, thus:

$$(XB)(Xb) \times (XB)Y$$
$(XB)(XB)$ broad-leaved female
$(XB)Y$ broad-leaved male
$(Xb)(XB)$ broad-leaved female
$(Xb)Y$ narrow-leaved male

Pollen   Ovule

Fig. 102.—Sex chromosomes in Melandrium.   (*After Bělař.*)

Winge has found other traits in this species which are inherited in somewhat the same fashion. These evidently conform in their essential features to the types of sex-linked inheritance found in Drosophila and many other animals.

The cytological basis for sex differences in dioecious plants has also been determined in many cases. Female plants of Melandrium, for example, have been shown to possess two large X chromosomes, and male plants an X and a much smaller Y (Fig. 102). A similar distribution of heterochromosomes has been found in over 50 other species of dioecious plants, as in Elodea, Rumex, and Humulus. In many other dioecious forms, however, such as Bryonia, there are no visible chromosome differences between the sexes.

Origin of Dioecious Maize (Fig. 103).—In a case investigated by Jones, the parts played by specific genes in determining the sexual type of the plant and the method of reproduction (monoecious or dioecious) have been disclosed. The maize plant is ordinarily monoecious, the terminal inflorescence (the tassel) being male, the lateral inflorescences with pistils, styles (silks), and stigmata being female. Mutant genes are known which suppress the development of the silks, and plants homozygous for such a gene function only as males; other mutant genes cause the production of female flowers and seeds in the tassel, and plants homozygous for such a gene function chiefly as females, although the

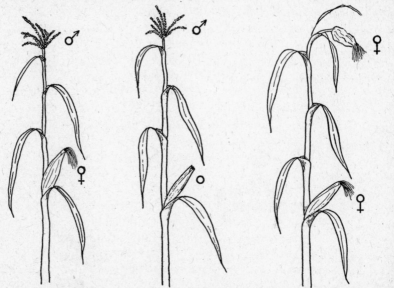

Fig. 103.—Normal hermaphroditic maize (left); silkless (male) center; tassel-seed (female) right.

tassel may also produce functional pollen. Jones crossed a silkless plant, *sk sk*, as male parent with tassel-seed plant, *ts ts*, as female. The F_1 plants, *Sk sk Ts ts*, were normal hermaphrodites with the usual tassels and cobs, that is, each mutant type contained the normal allele of the other and reversion to the normal monoecious condition occurred. When these F_1's were inbred, the F_2 consisted of normal hermaphrodites, silkless (male), and tassel-seed (female) plants in a ratio of 9 hermaphrodites:3 males:4 females. Breeding tests showed that the tassel-seed females were of three types: *Sk Sk ts ts*, *Sk sk ts ts*, and *sk sk ts ts*, that is, *sk* had no effect in the presence of *ts ts*. The results of crossing such double recessive females with silkless males heterozygous for *ts* produced exclusively males and females as shown below:

$$sk \; sk \; ts \; ts \; (♀) \times sk \; sk \; Ts \; ts \; (♂)$$

$$sk \; sk \; ts \; ts \; (♀); \; sk \; sk \; Ts \; ts \; (♂)$$

Continued breeding of these types gave always this clear segregation, that is, this stock had become dioecious. The differences between functionally male and functionally female plants in this family is determined by the segregation of a single gene pair *Ts ts*. Since *ts* is located in chromosome I, this chromosome has become in effect a sex chromosome, and since the male is heterozygous for the most effective locus in this chromosome, it resembles closely the male heterogamety found so frequently in animals and other dioecious plants. This is very similar to the assumption of sex-determining power by an autosome in Lebistes (p. 265).

Sex in Plants and Animals Compared.—Plants ordinarily are much less sharply differentiated as to sex than most animals, but in the essential features of sex determination the two groups seem to be fundamentally alike. In both there is evidently a balance between tendencies toward femaleness and tendencies toward maleness. In most animal individuals the balance has tipped definitely to one side or the other and, once established, is relatively constant, but it may be upset by changes in the genes or in the environment. In most plants there is a much more delicate equilibrium which is often subject to modification between different parts of the same plant and which, even in normally unisexual species, may be radically altered. The mechanism of heterochromosomes, so definitely associated with sex differentiation in animals, is relatively rare in plants, and many cases of sharp sex differences occur with no accompanying chromosome differences. There are enough instances of well-marked sex chromosomes in plants, however, so that we may feel sure that there is a similar relation between chromosomes and sex to that found in animals, even though it may often lack a morphological expression in the chromosomes themselves.

In both animals and plants, genetic modification of sexual characters may come about through the interaction of many genes, although under certain conditions one or few of these may play predominant roles.

REFERENCES

ALLEN, C. E. 1919. The basis of sex inheritance in Sphaerocarpos. Proc. Amer. Phil. Soc. **58.**

BAUR, E. 1912. Ein Fall von geschlechtesbegrenzter Vererbung bei *Melandrium album*. Zeitschr. Ind. Abst. Vererb. **8.**

BLAKESLEE, A. F. 1904. Sexual reproduction in the Mucorineae. Proc. Amer. Acad. **40.**

BRIDGES, C. B. 1925. Sex in relation to chromosomes and genes. Amer. Nat. **59.**

CORRENS, C. 1928. Bestimmung, Vererbung, und Verteilung des Geschlechtes bei den höheren Pflanzen. Handbuch der Vererbungswissenschaften 2. Berlin.

CREW, F. A. 1927. The genetics of sexuality in animals. Cambridge (England).

DOBZHANSKY, T. 1930. Genetical and environmental factors influencing the type of intersexes in Drosophila melanogaster. Amer. Nat. 64.

—— and J. SCHULTZ. 1931. Evidence for multiple sex factors in the X chromosome of Drosophila melanogaster. Proc. Nat. Acad. Sci. 17.

DODGE, B. O. 1931. Inheritance of the albinistic non-conidial character in interspecific hybrids in Neurospora. Mycologia 23.

GOLDSCHMIDT, R. 1931. Die sexuellen Zwischenstufen. Berlin.

JONES, D. F. 1934. Unisexual maize plants and their bearing on sex differentiation in other plants and in animals. Genetics 19 : 552–567.

LEBEDEFF, G. A. 1934. Genetics of hermaphroditism in Drosophila virilis. Proc. Nat. Acad. Sci. 20.

MORGAN, T. H. 1914. Heredity and sex. New York.

——. 1928. The theory of the gene. 2d ed. New Haven.

——, C. B. BRIDGES, and A. H. STURTEVANT. 1925. The genetics of Drosophila. Bibliographia Genetica 2.

SCHAFFNER, J. H. 1925. Sex determination and sex differentiation in the higher plants. Amer. Nat. 59.

SHULL, G. H. 1914. Sex-limited inheritance in Lychnis dioica. Zeitschr. Ind. Abst. Vererb. 12.

SONNEBORN, T. M. 1937. Sex, sex inheritance, and sex determination in Paramoecium aurelia. Proc. Nat. Acad. Sci. 23 : 378–385.

STURTEVANT, A. H., and DOBZHANSKY, T. 1936. Geographical distribution and cytology of sex-ratio in Drosophila pseudoobscura and related species. Genetics 21.

WHITING, P. W. 1935. Sex determination in bees and wasps. Jour. Hered. 26.

WINGE, O. 1931. X- and Y-linked inheritance in Melandrium. Hereditas 15.

——. 1934. The experimental alteration of sex chromosomes into autosomes and vice versa as illustrated by Lebistes. C. R. Lab. Carlsberg 21.

PROBLEMS

328. What prospect is there for influencing the sex of unborn offspring in man?

329. Riddle has found in pigeons that eggs with a relatively large amount of stored food and a relatively low metabolic rate tend to produce females and that those with less storage and higher metabolic rate produce males. With what general characteristics of maleness and femaleness may these differences in germ cells be related?

330. What evidence do you know of in man that sex is quantitative and that there are various degrees of maleness and femaleness?

331. If a hen which undergoes sex reversal, and thus becomes a functional male, produces gametes of the same chromosomal constitution as before (although they are now sperms instead of eggs), what will be the sex of her offspring when she is mated with a normal hen?

332. If such a sex-reversed hen were barred, what would be the appearance of her offspring when bred to a nonbarred hen?

333. In Drosophila what ratios of autosomes to sex chromosomes would you expect to get in the progeny from a cross of triploid females × diploid males, assuming that all eggs are viable and that all the autosomes have equal male tendency? What would you expect to be the sexual character of each of these offspring? (Fig. 97.)

334. How would you determine whether there are differences in the strength of the male tendency between the three autosomes of Drosophila?

335. Goldschmidt has discovered one race, *H*, of *Lymantria dispar* which is the weakest of all weak races. When an *H* female is crossed with a strong male, only sons are produced, half of them being sex-reversed females. The reciprocal cross (strong female × *H* male) produces normal sons and daughters in the F_1 and 3 females : 1 male in F_2. An F_1 female from this cross × *H* males produces only females. Explain these facts.

336. On the hypothesis of sex-determination and sex-linkage in Melandrium outlined on page 274, explain why it is that narrow-leaved female plants do not occur.

337. If a female Melandrium plant heterozygous for broad leaves is crossed with a broad-leaved male plant and the F_1 individuals are allowed to interbreed freely, what will be the appearance of the F_2 as to sex and leaf character?

338. What cytological explanation can you suggest for the fact that there may sometimes be genetic segregation in each of two successive cell divisions, as in the ascus of Neurospora?

339. Assume that in Neurospora a mycelium which is "plus" and carries the gene for the production of conidia fuses with a "minus," nonconidial mycelium and that, in a given ascus produced in the resulting perithecium, segregation for sex takes place at the first division and for conidia at the second. State the genetic constitution, as to these two traits, of each of the eight spores in this ascus, enumerating them in order.

340. What would you expect to be the mode of inheritance in Sphaerocarpos of a sex-linked trait which had its expression in the sporophyte? Of one which had its expression in the gametophyte?

341. If the F_1 of a cross between homozygous silkless and homozygous tassel-seed maize (p. 276) is crossed back on its tassel-seed parent, what will be appearance of the offspring?

342. In the following crosses, involving silkless and tassel seed in maize, what will be the appearance of the offspring?

$$Sk\ sk\ Ts\ ts \times Sk\ sk\ ts\ ts$$
$$Sk\ sk\ Ts\ ts \times sk\ sk\ ts\ ts$$

343. In the artificially produced race of dioecious maize where the female is *ls ts* and the male *Ts ts*, assume that gene *a* occurs in the same chromosome as *ts* and shows 10 per cent crossing over with it. If the female parent (*ts ts*) is *aa* and the male (*Ts ts*) is *AA*, what will be the appearance, as to sex and gene *a*, of the F_1? of the F_2?

344. In Habrobracon, assume that gene a is sex-linked and recessive; that recessive males are either aX or aY; and that heterozygous females are either AX/aY or AY/aX. List the phenotypes of the male and female offspring (including biparental males) of the four types of matings between a males and Aa females.

345. In Habrobracon a wild-type (black-eyed) female mated to a haploid male with orange eyes produced in F_1 black-eyed sons and daughters. F_1 females backcrossed to orange and to black males produced offspring as follows:

	Black-eyed		Orange-eyed	
	♀♀	♂♂	♀♀	♂♂
F_1 ♀ × orange ♂	44	221	59	243
F_1 ♀ × black ♂	102	19		21

Explain these ratios.

346. In Habrobracon, an orange-eyed female heterozygous for the recessive fused antennae (fu) mated to a black-eyed fused male produced offspring as follows:

Black-eyed				Orange-eyed		
♀♀		♂♂		♀♀	♂♂	
+	fu	+	fu		+	fu
105	6	2	7	none	112	120

Explain the inheritance of fused.

CHAPTER XII

INBREEDING AND HETEROSIS

Most of the hereditary differences between individuals belong to the types discussed in the preceding chapters and owe their origin to genic changes or to alteration in the number or character of the chromosomes. A number of important differences, however, which are concerned chiefly with size and vigor, have been regarded by practical breeders as being due to other causes, among which is the degree of relationship between the parents. The frequently deleterious effects of "inbreeding," or the mating of individuals closely related in descent, have long been recognized and assumed to be due chiefly to the close relationship of the parents. Conversely, the stimulatory effect of a cross between parents belonging to different races or stocks has often been observed by practical breeders and used as a means of improving size and constitutional vigor. The essential truth of these observations is not to be doubted, but they may now be interpreted as consequences of the Mendelian mechanism.

Inbreeding.—Breeders, especially of animals, have found that, although inbreeding has been the means by which superior varieties have been developed since the earliest times, it will often, if too close or too long continued, result in reduced size, lessened fecundity, and ultimate inability of the stock to survive. The fact that in many of the higher plants self-pollination is prevented or rendered relatively infrequent by various structural or functional means and similarly in most animals that the progeny arise from matings between different individuals, convinced many earlier biologists that self-fertilization was an unnatural and thus presumably harmful process. The extensive experiments of Darwin with plants seemed to lead to the same conclusion, since in most species the offspring arising from self-fertilization were clearly less vigorous than those from cross-fertilization. It was his opinion, shared by most biologists until recent years, that *the process of inbreeding itself* in some way produced these injurious effects.

Objections to such a general conclusion, however, began to appear when the problem was reinvestigated by carefully controlled experiments and in the light of a knowledge of Mendelian inheritance. Attention was called to the fact that many species of plants, such as peas, beans, barley, and oats, are normally self-fertilized but nevertheless compare favorably with cross-fertilized species in size, fecundity, and ability to survive. Furthermore, several animals with which careful inbreeding experiments

281

have been carried out do not invariably show the expected decrease in size and vigor. Thus in the strain of albino rats studied by King, brothers were mated to sisters for 25 generations, at the end of which period the animals compared favorably with crossbred stock used as controls. It should be noted, however, that in the inbred race only the most vigorous animals were selected for breeding. In Drosophila, inbreeding through brother-sister matings was carried on by various workers for a much larger number of generations, and although vigor and fecundity were somewhat reduced at first, in later generations these were maintained at essentially the level of cross-fertilized stocks.

Most experiments, however, confirm the results of earlier workers and show that long-continued inbreeding of normally cross-fertilized organisms does result in the appearance of certain traits that are unfavorable for survival.

Important evidence here is provided by extensive series of experiments on plants, in which the effects of the closest sort of inbreeding—self-fertilization—could be studied. Work with maize has been particularly fruitful in results. This was begun independently by Shull and East in 1905, the latter's experiment having been carried on in an enlarged form to the present time by Jones. Maize is normally cross-pollinated but can readily be self-pollinated experimentally. Results showed that the first generation following the self-pollination of a normal crossbred plant was generally inferior to the parental generation in size and fruitfulness and that this decline continued for seven or eight generations at a *progressively decreasing rate* until a point was reached (unless the line became extinct) where no further decline was manifest, no matter how long the inbreeding continued (Table XXI). Parallel with these changes was the isolation of subvarieties differing in characters, such as color, branching, length and position of ears, character of silk, tillering, seed size, arrangement of kernels, and other respects, all of which gradually became fixed and constant. The general results of inbreeding in maize are summarized by East and Jones (1919) as follows:

1. There is a reduction in size of plant and in productiveness which continues only to a certain point and is in no sense an actual degeneration.
2. There is an isolation of subvarieties differing in morphological characters accompanying the reduction in growth.
3. As these subvarieties become more constant in their characters the reduction in growth ceases to be noticeable.
4. Individuals are obtained with such characters that they cannot be reproduced or, if so, only with extreme difficulty.

Evidence of the same sort has been obtained from animals. Thus the long-continued inbreeding experiments with a series of guinea pig families

TABLE XXI.—THE EFFECT OF CONTINUED SELF-FERTILIZATION UPON THE HEIGHT OF FOUR LINES OF DENT CORN (*Data from Jones*)

Number of generations selfed	A, height, inches	B, height, inches	C, height, inches	D, height, inches
0	117	117	117	117
1 to 5	87	81	91	77
6 to 10	97	84	88	82
11 to 15	97	84	87	83
16 to 20	88	85	*	75
21 to 25	81	75		71
26 to 30	92	80		

* Lost.

begun by the United States Department of Agriculture in 1906 and carried on in later years by Wright involved records of 30,000 animals and 23 generations of brother-sister inbreeding. The effect of this was to produce a decline in size and other elements of vigor. The mortality at birth and between birth and weaning, body weight, growth, size and number of litters, and resistance to tuberculosis were adversely affected, and the inbred animals were inferior to outbred controls in these respects. Just as in maize, there was here observed a conspicuous differentiation among the various inbred families, with a fixation of various traits in each.

The genetic interpretation of these results of inbreeding has been concisely stated by East and Jones (1919) as follows:

From the preceding observations it can be said that inbreeding has but one demonstrable effect on organisms subject to its action—the isolation of homozygous types. The diversity of the resulting types depends directly upon the number of heterozygous hereditary factors present in the individuals with which the process is begun; it is likely, therefore, to vary directly with the amount of cross-breeding experienced by their immediate ancestors. The rapidity of the isolation of homozygous types is a function of the intensity of the inbreeding.

A decline in heterozygosity should result automatically under continued self-fertilization or close breeding. Thus an individual heterozygous for a single factor pair Aa will produce, if selfed, offspring of which one-fourth are AA, one-half Aa, and one-fourth aa. Under continued selfing the homozygous types breed true and are progressively augmented by segregates from the dwindling group of heterozygotes. The proportions of the three groups may be determined for any generation by the formula developed by Mendel:

$$2^n - 1 \ AA \ : 2 \ Aa \ : 2^n - 1 \ aa$$

where n is the number of generations of self-fertilization.

Similar formulas have been developed by which it is possible to compute the results of other systems of mating. Thus in brother-sister mating the proportion of homozygosity progressively increases but at a slower rate, 6 generations of self-fertilization being approximately as effective as 17 generations of brother-sister mating (East and Jones 1919, p. 97).

This reduction in heterozygosity takes place automatically in all other factor pairs regardless of the number of pairs involved (Fig. 104). Thus

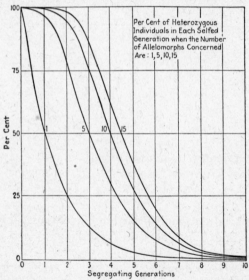

Per Cent of Heterozygous Individuals in Each Selfed Generation when the Number of Allelomorphs Concerned Are : 1, 5, 10, 15

Fig. 104.—Graphs showing the reduction in the proportion of heterozygous individuals and of heterozygous factor pairs in successive generations of self-fertilization. (*After East and Jones.*)

continued self-fertilization leads to a decline in heterozygosity for about seven generations, about 99 per cent of homozygosity being attained in the seventh generation. This resembles the actual results of inbreeding, for here there is a decline in size and variability for about seven or eight generations, after which a line becomes essentially stable.

All the evidence can best be interpreted, therefore, as indicating that the reduction in size and vigor is related in some way to the attainment of homozygosity and that the mere process of inbreeding, *of itself*, does not produce this result. The automatic reduction of heterozygosity will occur, of course, only if new mutations in inbred lines are very rare. If the mutation rate is high, this may defer or prevent the attainment of homozygosity.

Hybrid Vigor.—The phenomenon precisely converse to that of lack of vigor following inbreeding is the marked increase in size following crossing or outbreeding. This, too, has long been observed by both animal and plant breeders. The beneficial effect, technically called *heterosis*, is in greater or lesser degree almost universal and is evident even among forms in which inbreeding seems not to be deleterious. It is readily recognized, since its maximum effects are evident in the generation immediately following the cross.

Plants show the phenomenon of heterosis particularly well. Thus in maize the F_1 hybrids between inbred homozygous strains show a marked increase over the parent strains in height, frequently show a gain of 150

Fig. 105.—Heterosis followed by decline in height after inbreeding in maize. Representative plants of the two parent strains at right, followed by plants from the F_1, F_2, F_3, F_4, . . . F_8 generations of inbreeding toward the left. (*From Jones.*)

to 200 per cent in yield, and have thicker stalks and larger leaves, ears, and seeds than have their inbred parents. This immediately restores all the size lost by inbreeding, and the F_1 plants are frequently as large as the original heterozygous stocks. They further show a striking uniformity in physical traits as compared with normal crossbred stock, a result evidently due to the homozygosity which their parent lines had attained. A remarkable feature of this vigor, which reaches its maximum in the first hybrid generation, is that it cannot be fixed but rapidly disappears again under inbreeding (Fig. 105).

Many other plants show a similar heterosis. This is usually reflected in greater size and more numerous and larger parts, but in some cases shows itself in more strictly physiological characters, such as increased longevity and higher resistance to disease. Hybrid vigor arising through crossing may apparently be maintained indefinitely by vegetative reproduction, a fact of particular economic importance in fruit and nut trees and such crop plants as potatoes.

Heterosis also occurs in animals. The mule is perhaps the most familiar example of a hybrid animal, and its vigor, hardiness, and resistance to disease are well known. Crossbred animals and "mongrels," although of little value for breeding, may be superior to purebred animals in size and other bodily characters. Use is often made of this fact in breeding them for market. In only a few animals, however, have controlled experiments been carried out. In Drosophila much evidence has been obtained which indicates that size and fecundity increase when

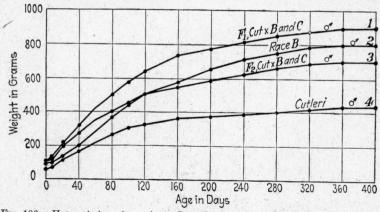

Fig. 106.—Heterosis in guinea pigs. Growth curves of males of a large domesticated race of guinea pigs (race *B*, line 2); of a small wild race from Peru (*Cavia cutleri*, line 4); and of the F_1 (line 1) and F_2 (line 3) males from a cross of race *B* (and race *C* of similar size) with *Cavia cutleri*. The F_1 animals exceeded both parent races in growth rate and final size. The F_2 animals were distinctly smaller. (*After Castle.*)

strains are crossed, particularly if they have been inbred previously. The same results have been found in guinea pigs, fowls, and other animals (Fig. 106).

Early students of hybrid vigor, especially Darwin himself, were inclined to attribute it (as in the opposite case of the ill effects of inbreeding) to something inherent in crossbreeding itself, perhaps a physiological stimulus from the act of crossing or the mixture of two types of protoplasm. When Mendelian inheritance was understood, however, it was seen that there was a definite parallelism between hybrid vigor and heterozygosity, both immediately attaining a maximum in the F_1 and both declining steadily under inbreeding. The suggestion is obvious that the condition of heterozygosity, rather than the breeding methods by which it is obtained, is what results in the appearance of hybrid vigor.

Genetic Interpretation of the Effects of Inbreeding and Crossing.—
That homozygosity *of itself* should be the direct cause of reduction in

size and vigor, and heterozygosity of the opposite condition, is difficult to believe. A closer analysis of the problem suggests an explanation more in harmony with genetic theory and not requiring the assumption that the condition of heterozygosity exerts a stimulatory influence.

Within a species, different races or lines may differ in the various elements of size and vigor. Some may excel in height, some in number of parts, and some in resistance to disease. None is likely to be superior to all others in every respect. These differences have arisen in the process of genetic divergence, slight though it may be, which has separated the races. They are intensified through the breeding of related individuals. It is significant that traits of lesser size or vigor, especially if they differ from their alleles sufficiently so that they are obviously defects, are usually recessive in their inheritance.

For the recessive gene controlling each of these deleterious traits there is a dominant allele which produces a relatively more vigorous condition. The number of pairs of such genes is apparently very great, and they are distributed diversely among various related races or lines. One race may contain one series of genes determining reduced size and vigor and another race quite a different series. Each race should have the dominant normal alleles of the genes causing the deficiencies in the other race. When these two races are crossed, the offspring should show the effects of *all* these dominant genes and none of the recessive ones and thus should show maximum size and vigor immediately, an effect which rapidly disappears again under inbreeding as the recessive defects begin to appear through segregation. The more highly inbred and lacking in vigor a race is, the more pronounced should be the gain made by its hybrid offspring, provided that the two parents lack *different* elements of size and vigor. Thus if two different lines of maize, reduced in size from long-continued inbreeding, are crossed, the immediate return to full stature shown by their offspring may be due to the fact that dominant genes, which have been separated from each other during the isolation of these lines, are brought together again, each contributing some element of vigor to the hybrid type.

A simple example will illustrate how such a result is presumably obtained. Keeble and Pellew crossed two varieties of garden peas. One variety had short, thick internodes but many of them. The other, equally tall, had fewer but longer internodes. The F_1 plants had both many and long internodes and were therefore considerably taller than either parent because of this complementary action of two dominant genes. Heterozygosity in such cases is thus to be related to hybrid vigor merely as the necessary result of bringing together two diverse groups of factors, and the rapid loss of hybrid vigor under inbreeding thus receives a simple Mendelian explanation.

If this hypothesis is correct, however, it should be possible to obtain individuals homozygous for all of the dominant factors present in the hybrid and thus make hybrid vigor permanent in a true-breeding race; but in actual practice this has been found very difficult or impossible to do. Jones has reconciled this result with the hypothesis, however, by assuming that there are a relatively large number of factors affecting size and vigor and that each chromosome ordinarily may contain several of them. In inheritance they must therefore occur in groups of linked genes. A single group would be expected to contain some dominant alleles for increased size and some recessive ones for lesser growth. The hybrid would possess the dominant member of each pair, but the recombination of all of these together in one gamete would be extremely rare, since the genes do not assort independently as they would if there were but one to a chromosome. Their genetic behavior is necessarily complicated by their linkage relations, and a series of rarely occurring crossovers of a very precise sort would be necessary to obtain all the dominant genes in the same gamete. By proper genetic manipulation, however, it should be possible to do this, and the fact that markedly vigorous, true-breeding races have been obtained in both plants and animals indicates that such combinations have sometimes been at least partially fixed.

The genetic interpretation of heterosis is not quite as simple as this in all cases, however. Much of the reduction in size which accompanies inbreeding seems not to be the result of this appearance of real defects but rather to belong to the category of general size differences. Obvious defects which often appear as the result of inbreeding may readily be eliminated by the selection of individuals which do not display them, and the stock itself thus purged of genes which produce such weaknesses. The remaining inbred individuals are small but often otherwise normal, and it is significant that when two such inbred types, genetically diverse, are crossed, the F_1 at once shows the maximum heterotic size. Evidently in such cases it is not the so-called "defect" genes which are responsible either for the reduction in size due to inbreeding or for the increase due to crossing.

Another difficulty arises from the fact that for ordinary size traits, which seem here to be chiefly involved, there is no clear evidence that large size is dominant over small. The F_1 in most cases seems to be essentially intermediate. Some degree of dominance, however, must be assumed if the genetic explanation of heterosis proposed above is to hold, for if the heterozygous condition is precisely intermediate, there can be no cumulative effect of heterozygosity. East has recently suggested a possible explanation of heterosis which does not require dominance. The essence of this suggestion is that allelic genes may affect different processes and so in heterozygous combination produce cumulative effects. Thus if a gene a_1 affects a slightly different physiological process from its allele a_2, then a_1a_2 would be expected to show a cumulative effect, that is, a greater positive effect than a_1a_1 or a_2a_2. This implies a complementary action of different mutations at the same locus, but unlike the complementary action of two nonallelic genes (p. 90), it does not require the assumption of dominance. If genes with such effects on growth occur as members of multiple allelic series then various degrees of heterosis might be accounted for by varying degrees of divergence in physiological effect among genes at the same locus. Apparently the only actual case to which such an interpretation may be directly applied is one reported by Dunn, in which each of two recessive genes in the mouse (t^0 and t^1) is lethal when homozygous (t^0t^0 and t^1t^1) but the heterozygote (t^0t^1) is viable and normal in character. Since these two genes are probably alleles (they show no crossing over), their action is thus complementary in the sense required by the above interpretation, that is, t^0 supplies what is lacking in t^1.

Assuming that heterosis is due to combination of unlike genes affecting growth either by dominance or by divergence of alleles, the problem still remains as to how such an initial hybrid genetic constitution produces greater size. The two chief explanations that have been brought forward are (1) that the hybrid reaches greater size and vigor by more rapid and efficient growth than its purebred parents and (2) that the greater size of the hybrid is due to its greater initial size (embryo or primordium size). Although earlier work appeared to support the first interpretation, Ashby has recently questioned this. He finds that in both maize and tomato there seems to be no difference in photosynthetic or respiratory activity between heterozygous plants and their parents, nor any higher rate of growth (in terms of percentage rate) in one than the other. The increased size of heterotic plants he finds to be due merely to the maintenance of an initial size difference, presumably in the mass or "capital" of the meristematic tissues, in the embryo. In other words, the relative difference in size between plants of the F_1 and their parent forms is no greater than the relative difference between their embryo sizes. Ashby thus assumes that the major effect of heterosis occurs in the very early development of the individual rather than throughout its life. Ashby's results have been confirmed for tomatoes by Luckwill but are called in question by Sprague, who repeated similar experiments with maize. The hypothesis of meristematic "capital" as the prime factor in hybrid vigor has been of value in directing attention to the need for a fuller understanding of the physiology of heterosis. It fails to touch a number of important questions, however, such as the frequently greater duration of growth in heterotic plants, the fact that heterosis may be transmitted in vegetative reproduction, and the cases where heterozygous individuals are apparently superior to inbred ones in truly physiological characters such as immunity and fecundity.

Altogether, the problems presented by the effects of inbreeding and crossing are still very puzzling ones genetically and require much more intensive study. They are clearly related to those involved in the inheritance of quantitative characters and will not be solved until much more definite information is obtained as to the physiology and genetic control of growth processes.

REFERENCES

ASHBY, E. 1930. Studies on the inheritance of physiological characters I. A physiological investigation of the nature of hybrid vigour in maize. Annals Bot. **44.**

———. 1932. II. Further experiments upon the basis of hybrid vigour and upon the inheritance of efficiency index and respiration rate in maize. Annals Bot. **46.**

EAST, E. M. 1936. Heterosis. Genetics **21.**

——— and D. F. JONES. 1919. Inbreeding and outbreeding. Philadelphia. (Contains extensive bibliography of this field.)

JONES, D. F. 1917. Dominance of linked factors as a means of accounting for heterosis. Genetics **2.**

KEEBLE, F., and C. PELLEW. 1910. The mode of inheritance of stature and flowering time in peas. Jour. Genetics **1.**

LUCKWILL, L. C. 1937. Hybrid vigour in the tomato. 2. Manifestation of hybrid vigour during the flowering period. Annals Bot. n.s. **1.**

SPRAGUE, G. F. 1936. Hybrid vigor and growth rates in a maize cross and its reciprocal. Jour. Agr. Res. **53.**

WRIGHT, S. 1922. The effects of inbreeding and crossbreeding on guinea pigs. U.S. Dept. Agr. Bulls. **1090** and **1121.**

PROBLEMS

347. Why may persistent inbreeding in a number of lines, later followed by crosses between them, result in more vigorous individuals than are produced by crosses between members of lines which have not been inbred?

348. The inbreeding of normally cross-fertilized animals and plants is usually followed by a reduction in vigor. How is it, then, that many species of plants in nature are almost always self-fertilized and thus closely inbred but still continue to thrive and maintain themselves successfully?

349. Will inbreeding result in the reduction of a heterozygous to a homozygous condition more rapidly in a species with a large number of chromosomes or in one with a smaller number? Explain.

350. If heterozygous individuals are more vigorous than homozygous ones, why is so much emphasis laid by animal breeders on the desirability of purebred animals, which are relatively much more homozygous than ordinary stock?

351. Why is selection for vigor in inbred lines likely to delay the attainment of complete homozygosity?

352. In the tenth generation of the offspring of a self-fertilized plant heterozygous for *Aa*, what proportion would there be of heterozygous individuals?

353. Why should six generations of self-fertilization be as effective in reducing heterozygosity as seventeen generations of brother-sister mating?

354. When a farmer procures from his experiment station some "crossbred" maize seed which gives him a high yield through heterosis, he is tempted to grow his own seed for the next season, hoping to perpetuate these favorable traits. Why is such a procedure doomed to failure?

355. To obtain maize seed which will produce plants having the large size and yield and other advantages of heterosis, it is impractical to use the seed from crossed inbred lines since the yield is relatively small. What means can you suggest for obtaining a high yield of seed which will produce heterotic plants?

CHAPTER XIII

THE ORIGIN OF HEREDITARY DIFFERENCES. I
GENE MUTATION

For many years our knowledge of how hereditary differences originate has lagged behind the rapidly growing information of the mechanism by which they are inherited. The reasons for this are not far to seek: it was first necessary to discover through what structures in the organism the differentiating characters are transmitted and to reach some general classification of the variations found in nature with regard to their transmissibility. The preceding chapters have shown that the main features and many of the details of the transmission mechanism are now known. This by itself restricts the locale of those changes that become hereditary to the chromosomes with their contained genes. Except for a few cases of cytoplasmic inheritance it is correct to say that hereditary variations that arise in nature are due to changes in the chromosomes. Moreover, knowledge of the mechanism of transmission has made it possible to devise methods by which heritable changes may be induced and studied experimentally. The induced changes which are inherited follow the same general rules as the natural ones—they are due to changes in chromosomes or genes or both. Since these basic hereditary materials are present in all living cells, changes in them may arise, and have in fact been demonstrated, both in the reproductive cells (germinal variations) and in the somatic or vegetative tissues (somatic variations) in both animals and plants.

Autogenous Variations.—We have called such variations *autogenous* to distinguish them from the other great class of variations which are due to the direct action of the environment (Chapter II). It was not possible to separate these classes sharply until the transmission mechanism was known; now it is clear that the latter class (environmental) does not furnish the variations which are inherited according to Mendel's principles. This does not mean that the chromosomes and genes are completely insulated from environmental changes. On the contrary transmissible changes may be induced by exposure to X rays, radium, heat, and chemical agents. It means rather that the changes directly evoked in the organism in response to changes in the environment do not themselves give rise to the hereditary differences, but that the latter are induced directly in the ultimate hereditary materials. It is the internally restricted character of the change to which the term auto-genous refers. Autogenous variations may now be classified for con-venience into three main categories.

1. *Recombinations.*—Although these constitute the commonest source of new phenotypes, they are not, properly speaking, new differences at all but are due to rearrangements of the elements within a genetic diversity already in existence. They can be diagnosed as such only after knowledge of the separate elements has been obtained by experi-mental tests. They may be as simple as the segregation of a recessive which may have been carried in the stock for many generations, or as complex as the release of a gene from a balanced lethal association. They may arise also in somatic cells through somatic segregation or somatic crossing over (p. 207). This type of variation has been sufficiently discussed in other connections and in this chapter we shall confine our attention to those differences that express the origin of something actually new.

2. *Gene Mutations.*—Of first importance is the change in a single gene, which we shall term *gene mutation* or *point mutation* or, more briefly, *mutation.* If the mutation occurs in a germ cell, it is signalized by the sudden appearance of a new form, such as a white-eyed fly in an inbred culture of red-eyed ones, which proves on test to show a monohybrid difference from the parent form. The individual showing a mutation is referred to as a *mutant.* Such mutations may also arise in somatic cells, as in the appearance of a few white facets in an otherwise red eye or the occurrence of patches of tissue in leaf, stem, flower, root, or seed, differing in character from the neighboring tissues. When such a change can be shown to be restricted to a single locus or gene, it may be ascribed to *somatic mutation.* If no reproductive tissues have been affected by the change the proof that a point mutation has occurred may be difficult or impossible to obtain.

3. *Chromosome Changes.*—Variations due to alterations in chromo-somes of greater extent than single gene loci may be grouped under the general term chromosome changes. Here may be placed:

a. Changes in the number of chromosomes (haploidy, polyploidy, heteroploidy);

b. Changes in the number or arrangement of the genes (deficiency, duplication, translocation, inversion). Here too should be placed those variations (like Bar eye in Drosophila) which behave like gene mutations in inheritance but which on analysis prove to be chromosomal rearrange-ments showing a position effect (p. 336).

Rearrangements likewise may occur either in germinal or somatic tissues. The chromosome changes that occur spontaneously and those induced by irradiation fall into the same categories.

The first of these three types of autogenous variations has already been sufficiently discussed. The second (gene mutation) is the subject of the present chapter. The third (chromosome changes) will be considered in Chapter XIV.

The Mutation Theory.—New, suddenly appearing types have been known among breeders as "sports," and their importance as points of departure for new varieties or species has been recognized for many years. Darwin had collected many instances of sudden heritable changes but did not ascribe to them an important role in the origination of new species because he thought that major sudden changes of this sort would be likely to upset the harmonious correlation between the parts of the organism and between the organism and its environment. The variations to which he chiefly appealed as leading to progressive change were the small, continuous, intergrading variations which seemed to be called forth by the environment itself. Galton (1889), however, and especially Bateson (1894), were led to another view: that *discontinuous* variations, appearing as distinct new steps, were the chief sources of the new heritable differences on which natural selection acted.

This view was most forcibly developed and supported by Hugo de Vries, who in his "Mutation Theory" (1901–1903) introduced the term "mutation" and laid the foundations for the modern theory of the origin of heritable variations by sudden, discontinuous, random changes in the hereditary material.

Mutation in Oenothera.—De Vries' evidence was drawn from observations on wild and cultivated plants but chiefly from breeding experiments with Lamarck's evening primrose, *Oenothera Lamarckiana.* He found this plant growing wild in Holland, where it had escaped from cultivation. He noticed its great variability, for in the field it produced a number of new types each season (Fig. 107). This tendency to sport or mutate continued after the wild plants had been transferred to his garden, and during one period of eight generations, seven different new types appeared from the wild form and many of these bred true from the time they first arose.

De Vries' chief contention, that new forms arise by a process of discontinuous variation (mutation), has been amply sustained by later work. Intensive genetic and cytological studies of Oenothera species, however, have shown that not one but a number of different processes are involved in the origin of the new types in this genus. These are discussed in detail in Chapter XIV.

Gene Mutation.—The classic example of gene mutation has been the sudden appearance in a true-breeding stock of red-eyed Drosophila of a *single white-eyed* individual, which when bred behaved as though a specific change had taken place in one point in the X chromosome.

FIG. 107.—*Oenothera Lamarckiana*, the evening primrose (center) with two mutant types which arose from it; *O. gigas*, the giant form (right), and *O. nanella*, the dwarf (left). (*From B. M. Davis.*)

Here a wild-type gene had suddenly changed in such a way that processes in development which before had resulted in red color of the compound eye now resulted in uncolored eyes. This change was a permanent one, for the white-eyed stock derived from the mutant bred true from its origin. Subsequently several hundred other gene changes occurred in Drosophila, each one resulting in specific and permanent hereditary differences. The same kind of evidence has been obtained from several other species of Drosophila, from maize, snapdragon, rodents, and many other varieties of plants and animals which have been bred in large numbers. There is little doubt that the differentiating characters which Mendel studied in peas had arisen as gene mutations. The specificity of such changes, their stability, and their restriction to single loci in the chromosomes are therefore direct inferences from controlled breeding experiments. A gene mutation may from this evidence be defined simply as an *alteration of a gene*.

Diagnosis.—A new inherited variation can be diagnosed as a gene mutation only after proof that it is not due to one of the several other types of genetic change, and this generally presents considerable difficulty. In the case of a new character appearing only in certain somatic tissues of animals, as in mosaics, a test of the nature of the change is possible only in case it duplicates a previously known mutation, or in the rare event that a part of the reproductive tissues have also changed in the same way so that some of the gametes transmit the mutation. Somatic variations in plants may often be propagated vegetatively and gametes derived from the variant tissues may thus eventually be tested.

Even when the variation has occurred in the germinal tissue or gametes, proof that it shows monofactorial segregation is not always adequate. Thus the Bar-eyed variation in Drosophila (p. 236) met all the criteria of a gene mutation until it was shown to be due to a minute duplication of wild-type genes. The phenotype "Bar eye" thus depends on changed relations between unmutated genes—the so-called "position effect" (p. 336). Similarly the Notch mutation in Drosophila met the usual criteria of segregation but proved on analysis to be due to a section deficiency.

Moreover it is now known that only a small fraction of the gene mutations that occur are accompanied by marked and visible character changes. The changes to which the gene is subject constitute a wide spectrum from those with effects that are too small to be detected, through the large class of "small mutations" in which the character changes are barely perceptible, to those whose effects are lethal or semi-lethal. A large proportion of natural gene mutations probably belong in the latter category and special methods are required for detection and diagnosis of these (p. 302). Finally it must be remembered that whether a change in a gene produces any character change at all depends upon the function of the particular gene locus affected in relation to the other processes of the organism. A locus chiefly concerned with eye color might mutate within digestive or muscle tissue and produce no detectable effects; a change which in one genotype may be lethal may not have this effect in another, or under other external conditions.

SPONTANEOUS MUTATION

Gene mutations occurring in nature or in cultivated animals or plants that have not been treated to produce mutations are called spontaneous mutations, although it is well recognized that "spontaneous" expresses merely the fact that we do not know the causes of these.

Frequency of Gene Mutation.—Although it has usually been held that spontaneous gene mutation is a rare event, this opinion has rested rather on the stability and conservatism of wild species and on the low frequency with which mutant phenotypes are found in nature than on data from deliberate attempts to measure the exact frequency of mutation. Recent experience indicates that mutation frequency varies in different species and in the same species under different conditions and that the different loci of the chromosomes have different mutabilities. Muller has devised special techniques for measuring mutation rate in Drosophila and has estimated that under ordinary laboratory conditions a mutated gene (lethal) may be expected in *Drosophila melanogaster* in from 1 in 100 to 1 in 1,000 chromosomes. Schultz (1936) gives a mutation rate of .18 per cent for sex-linked lethals in this species. Tschetverikoff (1927) and his students sampled wild Drosophila populations in southern Russia and inbred the offspring of single females in the laboratory. The offspring of 239 wild flies segregated for a total of 32 mutant genes. Dubinin and his associates (1934), in a more extensive experiment of the same sort, inbred the descendants of wild females of *D. melanogaster* collected at several stations in the Caucasus. A large percentage of the flies were found to carry mutant genes. The frequency of lethals varied in different populations from 0 to 21.4 per cent; and the frequency of mutations with detectable visible effects from 3.9 to 33.1 per cent (Table XXII). In one year 151 salivary chromosomes containing lethals were studied and not one was found to show a chromosomal aberration, indicating that the lethals were probably gene mutations. No sex-linked mutations were found in any year. Systematic study of certain variable characters (bristles) revealed an even greater frequency of mutations with minor or modifying effects. Baur had also found such "small mutations" to be very frequent in Antirrhinum (10 per cent) and attributed to them especial importance in evolutionary change. Dobzhansky (1938) has recently found that the majority (75 per cent) of the chromosomes of wild *D. pseudoobscura* contain at least one mutant gene, most of them with small effects on viability.

TABLE XXII.—MUTATIONS FOUND IN THE INBRED F$_3$ DESCENDANTS OF WILD FEMALES OF *Drosophila melanogaster* CAPTURED AT GELENDZHIK, U.S.S.R. (*Data from Dubinin, Heptner, Demidova, Djachkova, 1936*)

	1933	1934	1935
Number of wild females tested...............	877	616	797
Number of autosomes (II and III) tested.....	1,754	1,232	1,594
Percentage of autosomes carrying gene mutations...................................	21.78	56.17	36.75
Percentage of autosomes carrying lethal mutations...................................	7.98	12.66	8.78
Percentage of autosomes carrying visible mutations..............................	13.80	43.51	36.75

These extensive studies of Dubinin and his coworkers, of Dobzhansky, and of others do not, of course, measure actual mutation frequency in wild populations. The frequency of mutations found must, as Dubinin concludes, represent a resultant of two phenomena: the mutation rate and the force of natural selection which tends to restrict the spread of harmful mutations. The data show clearly, however, that mutations do occur with appreciable frequency in nature and that large fractions of them are at the extremes of the spectrum of magnitude of effect, that is, "small mutations" and lethals.

Spencer (1935) found that the rate of occurrence of visible mutations in several species of Drosophila, while in general of low order (37 mutants out of about 750,000 flies observed), differed greatly at different times, and he attributed this to variations in environmental factors. Demerec (1937), however, has proved that different strains of the same species (*melanogaster*) may show very different mutation rates and that some of these differences are due to genic differences between the strains. If such genes stimulating mutability are of common occurrence then "mutation rates" may be due chiefly to such inherent factors; and mutation-frequency estimates obtained in the usual way are not likely to be applicable beyond a particular strain and a particular time.

Plants show a similar situation. Thus in *Antirrhinum majus* Baur estimated that 5 to 7 per cent of the sexual progeny of an individual plant contained a new mutant gene in at least one locus, while in the nearly related *A. siculum*, on the other hand, not a single gene mutation was found in twenty years of breeding.

Individual genes likewise vary greatly in their tendency to mutate. In maize Stadler has made an extensive and carefully controlled study of the frequency of mutation of eight genes. His data (Table XXIII) show that some loci (such as *R*) are relatively mutable, while others (such as *Wx*) are extremely stable. In Drosophila a similar situation probably exists.

TABLE XXIII.—THE FREQUENCY OF CHANGES IN SEVEN GENES OF MAIZE.
(After Stadler)

Gene	Gametes tested	Number of mutations	Average per one million gametes
R	554,786	273	492
I	265,391	28	106
Pr	647,102	7	11
Su	1,678,736	4	2.4
Y	1,745,280	4	2.2
Sh	2,469,285	3	1.2
Wx	1,503,744	0	0

In Drosophila many spontaneous mutations at such loci as white, cut, forked, ebony, and vestigial have now been observed, forming long series of multiple alleles and including recurrent mutations to the same allele; many mutations at these loci have also been observed following irradiation; while at other loci only one or a few mutations have been found. There are known, for example, at least 14 alleles of the gene for white eyes in *D. melanogaster* (p. 103); in several of the rodents from 3 to 7 alleles at the albino locus are known; and other genes which have been observed just as continuously have mutated but once to produce a single pair of alleles. Apparently some regions of the chromosome tend to mutate more frequently than others.

Mutations to and from the different alleles at the same locus also occur with different frequencies as Timofeeff-Ressovsky has shown in the case of the white locus of *Drosophila melanogaster*.

These and other observations show that mutations may occur in two directions, from an old or wild-type gene to a new allele (direct mutation) and from the mutant allele back to or toward the wild-type (reverse mutation). The frequencies of these two processes may be equal or unequal in different strains or in different loci of the same strain.

Mutable Genes.—The wide range of mutation frequency that Stadler found is probably representative of a general variation in gene stability. At one end of the range are stable genes which change very rarely; at the other are the so-called mutable genes, which mutate with frequencies that under certain conditions approach 100 per cent. Many of these, as for example the gene for variegation in the pericarp of maize, studied by Emerson, mutate only in somatic tissue. The mutated areas show the dominant self-colored condition, indicating that the recessive gene (variegation) has mutated back to its dominant allele again. Emerson also found evidence of another gene in maize which increased the frequency of these reverse mutations. Demerec has discovered several mutable genes in Drosophila and in Delphinium. In *Drosophila virilis* one strain of miniature-winged flies, known as miniature alpha (miniature is a recessive sex-linked gene as in *D. melanogaster*), regularly produces from 5 to 10 per cent of wild-type (long-winged) flies as well as some mosaics in which patches of wild-type tissue appear in the miniature wing. Demerec has shown that the appearance of the wild-type flies is due to reverse mutation of a miniature gene to its wild-type allele in the germ cells, whereas the mosaics are due to the same type of mutation in the somatic cells. He has, moreover, demonstrated the inheritance of several genes that stimulate the mutability of the miniature gene. One of these, *M*, behaves as a dominant and when present in miniature alpha flies may result in the production of over 75 per cent of wild-type progeny. The mutability of the same miniature gene in the somatic cells may be unaffected.

This may provide an explanation for many of the cases of continually variable traits such as variegation which have puzzled geneticists and breeders for so long. When considered in connection with the evidence from *Drosophila melanogaster*, *Antirrhinum majus*, and Stadler's proof of different mutation rates in maize genes, the evidence from mutable genes shows that different genes may have very different stabilities, even under normal conditions.

Stages at Which Gene Mutations Occur.—New mutations may occur at various stages in development. They may affect only a single somatic cell which, as in color variation in the endosperm of maize or in the epidermis of flowers or leaves, shows a specific difference from surrounding cells; or they may occur at earlier stages, in which case all the descendants of the mutated cell may, under certain conditions, exhibit the changed condition and thus produce sectors of greater or smaller size which differ from the rest of the individual. In Delphinium, Demerec has found that somatic mutation in flower color occurs at very early stages and at the latest stages of development of the flower with higher frequency than in intervening stages (Fig. 108). Mutations in cells ancestral to the gametes may affect from one to many gametes, but judging from the manner in which new germinal mutations first appear, the change seems more often to occur (or to be preserved) during the maturation process itself. Many mutants have appeared as single aberrant individuals, as though one gamete contained a changed gene. When the new gene is dominant, or where it is recessive but not hidden by a dominant allele, as in the sex chromosome of the male Drosophila, it is noted immediately.

In such cases it can be traced to a single changed gamete. Bridges has found that about half of the mutations in the X chromosome of Drosophila have appeared first in single males and the other half in single heterozygous females. In the snapdragon the dominant gene mutation Crispa with short, curled leaves has arisen 39 different times, in each case in only one or a few progeny of a normal plant. The parent plant itself has never shown any evidence of the Crispa gene, so that only one or a few of the cells during or just preceding maturation were affected. All these Crispa mutants were heterozygous for the normal gene, showing that only one gene of the pair had mutated.

Recessive gene mutations have frequently appeared for the first time in one-fourth of the progeny of an inbred pair, showing that both

Fig. 108.—Flowers of Delphinium showing somatic mutations from rose to purple. Large areas result from early mutation, small ones from later mutation. (*From Demerec.*)

parents were heterozygous for the new gene and that the mutation had occurred in a common ancestor. Under outbreeding or crossbreeding the recessive may remain hidden for many generations until a mating of two heterozygotes occurs.

Recessive Nature of Most Gene Mutations.—One characteristic of new gene mutations is that they are generally recessive to the wild type or to the condition from which they arose. In the several species of Drosophila relatively few dominants have been found, and this holds for other animals, for example rodents, and for plants such as maize, snapdragon, and barley, in which many gene mutations have been observed. Several mutations which appeared at first to be due to dominant genes have been shown to be actually deficiencies (such as Notch in *D. melanogaster*) which are usually lethal. The fact that most of the dominants of Drosophila are also lethal when homozygous may mean that some of them are also deficiencies, but it may also mean, as Muller has pointed out, that lethal mutations are frequent and that, when one happens to produce also a visible effect on some external character of the heterozygote, it will be selected by the experimenter and kept as a mutant. Dominance of visible effect may thus offer the opportunity for detecting one of the numerous class of lethals, and this rather than a necessary physiological correlation of dominance with lethal action may explain the greater frequency with which lethals have been noted in cultures.

There have been found, however, a sufficient number of mutations which are at once partially dominant to the normal type and *not* lethal to indicate that gene mutations do not occur exclusively in one direction, that is, from normal or wild-type gene to recessive allele. The fact remains that most new mutants *are* recessive to the wild type. R. A. Fisher has suggested that this is due not to a preferred direction of mutation itself but to a peculiarity of the wild type, by which it has acquired, through long exposure to natural selection, a genetic constitution which favors the dominance of wild-type genes.

THE INDUCTION OF MUTATIONS

Most of the above statements are derived from observations of spontaneous or naturally occurring mutations, and indeed until 1927 no other good means of studying the mutation process was available. In that year, however, Muller reported that by use of new methods the rate of mutation in Drosophila could be accurately measured and that this rate could be enormously increased by subjecting organisms to treatment with X rays. Shortly thereafter Stadler showed that treatment with X rays and radium causes large increases in mutation frequency in maize, barley, and wheat.

Methods.—The investigation of mutation in Drosophila, the most favorable animal for this purpose, has depended upon the development of special genetic methods. In the first place, mutations occur with rather low frequency even after radiation, and it is necessary to be able to deal with very large numbers of individuals in order to establish significant differences in mutation rate. Secondly, most mutations are lethal, and to detect these a method is needed by which each new lethal that occurs shall produce a change in results of such a striking character that it cannot escape observation, such as the presence or absence of one whole class of individuals in a population. Finally, the possibility that mutational changes had occurred prior to the treatment and had been retained in the stock must be excluded. The following methods devised by Muller meet these requirements.

Detection of Lethal Mutations. The ClB Method (Fig. 109).—This method is designed to detect new lethal mutations occurring in the X chromosome of Drosophila. It depends on the presence in one of the

X chromosomes of a female of a known lethal gene, l, which will kill that half of the male progeny that receives this X chromosome, since these receive no normal allele in the Y chromosome from the father. In this chromosome is a factor, C (a general symbol for a crossover suppressor, probably an inversion, p. 234), which prevents crossing over in the X, thus insuring that this chromosome will not lose its lethal by crossing over; and a dominant gene, in this case B (Bar eye), to mark this chromosome and identify the offspring that receive it.

In practice a male is treated with X rays, radium, or other agents and crossed with a ClB female. From the offspring of this cross the Bar females are selected (since these must contain the ClB chromosome and the treated chromosome) and crossed with a wild-type male. Such

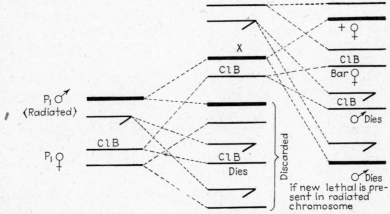

FIG. 109.—The ClB method for detecting lethal mutation in the X chromosome in Drosophila.

a cross will normally produce Bar and not-Bar daughters; half the sons will die because of the ClB lethal, *and if a lethal mutation has occurred in the treated X chromosome,* the other half of the sons will also die. The experimenter is thus required only to distinguish between progenies that contain a ratio of 2 females: 1 male and those that contain no males at all. Each progeny of the latter sort indicates one new sex-linked lethal mutation in the F_1 female tested. In this method the culture rather than the fly becomes the unit of the experiment and large numbers of observations can be quickly and accurately made. It may also be used for the detection of semilethal and visible mutations by examination of the surviving F_2 males.

With a method of this sort and using two treatments of X rays differing only in time of exposure (t_2 for 24 minutes, t_4 for 48 minutes), Muller obtained the following results:

TABLE XXIV

Treatment	No. of fertile F₂ cultures	New mutations		
		Lethals	Semi lethals	Visibles
Untreated.....................	198	0	0	0
X ray t_2.....................	676	49	4	1+
X ray t_4.....................	772	89	12	3+

Thus a total of at least 138 new lethal mutations occurred following X radiation of the grandfather. A few "visible" mutations, *i.e.*, external changes shown to be due to mutation, were also observed incidentally, but their frequency was not accurately measured in this experiment. The frequency of mutation varied with the X-ray dosage, those treated for 48 minutes producing nearly twice as many mutations as those treated 24 minutes.

In a similar experiment in which the effects of radiation on either of the grandparents was measured, the following results were obtained:

TABLE XXV

Treatment	No. of fertile F₂ cultures	Lethal mutations	Visible mutations
X ray $t_1 - t_4$.....................	783	91	37
Untreated.....................	947	1	0

Whereas the untreated controls showed about .1 per cent of sex-linked mutations, the X-rayed cultures produced about 16 per cent, or an increase of some 150-fold due to the radiation.

Detection of Visible Mutations. The "Attached-X" Method (Fig. 110). Another method has been devised especially for the detection of visible mutations in the X chromosome of Drosophila. This utilized the peculiar stock discovered by L. V. Morgan in which the X chromosomes show 100 per cent nondisjunction in the female and in which it has been shown cytologically that the females contain two X chromosomes attached to each other and in addition a Y chromosome (Chap. VII). When crossed with normal males, the daughters (XXY) receive their X chromosome from the mother and the Y chromosome from the father, while the sons get their Y chromosome from the *mother* and their X from the *father*— just the reverse of the usual method. This obviously provides the opportunity for any new recessive mutation arising in the X chromosome of the father to appear immediately in the sons.

In practice, the X chromosomes of both parents are "marked" by recessive genes, for example, y = yellow body in both maternal X's, m = minature wing in the paternal X. The P_1 males are radiated

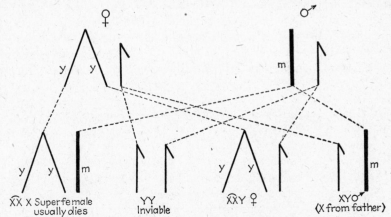

Fɪɢ. 110.—The "attached-X" method for detecting visible (and lethal) mutations in the X chromosome in Drosophilia.

and bred to attached-X females. Some sons exhibit directly the effects of new sex-linked genes which have arisen as a result of the treatment of the father. The result of one such experiment is shown below.

TABLE XXVI

Treatment	Total F_1 ♂♂	Visible mutants
P_1 ♂ X-rayed t_2............................	1,490	61
P_1 ♂ X-rayed t_4............................	1,150	86

It was soon found that various kinds of short-wave radiations (ultraviolet, radium, hard and soft rays) were also effective in inducing mutation, and later heat and certain chemical substances gave positive, though much less striking, results. Not only germinal mutations but also somatic mutations have been obtained by treatment of larvae.

Induced Mutations in Plants.—The same types of change have been brought about in plants by the application of various stimuli. The clearest evidence is that which Stadler has obtained from the irradiation of barley and maize. In the former plant new gene mutations have been produced in such high frequency that it has been possible to make quantitative studies of the nature of the effects produced, by varying the time and intensity of the treatment and applying it to different stages of the life cycle and under different conditions.

Gene Mutations in Barley.—Barley provides good material for studying the effect of radiation on mutation frequency since, when planted at sufficient distance, each plant produces several tillers and each tiller bears a terminal flower and seeds. Each tiller arises from a separate primordium in the seed, and a mutation occurring in one primordium affects only a single head; if the mutation is recessive, its effects will appear only when the gametes produced by this head unite in self-fertilization and produce another generation of plants. In prac-

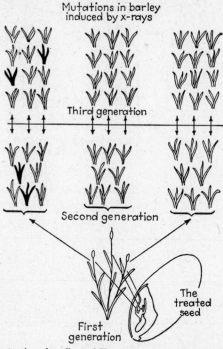

FIG. 111.—Method for testing the effect of X rays on the induction of mutations in barley. (*From Stadler.*)

tice, normal barley seeds in which primordia have separated are irradiated and planted, and the self-fertilized seeds on each head of the resulting plant are harvested and planted separately.

If a recessive mutation has occurred in the cell from which the entire head is derived, all cells in this head will be heterozygous for it, and about one-fourth of the seedlings produced by self-fertilization will show it. If, as often happens, only part of the head is derived from the cell in which the mutation occurred, less than one-fourth of the offspring will show the change. Other head progenies from the same parent plant will all be normal, proving that the mutation had not occurred prior to the treatment, for then it should appear in the offspring of all the heads.

The correctness of these assumptions can be tested in later generations, for in the progeny of a head that segregates three-fourths normal to one-fourth mutant, two-thirds of the normal individuals should be heterozygous for the mutation and should segregate for it when self-fertilized. This was found to be the case (Fig. 111). Since observations have been confined chiefly to seedling characters, it has been possible to observe large numbers of head progenies. In experiments of this type some

Fig. 112.—Induced mutation in barley. Right, normal barley plant; left, "vine," a mutant which arose after application of X rays. (*From Stadler.*)

800 seedling mutations were recorded. Most of them affect chlorophyll characters (albinism, striping, etc.), although many other kinds of mutants have been found (Fig. 112).

In general, these new mutant characters are similar to those that appear in barley under natural conditions, but they are much more frequent in the progeny of irradiated seeds.

Types of Changes Produced.—The "mutations" obtained from plants and animals treated with X rays include all the types of variations that have been found to occur spontaneously. The lethals obtained from the *ClB* method in Drosophila prove on subsequent breeding tests to consist of deficiencies, translocations, inversions, and point mutations. Haploid, heteroploid, and polyploid types have also been obtained in large numbers, chiefly in plants. In Drosophila, these mutants may be

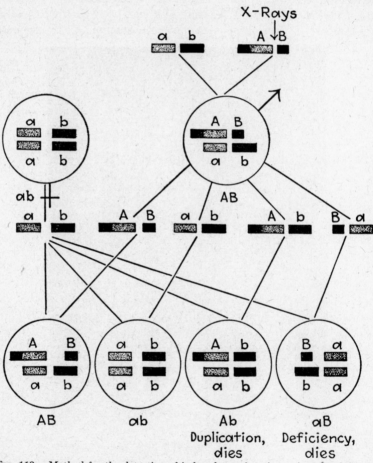

Fig. 113.—Method for the detection of induced translocation. At upper left, normal female with genes *a* and *b* in different chromosomes. When crossed with *AaBb* male containing translocation between these chromosomes (due to previous treatment with X rays), two of the four expected classes (*Ab* and *aB*) die, so that there appears to be complete linkage between *A* and *B*. (*From Dobzhansky,* 1936.)

analyzed by the usual breeding methods (Fig. 113); or more rapid and reliable results may now be obtained by examining the salivary gland chromosomes of larvae from a treated parent. Most of the visible changes have been found to be recessive point mutations, although some dominants have appeared. just as in spontaneous mutation.

Oliver has studied the frequency, among the lethals obtained by radiation in *Drosophila melanogaster*, of sex-linked lethals and chromosomal rearrangements. The results of one experiment are shown in Table XXVII.

TABLE XXVII.—(*After Oliver*)

Dosage	Percentage of lethal mutations	Percentage of chromosome rearrangements
t^{16}	16.09	5.52
t^8	9.87	2.43
t^4	4.90	.35
t^2	3.23	.40
t^1	1.42	.075
Control.............	.24	

Only those chromosomal changes were detected which caused a large change in linkage and crossing over (inversions and translocations), but it is certain that the same agency brought about both point mutations and chromosome changes.

Although many induced lethal changes have been found to be deficiencies, it is certain that not all of them represent loss of genic material. Mutations have been induced both from the wild-type allele to a new mutant allele, and from mutant to wild type (reverse mutation). In a few cases a recessive mutant obtained by irradiation has been bred pure, then radiated, and reverse mutation to wild-type observed. As Muller has aptly said of this experiment, if the first treatment punched something out of the chromosome, then the same treatment reapplied punched it in again. It is thus true of induced, as of spontaneous gene, mutations that they do not occur exclusively in one direction and therefore cannot be interpreted simply as losses of gene material.

In plants also all the types of changes have been found. Stadler has used special methods by which the frequency of induced deficiencies can be measured in maize. These were made possible by the careful mapping of the chromosomes carried out cooperatively by numerous investigators.

When a maize plant with a number of recessive mutant genes controlling endosperm characters is used as the female parent in crosses with a male carrying the dominant alleles of these, the characters of the male parent are ordinarily transmitted intact through the pollen, and the progeny show only the dominant characters. When the pollen of such a male parent is irradiated and then placed on the silks of such a recessive female, the seeds that develop are frequently defective in various ways, and many of them show the *recessive* endosperm characters, indicat-

ing that the dominant alleles in the pollen have been deleted or inactivated by the treatment.

When linked genes in the same chromosome are used, it is found that
several neighboring alleles usually disappear from the pollen at the same
time, indicating that a sectional deficiency has been brought about by
the irradiation (Fig. 114). Thus when a *c, sh, wx* (white, shrunken,

Fig. 114.—Deficiencies induced by irradiated pollen. An ear from a plant pure for
recessive genes *a, pr, su* affecting endosperm characters pollinated by irradiated pollen
bearing the dominant alleles of these genes, *A, Pr, Su*. Colorless (*a, pr*) and sugary
(*su*) seeds show absence (deficiency) of dominant alleles from irradiated pollen. (*From
Stadler.*)

waxy) ear is pollinated with X-rayed *C, Sh, Wx* (colored, full, starchy)
pollen, many of the seeds are colorless, indicating absence of the *C* gene,
but the majority of these are also shrunken and waxy. When *C* disappears from the pollen, *sh* and *wx* usually disappear also. This means
that a rather long section of chromosome VII (Fig. 89, p. 238) is deficient.
Deficiencies induced in *ripe pollen* do not seem to be lethal to the pollen

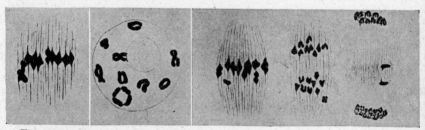

Fig. 115.—Chromosome abnormalities induced by irradiation in maize. Stages
in microsporogenesis showing ring formation and lagging chromosomes in the mutant
"semisterile." (*From Randolph.*)

tube or generative nuclei, although those present before maturation *are*
lethal to the gametophyte and are not transmitted through the pollen.
Many other types of chromosome changes have been thus produced in
maize, and some of these have been demonstrated by cytological methods
(Fig. 115).

Recently Stadler and collaborators have treated maize pollen with
ultraviolet light, using filters to obtain monochromatic light of specific
wave lengths. The pollen was then used to fertilize ovules containing a

number of recessive genes for endosperm characters. Ultraviolet light greatly increased the frequency of point mutations and deficiencies and of a type of change, found only after such treatment, in which only a part of the endosperm of the resulting seed is changed; but the rate of occurrence of translocations was not increased. Certain wave lengths were found to produce prevailingly one type of change, indicating a specific relationship between the type of mutation and the part of the spectrum from which the energy was introduced.

Analysis of the Effect of Radiation on Mutation.—The application of quantitative methods to the study of mutations following irradiation has

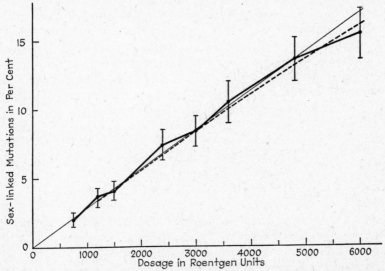

FIG. 116.—The proportionality between the frequency of sex-linked mutations and the radiation dosages applied, in *Drosophila melanogaster.* (*After Timofeeff-Ressovsky.*)

yielded several significant results. The clearest of these is that mutation frequency is directly proportional to the amount of energy applied. This is illustrated for Drosophila by the results of various workers shown in Fig. 116. Intensity of radiation was measured by its ionization effect on air. The results show clearly that the greater the quantity of radiant energy reaching the flies the greater the percentage of mutations induced. Similar demonstrations have been given by Stadler for gene mutations in barley and for induced deficiencies in maize.

This proportionality has been shown to apply also to the changes induced at a single locus, as for example the mutations induced at the white locus.

The proportionality relationship has been interpreted to mean that the induced mutations are due to direct hits of electrons in the gene and chromosome materials, the greater the number of hits, the greater the likelihood of an induced change. This may be the case, but it should not be forgotten that not only are the mutabilities of different loci not equal, but as Demerec (1937) has recently shown, genetic factors (genes stimulating mutability) affect the surroundings of the genes in such a way as to affect the general mutability rate. Some effects on mutability may thus occur through less direct channels.

The frequency of induced gene mutations may also depend upon the number of times the normal or wild-type genes are represented in the genotype. Stadler found that polyploid species, subjected to the same treatments, yield many fewer gene mutations than related species with fewer chromosomes. Thus cultivated species of wheat and oats with 21 pairs of chromosomes gave only about a hundredth as many mutations as common barley, which has only 7 pairs. But when 7-chromosome species of wheat and oats were treated, they showed a mutation rate about as high as that of barley, while a 14-chromosome species of wheat was intermediate in mutation rate between the 7- and 21-chromosome species. On the assumption that the 14-chromosome species of wheat, for example, have evolved from the 7-chromosome species by duplication of the whole chromosome complement, then any recessive mutation in only 1 of a set of 4 chromosomes would be unlikely to produce any effect, since it would be masked or hidden by the unmutated wild-type genes at the same locus in the other pair of duplicate chromosomes.

Thus in a 7-chromosome type a wild-type gene R_1 would be represented in each of a pair of chromosomes; in a 14-chromosome type it would be represented four times; and in a 21-chromosome type, six times. Mutation would affect these loci as follows:

Number of chromosome pairs	Genetic formula for a wild-type gene	Mutation $R \rightarrow r$	Segregation of rr
7	R_1R_1	R_1r_1	$3R:1r$
14	$R_1R_1R_2R_2$	$R_1r_1R_2R_2$	All R
21	$R_1R_1R_2R_2R_3R_3$	$R_1r_1R_2R_2R_3R_3$	All R

A new visible mutation in the 14-chromosome type would appear only if two mutations occur, that is, $R_1 - r_1$ and $R_2 - r_2$, to produce the type $r_1r_1r_2r_2$, which as we have seen is a condition required for the appearance of the full recessive type in the case of duplicate genes (p. 105). This coincidence of two rare events would be very rare in nature, and in the 21-chromosome type its frequency would be almost negligibly low. Polyploidy may not introduce any barrier to the *occurrence* of gene mutations, but it tends to prevent their *appearance*. The facts that

Stadler has obtained by irradiation thus support the interpretation of the origin of polyploid forms by duplication of chromosomes.

Theoretical Contributions of Radiation Genetics.—The increase in mutation rate obtained through radiation methods has provided a valuable technique for the quantitative study of mutation and of many problems of genetics.   Although it has not led to the formulation of new principles, it has provided such a wealth of new mutants and of chromosome changes that it has been possible, for example, firmly to establish the linear order of the genes as both a genetic and cytological fact, through the comparison of the maps based on crossing over and on gonial and salivary chromosomes broken by X radiation at specific points; to elucidate further the relation of chromosome rearrangements to lethal and to visible effects (position effects); and in many other ways has confirmed and extended the principles and increased the speed of discovery concerning the mechanism of hereditary transmission.

The results as they relate specifically to the mechanism of the effect and its application have been recently reviewed by Timofeeff-Ressovsky. The student may consult his book.   Here it need only be emphasized that the radiation work of the last decade has already shown that the physical basis of heredity, which is ordinarily fairly stable, may be changed to new stable conditions by introduction of energy from outside the living system and that the changes induced are in many respects similar to those that arise spontaneously.   This has, of course, raised the question as to whether natural radiation is the cause of the mutations that occur in nature.   Some calculations of Muller and Mott-Smith seem to indicate that the amount of natural earth radiation is insufficient to account for the frequency of natural mutations.

REFERENCES

Bateson, W.   1894.   Materials for the study of variation.   London and New York.

Baur, E.   1930.   Einführung in die Vererbungslehre.   11th ed.   Berlin.

Bridges, C. B.   1919.   The developmental stages at which mutations occur in the germ tract.   Proc. Soc. Exp. Biol. Med. **17.**

Demerec, M.   1931.   Behavior of two mutable genes of *Delphinium ajacis*.   Jour. Genet. **24.**

———.   1933.   What is a gene?   Jour. Hered. **24.**

———.   1935.   Unstable genes.   Bot. Rev. **1.**

———.   1937.   Frequency of spontaneous mutation in certain stocks of *Drosophila melanogaster*.   Genetics **22.**

De Vries, H.   1910.   The mutation theory.   Chicago.

Dobzhansky, T.   1936.   Induced chromosomal aberrations in animals *in* Biological Effects of Radiation.   (Edited by Duggar.)   Vol. II.   Pp. 1167–1208.   New York.

———.   1937.   Genetics and the origin of species.   New York.

—— and M. L. Queal. 1938. Genetics of Natural Populations. II. Genic variation in populations of *Drosophila pseudoobscura* inhabiting isolated mountain ranges. Genetics **23**.

Dubinin, N. P., and collaborators. 1934. Experimental study of the ecogenotypes of *Drosophila melanogaster*. (Russian, English summary.) Jour. Biol. **3**. (Cited from Dobzhansky, 1937.)

—— M. A. Heptner, Z. A. Demidova, and L. I. Djachkova. 1936. Genetic constitution and gene-dynamics of wild populations of *Drosophila melanogaster*. Jour. Biol. **5**.

Duggar, B. M. (editor). 1936. Biological effects of radiation. 2 vols. New York.

Emerson, R. A. 1917. Genetical studies of variegated pericarp in maize. Genetics **2**.

Galton, F. 1889. Natural inheritance. London.

Hanson, F. B., and F. Heys. 1929. An analysis of the effects of the different rays of radium in producing lethal mutations in Drosophila. Amer. Nat. **63**.

Muller, H. J. 1930. Radiation and genetics. Amer. Nat. **64**.

Oliver, C. P. 1934. Radiation genetics. Quart. Rev. Biol. **9**.

Schultz, J. 1936. Radiation and the study of mutations in animals *in* Biological Effects of Radiation. (Edited by Duggar.) Vol. II. Pp. 1209–1261. New York.

Spencer, W. P. 1935. Visible mutations in Drosophila. Amer. Nat. **69**.

Stadler, L. J., and G. F. Sprague. 1936. Genetic effects of ultra-violet radiation in maize. Proc. Nat. Acad. Sci. **22**.

Timofeeff-Ressovsky, N. W. 1934. The experimental production of mutations. Biol. Rev. **9**: 411–457.

——. 1937. Experimentelle Mutationsforschung in der Vererbungslehre. Dresden and Leipzig.

Tschetverikoff, S. S. 1928. Über die genetische Beschaffenheit wilder Populationen. Zeitschr. Ind. Abst. Vererb. Suppl. Bd. II.

PROBLEMS

356. Most mutations are thought to be harmful rather than helpful to the organism in which they appear. Why?

357. What difference will there be in the way in which dominant mutations and recessive mutations, occurring in gametogenesis, come to expression phenotypically?

358. In studying the origin of gene mutations, is it easier to use dominant or recessive mutations? Explain.

359. From an examination of the chromosome maps of Drosophila do you think that mutations are equally likely to occur in all regions of the chromosome?

360. What suggestion can you make as to the reason for the high mutability of some loci as compared with others?

361. Why is it to be expected that gene mutations should occur more frequently at or just before the formation of gametes than at any other time?

362. Assuming an equal frequency of gene mutation, will sporophytic or gametophytic tissue be more variable, phenotypically?

363. It has been suggested that so-called mutations are really the results of segregation from remote hybrid ancestry. Of what significance in this question is the fact that such variations are also found among the offspring of diploids which have had their origin through the (rarely occurring) self-fertilization of haploids?

364. Gametic lethals are unknown in animals but pollen lethals are of common occurrence in plants. Explain.

365. In the *"ClB"* method of determining the appearance of a new lethal mutation in the sex chromosome, why is it that the presence of a new lethal in the chromosome from the irradiated male parent does not prove lethal to this female, since she already possesses one lethal in the other chromosome?

366. In the "attached-X" method how would the results be affected if the attached X's should break apart in the test female?

367. How would you determine whether a case of variegation or spotting is due to gene mutation in somatic tissue or to a gene for variegation?

368. It is claimed that some types of plants which are propagated vegetatively in time "run out" or fail to maintain their original character. To what might this change be due?

369. If two apple trees of the same variety differ markedly in their yield, and buds taken from the better one consistently produce better yielding trees than buds taken from the poorer one, what conclusion would you draw? If buds taken from these two trees produce trees which are essentially similar in yield, what conclusion would you draw?

370. There are persons with one brown eye and one blue one. Suggest an explanation.

CHAPTER XIV

ORIGIN OF HEREDITARY DIFFERENCES. II
CHROMOSOME CHANGES

The remaining type of heritable variations consist in departures from the normal number of the chromosomes, or from the normal arrangements of the genes within the chromosomes. Their physical basis has been ascertained during recent years through a coordinated application of cytological and genetical methods.

The species and varieties of animals and plants are characterized each by a certain number of chromosomes, and each chromosome is characterized by the possession of a definite series of gene loci arranged in a linear order. These two aspects of nuclear structure, chromosome number and gene arrangement, constitute the *karyotype* of the group, just as the sum total of the particular genes of an individual is referred to collectively as its genotype. The constancy of the species or group characters is due to the stability with which both the genotype and the karyotype are transmitted in heredity.

The sexual reproduction of most animals and plants takes place by means of the orderly reduction of the diploid chromosome number of the zygote to the haploid number of the gamete, and the general occurrence of Mendelian segregation, which is a by-product of this mechanism, shows that this is the usual or normal condition. The genotype, as we have seen, is subject to variation by gene mutation. In a like way the karyotype is subject to variation in the number and form of the chromosomes, and the spatial arrangement of the genes. The constancy of both genotype and karyotype is thus relative rather than absolute; departures take place within the framework of the normal methods of reproduction, and changes which do not disrupt the mechanism are transmitted by heredity. Whether they become incorporated in the genotype and karyotype of some part of the group depends upon the stability of the particular changed condition and upon the interaction of the new condition with the internal constitution and the environment of the changed individuals.

Classification of Chromosome Changes.—Among the many variations in the karyotype, those which have been analyzed may be grouped under two main types, those which differ from the normal or ancestral *number of the chromosomes*, and those that differ in the *number or arrangement of the loci* within the karyotype.

I. Changes in the number of chromosomes.
  A. Changes involving entire sets; n = basic or monoploid number.
    1. *Haploidy* (n); each chromosome represented singly.
    2. *Polyploidy;* each chromosome represented by more than two homologues. Triploidy ($3n$); tetraploidy ($4n$); pentaploidy ($5n$), etc. An autopolyploid is one derived by chromosome multiplication from a single diploid, so that the homologues come from the same source as in pure strains or homozygotes. An allopolyploid is one derived from a hybrid between two diploids, so that the homologues come from different sources.

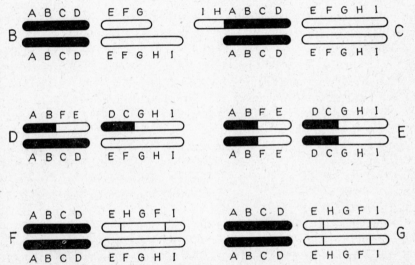

Fig. 117.—Classification of chromosome changes. *A*, normal chromosomes; *B*, deficiency; *C*, duplication, *D*, heterozygous translocation; *E*, homozygous translocation; *F*, heterozygous inversion; *G*, homozygous inversion. (*From Dobzhansky.*)

  B. Changes involving the numbers of chromosomes in a set (*heteroploidy*).
    1. *Monosomics* represent the loss of one chromosome from one set. Where this occurs in the diploid the chromosome complement is $2n - 1$.
    2. *Polysomics* represent the addition of one or more chromosomes to one set. *Trisomic* = $2n + 1$, tetrasomic, $2n + 2$, etc. (More than one set may be affected: double trisomics = $2n + 1 + 1$, etc.)
  II. Changes in the number or arrangement of gene loci within a chromosome (Fig. 117).

A. In number.
  1. *Deficiency* or deletion—loss of one or more gene loci.
  2. *Duplication*—addition of one or more gene loci.
B. In arrangement.
  1. *Translocation.*
      a. Reciprocal tranlocation or segmental interchange. Mutual exchange of parts between nonhomologous chromosomes to form two new chromosomes, for example, left part of chromosome I with right part of II, and right part of I with left part of II.
      b. Simple translocation. Breaking away of a part of a chromosome and its attachment to another intact nonhomologous chromosome.
  2. *Inversion.* Within a chromosome, one section with its block of loci may be turned end for end, producing a new gene order; for example, a chromosome with loci in order A B C D E F G may become A B · E D C · F G (internal inversion), C B A · D E F G (terminal inversion) etc.

CHANGES IN NUMBER OF CHROMOSOMES

The classification of chromosome changes as given above is based on evidence both from breeding experiments and from cytological observation which in most cases confirm each other. That this agreement between two types of evidence holds over so wide a range of departures from the normal, bears striking witness to the correctness and the usefulness of the chromosome theory of heredity. It shows too that the order of the chromosome mechanism of meiosis, while relatively fixed, still permits the occurrence and preservation of many kinds of variants, and thus provides the opportunity for new chromosomes and new gene arrangements to evolve. In the further discussion, which follows, of these types of chromosomal changes, our interest will be centered on this latter question, that is, in how far does each of these types of change furnish the new hereditary variations upon which evolution must depend?

Haploidy.—It sometimes happens that an egg with the haploid number of chromosomes develops without fertilization and produces an individual with a single ($1n$) set of chromosomes. This happens normally in the reproduction of some animals (such as bees, wasps, certain moths, and rotifers), in which unfertilized eggs develop into haploid males. In some animals (as frogs) the egg may be artificially induced to develop parthenogenetically. Often in such cases the diploid number is restored by division of the chromosomes without division of the cell. Where this does not occur, such artificial haploids are likely to be weak and infertile. In lower plants one normal part of the life cycle (the gametophyte) is regularly haploid, while in higher plants this haploid generation is reduced to a few cells (in pollen tube and embryo sac) which are unable to lead an independent existence. In

FIG. 118.—Polypoid series in Datura.   Above, haploid; in center, diploid; below, tetraploid.
(*From Blakeslee.*)

such plants, however, an unfertilized egg cell may occasionally produce a haploid sporophyte such as the Datura plant shown in Fig. 118. Haploids have been found in several species, for example, Datura, Nicotiana, wheat, tomato. In each case the haploid plant showed close resemblance to the diploid parent type except for smaller size, lack of vigor, and rarity of viable gametes. In Datura the haploid, in the rare cases when self-fertilization occurs, produces only normal diploid offspring, showing that the few viable gametes must contain the normal haploid set of chromosomes. These are probably produced by direct division without reduction. Haploids are of interest in that they cannot be heterozygous, so that pure types are obtained immediately when a complex heterozygote passes through one such haploid generation. This method may be consciously employed to obtain genetically pure material. Haploids may be induced by cold, radiation, or other external changes, but because of their rarity and infertility the haploid forms probably play little part in adding to the supply of new natural variations.

Polyploidy.—Much more common than haploids are modifications of chromosome number in the direction of an increase over that of the diploid, with the formation of polyploids of various degrees. Among these are *tetraploids*, in which the diploid complement is doubled, each chromosome being represented by a set of four in the body cells and two in the gametes. *Triploids*, where each set consists of three homologous chromosomes, commonly arise from crosses between diploid and tetraploid. Higher members of the series, such as hexaploids and octaploids, are less common, and the increase in number of chromosome sets seems definitely limited.

Polyploids produced by multiplication of the basic (n) chromosome number characteristic of a given race are known as *autopolyploids;* where they arise from fusion of gametes having more than the haploid number but coming from different genetic origins, they are known as *allopolyploids.*

Tetraploids.—The sudden origin of the tetraploid ($4n$) condition from the diploid ($2n$) has been observed frequently under experimental conditions in plants, and the existence of tetraploid and diploid races of the same species indicates that the chromosome changes resulting in polyploidy occur frequently in nature (Fig. 118). Tetraploids arise by the doubling of the whole chromosome set. This has been shown to occur in several ways.

Autotetraploids.—Within a species a nuclear division unaccompanied by a cell division results in a cell with a double number of chromosomes, all containing similar genes. Flowers born on branches descended from such cells produce $2n$ gametes which, if they unite with similar $2n$ gametes, perpetuate the tetraploid condition through sexual reproduction. Such autotetraploidy in vegetative cells may occur spontaneously; or it may also be induced by cold treatment, as Belling and Blakeslee have shown in Datura; from adventitious buds arising at grafts or after decapitation as in tomatoes (*Solanum lycopersicum*) or in nightshade (*S. nigrum*) and by chemical treatments.

An especially simple and effective method of inducing polyploids has recently been developed through use of the alkaloid colchicine. Weak solutions of this substance are applied to buds by immersion, and spraying, or in agar or lanolin; or to seeds by soaking. In treated material a high proportion of dividing cells fail to carry division through to completion, the chromosomes dividing but the new cell wall failing to appear. Such cells are thus tetraploid, and often give rise to pure tetraploid branches. Polyploids of higher order may be produced in the same way. This treatment has proved effective in a wide variety of plants and with the eggs of certain animals.

Autotetraploids usually (though not invariably) differ from their ancestral diploids in a number of characters, especially greater stature of stem and size of leaves and flowers ("gigas" type), these being due to the increased size of their cells. Other structural differences involve the shape of various organs, as of the leaves and capsule of Datura and the fruits of cucurbits. Autotetraploids are often phenotypically different from diploids in less concentrated cell sap, slower growth, and greater hardiness.

Von Wettstein has recently reported a case in mosses (Bryum) where an autotetraploid ($2n$ gametophyte, $4n$ sporophyte) showed gigas characters (Fig. 119) and almost complete sterility at first but, during the course of eleven years of vegetative propagation, became reduced to the normal size as to body and cells and grew almost fully fertile (Fig. 119 right).

The reproduction of autotetraploids may be almost normal. The tetraploid Datura produces viable gametes with $2n$ chromosomes (24) and a few with irregular numbers. These regular gametes result from the reduction of the 48 chromosomes by the formation of 12 groups of four chromosomes each (quadrivalents) and the passage of two homologues to each gamete. This is apparently a random process as shown by the segregation of two genes in tetraploid Datura. A purple-flowered tetraploid (*PPPP*) crossed with a white-flowered tetraploid (*pppp*) gives purple in F_1, and an F_2 ratio of 35 purple to one white, from which it has been inferred that the gametes formed by the F_1(*PPpp*) were $1PP$: $4Pp$:$1pp$, the result expected from random assortment. Crane and Darlington have pointed out that such random segregation of chromatids is to be expected on the chiasma-type theory of crossing over only when there is the maximum (50 per cent) of crossing over between the gene studied and the spindle-fiber attachment. The random segregation found in Datura may thus be exceptional; according to Darlington a higher proportion of recessives may be expected in cases where less than 50 per cent of crossing over occurs between gene and spindle attachment.

Although the fertility of autotetraploids is generally somewhat reduced by the formation of gametes with abnormal chromosome num-

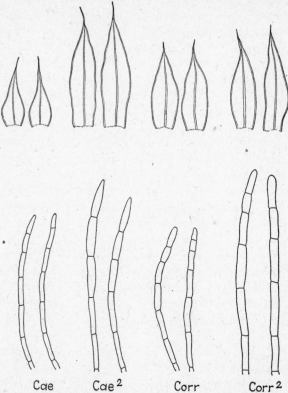

Cae   Cae²   Corr   Corr²

FIG. 119.—Leaves (above) and paraphyses (below) of 1n (Cae) and 2n (Cae²) of *Bryum caespiticium;* and of 1n (Corr) and 2n (Corr²) of *B. Corrensii.* (*From von Wettstein.*)

bers, some may reproduce normally enough to become established as new types. But a single tetraploid arising in a dioecious plant or in bisexual animals would have little chance of perpetuating its kind since its diploid gametes would meet in general only the haploid gametes of the normal population and produce not tetraploids but a new 3n or triploid type. Müntzing has reviewed the literature on autopolyploids and further details will be found in his paper.

Allotetraploids.—Allotetraploids commonly originate in a hybrid between two plant species or genera where the chromosome set contributed by each parent undergoes doubling and produces in the hybrid a chromosome number which is the sum of the diploid numbers of the two parent forms.   Such a type is sometimes referred to as an *amphidiploid*.   An example will make this clear.   Karpechenko (1928) crossed the radish *Raphanus sativus* (2n = 18), with the cabbage, *Brassica*

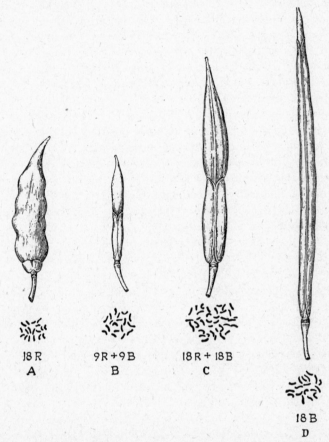

18 R
A

9R + 9B
B

18 R + 18 B
C

18 B
D

Fig. 120.—Pods and somatic chromosomes (R, Raphanus; B, Brassica) of radish (Raphanus) *A*, cabbage (Brassica) *D*, their diploid hybrid *B*, and their allotetraploid hybrid *C*.   (*After Karpechenko.*)

oleracea (2n = 18), (Fig. 120).   The F_1 hybrids had 18 chromosomes, 9 from the radish and 9 from the cabbage.   These hybrids were nearly sterile but under favorable conditions some F_1 plants produced a few seeds.   Some of the F_2 plants resembled the hybrid, others were intermediate between it and the radish parent.   Those which resembled the F_1 were found to have 36 chromosomes, the sum of the chromosome numbers of the two parent species.   They were thus tetraploid hybrids and proved not only to unite certain characters from both parents but to be fully fertile and to breed true to the hybrid and tetraploid characters.

A study of the meiotic divisions of the F_1 hybrids showed that pairing of radish and cabbage chromosomes did not occur and the 18 univalents were generally distributed at random to the gametes, each of which received from 6 to 12 chromosomes and were not functional. Occasionally, however, in pollen mother cells the first meiotic division was abnormal, resulting in nuclei with all 18 chromosomes, so that a few pollen grains formed from these contained 9 radish and 9 cabbage chromosomes.

Since the F_2 tetraploids had 36 chromosomes it is probable that these arose through union of such exceptional F_1 gametes so that the tetraploid had 18 radish and 18 cabbage chromosomes. Meiosis in the tetraploid was regular and normal; 18 pairs of chromosomes were formed. Undoubtedly the 9 cabbage chromosomes paired with their 9 cabbage homologues, and the 9 radish chromosomes paired with their homologues from the same parent species (autosyndesis). The gametes of the tetraploid thus each transmitted 9 cabbage and 9 radish chromosomes and perpetuated a new set of characters in a fertile intergeneric hybrid, breeding true to its own type and infertile with both parents, thus constituting essentially a new species.

Allotetraploids have occurred frequently in experimental material among plants and their occurrence in nature is highly probable. The doubling of the chromosome number has occurred in a variety of ways, as reviewed by Darlington and Dobzhansky. Since chromosome doubling may lead to the establishment of a new fertile type from a sterile hybrid, this kind of chromosome change is undoubtedly one of the important mechanisms by which new species of plants may originate.

Animal Polyploids.—Among animals polyploid series and experimental polyploids are much less frequent than in plants. As has been pointed out above this is probably due to the separation of the sexes in most animals, and to the sexual unbalance and sterility that is likely to result from changed ratios of autosomes and sex chromosomes (p. 263). Under parthenogenetic or asexual reproduction this bar to the reproduction of polyploids is less likely to operate, and of the few cases known in animals, two occur in connection with parthenogenesis (in the sow bug Trichoniscus and in the shrimp, *Artemia salina*). In the case of Drosophila where haploid, diploid, triploid, and tetraploid forms have been found, these are normal only when the ratio of X chromosomes to autosomes remains 1:1 (female) or 1:2 (male). Other ratios result in abnormality or sterility, and these are likely to occur when polyploidy is superimposed upon the X-Y mechanism.

Heteroploidy.—Some of the mutant forms which have appeared sporadically in Datura, Oenothera, Drosophila, and several other carefully studied genera have been shown to owe their peculiarities to departures from the normal number of chromosomes, by which one (or rarely two) chromosomes have been added to, or subtracted from,

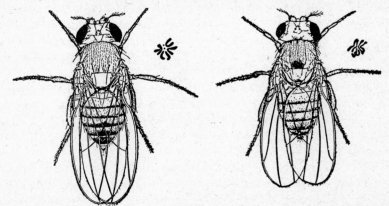

Fig. 121.—Normal (left) and haplo-IV individuals of *Drosophila melanogaster.* Their respective chromosome groups are shown at the right of each. (*From Bridges.*)

the usual diploid complement. These cases have been most thoroughly investigated in Datura and Drosophila, and our brief account will be confined to these genera. It is characteristic of such heteroploid forms $(2n + 1, 2n - 1, \text{etc.})$ that they appear sporadically but with greater frequency from triploids and from stocks in which nondisjunction is of frequent occurrence; that they show numerous and generally slight departures from the wild type in many characters; and that they never breed true and are of lower fertility than normal diploids so that they probably do not become established as new types in nature. The transmission of mutant genes also follows a different course in heteroploids from that with which we have become familiar in diploid inheritance. The case of haplo-IV in Drosophila is illustrated in Fig. 121.

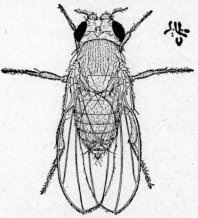

Fig. 122.—Triplo-IV individual of *Drosophila melanogaster.* Its chromosome group is at the right. (*From Bridges.*)

Triplo-IV Drosophila.—From triploid $(3n)$ females there appear frequently mutant forms with very slight departures from the wild type but in the opposite direction from those occurring in haplo-IV. Such flies have narrow pointed wings, coarse bristles and smooth eyes (Fig.

122).   Crossed to flies with a IV chromosome recessive, for example, eyeless, the mutants produce mutant flies like themselves and wild-type flies in about equal numbers. F_1 mutants backcrossed to eyeless give a regular trisomic ratio of five wild type to one eyeless.   On cytological examination the mutants prove to have three IV chromosomes.   Such heteroploids are known as extra-chromosome, or $2n + 1$, types; or they may be said to be *trisomics*, that is, having three chromosomes instead of two in one set.

Similar changes have affected the X chromosomes in Drosophila since haplo-X individuals (without a Y) have been found, always as sterile males; while triplo-X flies occasionally survive and are super-females (see Chap. XI).   Flies with one less or one more of the other chromosomes probably are not viable.

Datura Heteroploids.   *Primary Mutants.*—The most complete series of extra-chromosome mutants has been discovered and intensively studied in the Jimson weed by Blakeslee, Belling, and their collaborators. The normal Jimson weed has twelve pairs of chromosomes.   In breeding experiments, 12 mutant types have arisen, each of which has a typical set of plant characters which deviates from the wild type in numerous specific ways (Fig. 123).   Each of these 12 so-called *primary* types has an extra chromosome in one of the 12 sets, and it is a *different chromosome* which has become doubled in each of the 12 mutant types.   Thus the type known as Poinsettia was found always to be associated with an extra chromosome in the set which contains the genes for purple and white flowers.

When any one of these 12 primary $2n + 1$ types is crossed with normal, simple Mendelian ratios are not obtained.   The mutant characters are transmitted as a group (through the eggs only) to certain of the offspring and do not separate and recombine, as would be expected if the different traits depended on separate genes.

It is clear now that the complex of mutant characters is determined by the extra chromosome, which gives the plant an extra "dose" of all of the genes contained in the duplicated chromosome.   The presence of three instead of two of each kind of gene in one chromosome, acting in an individual in which genes in the other chromosomes are merely duplex, produces specific changes in many characters in accordance with the idea of genic balance.   The irregular transmission of the complex of characters brought about by the extra chromosome is due to the inviability of any pollen which has either more or less than 12 normal chromosomes. Extra chromosomes are thus not transmitted through the pollen but only through the egg cells.   Thus the Poinsettia $2n + 1$ form has an extra chromosome in the set which contains the gene pair purple and white.   If we let p stand for white and P for purple, the egg cells of a

NORMAL

ROLLED   GLOSSY   BUCKLING   ELONGATE

ECHINUS   COCKLEBUR   MICROCARPIC   REDUCED

POINSETTIA   SPINACH   GLOBE   ILEX

FIG. 123.—The seed capsules of primary heteroploid mutants in Datura. The extra chromosome in each is shown diagrammatically. (*From Blakeslee.*)

purple Poinsettia of the genotype Ppp have been shown to be in the ratio of $1P:2p$ $2Pp:1pp$, while the only viable pollen grains are P and p in a ratio of one purple (P) to two white (p). Segregating ratios for purple and white are therefore distorted not only by the triple representation of a gene but by inviability of pollen grains with the extra chromosome. The same is true for trisomic inheritance in maize. Except for this last pecularity, trisomic inheritance in Datura and maize follows the same course as in triplo-IV Drosophila.

Heteroploidy of the $2n + 1$ type has also been found in Oenothera, where seven primary types have been identified, each one probably corresponding to a duplication of one of the seven haploid chromosomes.

In Datura the analysis of heteroploidy has been carried much further. Primary mutants have been discovered not only in diploids, yielding $2n + 1$ types, but also in tetraploids $(4n + 1)$ and in haploids $(1n + 1)$. The changes in many of the plant characters shown by these primary mutants are much greater than those shown by the polyploid series $1n$, $2n$, $3n$, $4n$, since in the heteroploids the normal balance existing among the chromosomes is upset. If each of the chromosome sets possesses a specific complement of genes, characteristic of this chromosome and different from that of any of the other sets (an assumption entirely in accord with the known facts), then the addition of one member to a given set will increase the influence of this set on the development of the individual; and a study of the characteristics of the primary mutants thus produced may be expected to give some indication of the character of the genes in this particular chromosome. An extra chromosome of another set, if added to the normal diploid constitution, will tend to influence development in the direction characteristic of its own genes, which may be entirely different from the tendency given by the first chromosome. The balance may be shifted in this direction or in that, depending upon which chromosome or chromosomes are in excess. If each set possesses an extra chromosome, a triploid individual is produced in which the proportional influence of each set of chromosomes is the same as in the diploid and the balance is thus unchanged. Such individuals differ but little from normal diploids in appearance (Chap. XVI).

Secondary Mutants.—There can evidently be only as many primary heteroploid types as there are pairs of chromosomes. In Datura, however, with 12 pairs, there are many more than 12 recognizably different $2n + 1$ types, so that some of them must belong to a different category. Certain of these are termed *secondary* mutants. There are a number of differences between primary and secondary trisomics. Triploid plants, among the offspring of which forms with extra chromosomes are numerous, ordinarily produce only primaries and only as many of these as there are pairs of chromosomes. The primaries do not often give rise to secondaries but secondaries often give rise to primaries, usually to specific ones, so that it is possible by this fact and by structural resemblances to

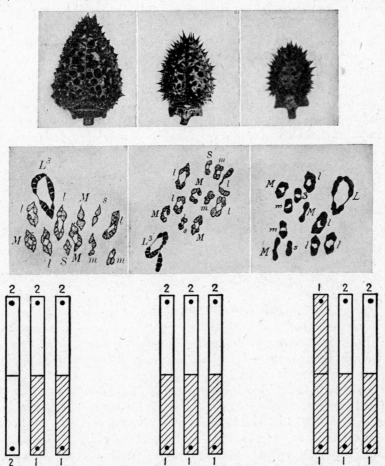

Fig. 124.—Capsules (above), chromosome configuration (in center) and chromosome diagrams (below) of a primary and its two secondaries in Datura. In center, the primary Rolled. At left, its secondary Sugarloaf. At right, its secondary Polycarpic. (*After Blakeslee.*)

relate a secondary to a definite primary. Four of the primaries in Datura each have two secondaries (Fig. 124), the others only one or none. Where there are two, the primary is intermediate between them in most respects. Where a gene is carried in the trisome of a primary it shows characteristic trisomic inheritance, since it is present three times, but in the secondary related to this primary it often gives normal disomic inheritance, suggesting that it is present only twice in the secondary. This led Belling to the hypothesis, now well substantiated, that the extra chromosome in a secondary contains one of the halves of the extra chromosome in the primary, but doubled.   Cytological evidence supports this view, for the trisome of a primary at synapsis is usually either a chain of three or a pair with the extra chromosome appended at one end whereas that of a secondary is a closed circle of three (Fig. 125).   This is to be expected if similar parts of a chromosome attract one another at synapsis, as they seem to do.   A doubled half could evidently intercalate itself between the ends of a pair to form a circle but a normal third chromosome could not.   This hypothesis explains satisfactorily the various differences in genetical and cytological behavior between primary

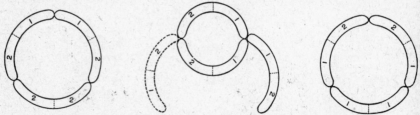

Fig. 125.—Diagram of a trisome in Datura.   In center, chromosome configuration of primary at synapsis.   At left and right, those of its two secondaries.

and secondary heteroploids in Datura and has been applied successfully to maize and other plants.   The origin of a primary involves but a single step away from normal—the presence of an extra chromosome; the origin of a secondary involves an additional step—a modification of the character of this chromosome.

Tertiary Mutants and Segmental Interchange.—In a third type of $2n + 1$ mutants, the tertiaries, the extra chromosome is made up of parts of two *different* chromosomes.   Such a type was first described in Datura.   Here the chromosomes in Line 1, the race first studied, are designated as $1 \cdot 2, 3 \cdot 4, 5 \cdot 6$, and so on.   The extra chromosome of the tertiary mutant seemed to resemble both chromosome $1 \cdot 2$ and chromosome $17 \cdot 18$, for it often united these two at synapsis, one of its ends apparently attracting the 1 end of $1 \cdot 2$ and the other the 18 end of $17 \cdot 18$.   This particular extra chromosome appeared only among offspring from a cross with another pure race, Line B, suggesting to Belling that in Line B there had been an interchange between chromosomes $1 \cdot 2$ and $17 \cdot 18$ of Line 1, so that these now were $1 \cdot 18$ and $2 \cdot 17$.   If this were the case, a hybrid between Line 1 and Line B should have all four of these chromosomes and should show at synapsis a circle of four chromosomes, thus:

This is the condition actually found. The chromosomal situation in these two lines and in their hybrid is shown diagrammatically in Fig. 126.

Segmental interchange evidently produces no alteration in the number or character of the genes and no external variation but changes only the distribution of the genes within the chromosome complement. The extent of the differences of this sort between two types and their distribution among the chromosomes can be determined by studying the cytological configuration of F_1 individuals resulting from crosses between the types. Where no segmental interchange has taken place, the reduc-

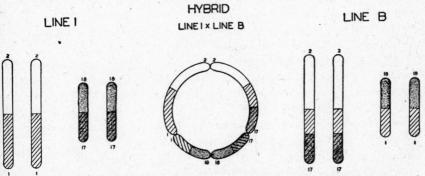

FIG. 126.—Diagrams of two pairs of chromosomes in two prime types in Datura, Line 1 and Line B, and (in center) of hybrid between them, showing ring formation.

tion division will show 12 pairs of chromosomes (bivalents). In Line B, as compared with Line 1, there has been only one interchange, as described above, producing a ring of 4 chromosomes and 10 separate pairs. In crosses between two other diploid lines, a ring of 4 chromosomes and 10 pairs is also found, indicating a single segmental interchange, but this can be shown to involve different chromosomes from the first. Between still others there are two rings of 4 chromosomes and 8 pairs. Such a result must have been brought about by two segmental interchanges, involving two independent sets or pairs. Thus if $1 \cdot 2$ and $3 \cdot 4$ showed an interchange to become $1 \cdot 3$ and $2 \cdot 4$; and $5 \cdot 6$ and $7 \cdot 8$ became $5 \cdot 7$ and $6 \cdot 8$, two rings would be produced:

More rarely the F_1 configuration shows a ring of six chromosomes, which can be explained by two segmental interchanges in three pairs of chromosomes.   Thus if one of the races is 1 · 2, 3 · 4, 5 · 6 and if 3 and 2 interchange and 4 and 5 interchange, the other race may be 1 · 3, 2 · 5, 4 · 6, and the ring of six is:

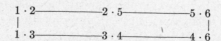

More rarely chains rather than rings appear in the F_1 configuration, and these are explained as due to the inversion of a segment in its interchange so that one end is turned inward and cannot become attached to the corresponding end in the other line.

Pure races differing in the arrangement within them of chromosome segments, which are, of course, merely blocks of genes, are known in Datura as *prime types*.   A number of these, widely distributed geographically, have now been isolated.

It should be noted that these prime types in Datura tend to maintain themselves unaltered due to the characteristic fashion in which the chromosomal components of the rings separate at reduction.   In the ring of four formed by the F_1 between Line 1 and Line B (Fig. 126), there are evidently two ways in which reduction might take place.   Chromosomes 1 · 2 and 1 · 18 might go to one pole, and 2 · 17 and 17 · 18 to the other; or 1 · 2 and 17 · 18 might go together, and 1 · 18 and 2 · 17.   The former method would result in nonviable pollen, since the 17 end would be lacking in one gamete and the 1 end in the other; and so all the pollen resulting from this sort of reduction would be bad, while that resulting from the alternate method would be good. If it were a matter of chance as to which type was followed, we should expect 50 per cent bad pollen in such F_1 plants.   This is actually the case in maize hybrids which arise from crosses between races differing by one segmental interchange.   In Datura, however, such types produce practically all good pollen, indicating that the second method alone occurs. This merely means that alternate chromosomes in a circle go to the same pole, a result that is perhaps to be expected in view of the probability that similar ends, which attract each other early in meiosis, repel each other later, so that a chromosome would tend to separate from both its neighbors.   As a result of this, the gametes of an F_1 are of two kinds, each preserving the arrangement of one of the parental types, and by this means the prime types tend to persist when once established even though intercrossing may take place between them.

Reciprocal Translocation in Maize.—In cases where the chromosomes assort at reduction by chance and thus half the pollen is bad, as in the so-called "semisterile" types of maize, the location of the breaks in the chromosomes which occur in segmental interchange can be determined by genetic methods. Thus if chromosomes $1 \cdot 2$ and $3 \cdot 4$ undergo translocation and the translocated race is crossed with the original one, a ring of four chromosomes is found at synapsis, just as in Datura (Fig. 126); but half of the pollen (that which results from the reduction to $1 \cdot 2 - 1 \cdot 3$ and $2 \cdot 4 - 3 \cdot 4$) is bad. If in the 2 arm of the original race, let us say, there is a gene a and in the corresponding locus of the other race its dominant allele, the semisterile hybrid is thus heterozygous for it (as in Fig. 127). If this plant is now crossed back on the original race $(1 \cdot 2, 3 \cdot 4 \text{ and } aa)$, the $1 \cdot 2 - 3 \cdot 4$ gametes will produce plants with all good pollen and of genotype aa, and the $1 \cdot 3 - 2 \cdot 4$ gametes will produce semisterile plants, genetically Aa. If, however, there has been crossing over in the 2 arm, involving the a locus, at synapsis, some of the normal plants resulting from the backcross will appear A and some of the semisteriles, a. Four classes of offspring will thus result; normal a and semisterile A (the noncrossovers) and normal A and semisterile a (the crossovers). The frequency of the latter will evidently serve as a measure of the distance between the break or translocation point and the gene a. If the location of a is known, the position of the break may thus be found just as if it were a gene. Rhoades has found that when the crossover percentages between several genes and the chromosome break are determined, the results are what would be expected from the known position of these various genes on the chromosome.

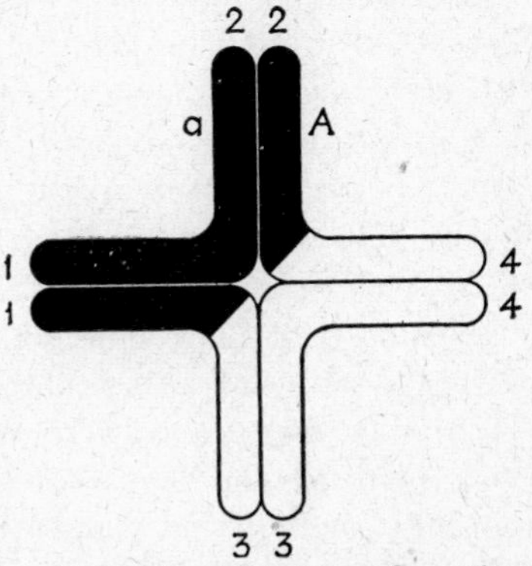

Fig. 127.—Meiotic configuration in a semisterile maize hybrid heterozygous for a reciprocal translocation between chromosome 1.2 (black) and 3.4 (white), at synapsis before the four chromosomes open out into a circle. The location of gene A-a is shown in arm 2.

The cause of these segmental interchanges is unknown. All involve chromosome breakage and reciprocal translocation. They have evidently occurred at rare intervals in nature but may be induced much more frequently by radiation or other environmental factors.

The investigation of heteroploidy in Datura and other plants has disclosed two mechanisms of great importance in the interpretation of (1) development through the theory of genic balance and (2) evolution through the theory of segmental interchange. We shall have to return to the applications of these theories to general problems in other connections.

CHANGES IN GENE ARRANGEMENT

The changes that occur within or between chromosomes (deficiency, duplication, translocation, and inversion) have already been described. It remains to inquire as to the mode of origin of these, their phenotypic effects, and the part they play in giving rise to new hereditary variations.

These changes in which blocks of genes are deleted or transposed occur spontaneously and, although we have little data on how commonly they occur, they probably have a lower frequency than gene mutations. In the sample of wild *Drosophila melanogaster* studied by Dubinin (p. 298), no chromosomal aberrations were found. They appear, however, in the offspring of irradiated parents and probably show proportionality between dosage and frequency as was noted in the case of gene mutations, although the different types have not been extensively studied from this point of view. The salivary chromosomes of Drosophila larvae from treated gametes show a high proportion of chromosomal changes. Many of these probably have little or no gross phenotypic effect and would not be detected by the usual methods.

What actually happens when new translocations or inversions occur is not known with certainty. In forms that have been most extensively studied (Drosophila, maize, Datura, Oenothera) most of the translocations are reciprocal, that is, mutual exchanges of sections between nonhomologous chromosomes. Belling suggested that this might be due to "crossing over" between nonhomologous chromosomes, and McClintock showed that this does occur in maize. Simple translocations, not involving exchange, are apparently rare or absent. This might be explained by the fact that fragments of chromosomes which do not contain a spindle-fiber attachment are always lost unless they become attached to another chromosome. By a similar exceptional event the same chromosome may possibly loop upon itself and break and re-form at the point of junction of the strands, and thus give rise to inversions, deficiencies, and duplications. It is fairly clear that the Ultrabar duplication arises as a result of unequal crossing over at the Bar locus (p. 336) and the original Bar mutation probably arose in the same way. Once one of these chromosomal rearrangements has occurred, it may lead directly to others.

Muller has suggested one way in which inversions may lead to other chromosomal changes. Assume two chromosomes R and R^1 with genes in the following order:

R ABCDEFGHIJKLMNOPQ

R^1 ABCDEFGHIJKLMNOPQ

These by inversion may become:

R ABC.MLKJIHGFED.NOPQ

R^1 ABCDE.NMLKJIHGF.OPQ

A cross of parents having R and R^1 would in the hybrid produce synapses as follows with like genes opposed:

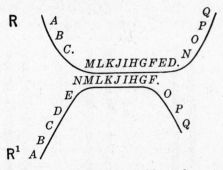

Crossing over in the central section would produce new chromosomes

r^1 ABC.MLKJIHGF.OPQ (deficiency for *DEN*)

r^2 ABCDE.NMLKJIHGFED.NOPQ (duplication of *DEN*)

Phenotypic Effects.—Chromosomal rearrangements are frequently accompanied by lethal effects. Deficiencies are nearly always lethal when homozygous, although in several cases in Drosophila very short deficiencies have proved to be viable. Large duplications are also generally lethal probably because of the disturbed genic balance. Small duplications, however, may be of normal viability. Bridges' finding of "repeats" in the Drosophila salivary chromosomes (p. 237) suggests that some loci may be duplicated at least once in the normal animal. Deficiencies nearly always show a dominant phenotypic effect which may be very marked and affect many parts of the life cycle as in the case of the Minute bristle deficiencies of Drosophila in which length of larval life, moulting, and many characters of the adult are changed. The same is true of duplications.

Translocations and inversions, which do not alter the number but only the arrangement of the genes, may have no lethal or other phenotypic effect at all. It happens that many of them are connected with lethal effects but this may mean that they were detected because they produced a lethal effect whereas many of those without this effect go undetected. The lethal in this case may be a deficiency or gene mutation at the point of breakage or a position effect. In plants translocations and inversions seem to produce no phenotypic effects at all; in Drosophila they may be accompanied by visible position effects (Fig. 128), although in many cases no effect has been detected.

SIGNIFICANCE FOR ORIGIN OF VARIATIONS

Although deficiencies and duplications produce the most marked character changes, they generally reduce viability to such an extent that they would soon be eliminated in nature.   They probably do not provide an important source of the continuing variability found in nature.

   Translocations and inversions on the other hand bring about important modifications of the mechanism of transmission, may lead to partial

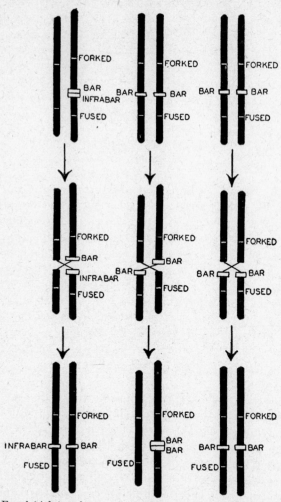

Fig. 128.—Equal (right) and unequal (middle and left) crossing over at the Bar locus in *Drosophila melanogaster*.   In the center column the origin of Doublebar from Bar is shown to involve crossing over between regions above Bar (marked by forked) and below Bar (marked by fused).   Doublebar (middle column below) shows greater effect on Bar eye than two Bar factors on separate chromosomes, the so-called "position-effect."   (*From Dobzhansky.*)

sterility between possessors of different gene arrangements, leading toward physiological isolation between different genotypes, and also make possible the retention in balanced lethal systems (p. 235) of the heterozygosity that arises from gene mutation. Two detailed examples will illustrate the mechanisms altered by translocations and inversions.

The Gene-complex Theory in Oenothera.—The hypothesis of reciprocal translocation, or segmental interchange, has made it possible to clear up the very difficult genetic situation in Oenothera and similar plants. Crosses between species in this genus have shown that many of them, like O. *Lamarckiana*, although breeding essentially true, are heterozygous for many genes, owing to the operation of balanced lethal factors. These genes often show almost complete linkage, as though they constituted a single linkage group. Species crosses also often result in two distinct types of hybrids, the so-called "twin hybrids."

These facts and others provided the clues for Renner's genetic analysis of these species. He showed that in most cases there are but two types of gametes produced, each containing an entire haploid set of closely linked genes, a *gene complex*. The particular genes in a given complex are constant for that complex and hold together in all crosses. The various complexes, however, are so different in the gene combinations which they contain that they are distinct and rather easily recognized; to each Renner gave a name. Each of the species, according to this hypothesis, contains two of these gene complexes, usually different; and at meiosis each separates from the other as a single entity. This analysis shows that *Lamarckiana* is composed of the gene complex called *gaudens*, containing the genes for green buds, nonpunctate stems, white nerves, broad leaves, and red flecks on the rosette leaves; and *velans*, containing genes for red-striped buds, punctate stems, narrow leaves, white nerves, and no red flecks on the rosette leaves. *Lamarckiana* may thus be described as *gaudens · velans*. Half of its pollen grains (and half of its eggs) contain the gene complex *gaudens* and the other half the gene complex *velans*.

If this is so, however, three types of offspring should arise from self-fertilization in this species: *gaudens · gaudens* (¼), *gaudens · velans* (½), and *velans · velans* (¼). Evidently the first and the last do not survive, an assumption which is supported by the fact that about half the fertilized ovules fail to produce seed, or they form seeds which are not viable. Thus only *gaudens · velans* (which is *Lamarckiana*) survives, and the species appears to breed true. The death of the two homozygous complex combinations is readily explained on the hypothesis of balanced lethal factors (p. 235) as originally suggested by Muller. One complex contains one lethal (l_1, let us say) and the other another (l_2), and each has the dominant allele of the other's lethal. The heterozygous types L_1l_1 and L_2l_2 thus survive, but the homozygotes l_2l_2 and l_1l_1 die.

It has been possible in this way to determine the genetic constitution of other species of Oenothera. Thus O. *biennis* is *albicans · rubens* and

O. muricata is *rigens · curvans.*   A very few species, notably *O. Hookeri,*
differ from the rest in being entirely homozygous and displaying normal
Mendelian breeding behavior.   It should be noted that even in the
heterozygous species a few genes occur which are independent of the
rest of the complex in their inheritance and that these genes have been
found to differ in their linkage relations in different complex combinations.

The problem now arises as to what the cytological basis is for these
remarkable phenomena.   A study of Oenothera species by Cleland
revealed the fact, long unrecognized, that in most of them at meiosis the
chromosomes are attached end to end in a large ring (Fig. 129) which
may include 12 or even all 14 of the chromosomes present in this genus.
At reduction, as in the rings of Datura, alternate members are assumed
to pass to the same pole, and thus the mechanism is at hand for preserving

FIG. 129.—Chromosomes of *Oenothera Lamarckiana* at meiosis, showing a ring of twelve
and one pair.   (*From Cleland.*)

intact two sets of 6 or 7 chromosomes each, which can be recombined
again at fertilization.   The persistence of these sets is further assured
by the fact that the end-to-end arrangement of the chromosomes seems to
preclude the crossing over of genes in them and renders each set a single
large linkage group.   The suggestion is obvious that the gene complexes
owe their existence and preservation to the fact that they are contained
in these relatively unchanging sets of chromosomes.   The fact that two
gametes containing the same chromosome set (or complex) fail to produce a viable embryo is evidently due, as has been suggested above,
to the presence in them of balanced lethal genes.   Thus each species is
composed of two complexes in two chromosome sets.

The origin of these rings may be explained by reciprocal translocation,
just as in hybrids between prime types of Datura (p. 331).   Doubtless
the original condition in the genus was like that in *O. Hookeri* today,
seven independent chromosome pairs.   A single interchange in one race
would result in a ring of four chromosomes in hybrids between this and the
original type.   The haploid set of *O. Hookeri* may be represented thus:
1 · 2, 3 · 4, 5 · 6, 7 · 8, 9 · 10, 11 · 12, 13 · 14.   Complex *flavens* combined

with *Hookeri* produces a ring and five pairs. This complex may therefore be given an arbitrary arrangement as follows: 1 · 4, 2 · 3, 5 · 6, etc. The combination *flavens-Hookeri* would thus appear:

$$1 \cdot 2 \text{------} 2 \cdot 3 \qquad 5 \cdot 6 \qquad 7 \cdot 8 \qquad 9 \cdot 10 \qquad 11 \cdot 12 \qquad 13 \cdot 14$$
$$| \qquad\qquad | \qquad (\quad) \quad (\quad) \quad (\quad\;\;) \quad (\quad\;\;) \quad (\quad\quad)$$
$$1 \cdot 4 \text{------} 4 \cdot 3 \qquad 5 \cdot 6 \qquad 7 \cdot 8 \qquad 9 \cdot 10 \qquad 11 \cdot 12 \qquad 13 \cdot 14$$

Two interchanges involving four chromosomes would produce two rings of four, leaving three pairs of chromosomes. Two interchanges involving only three chromosomes would make a ring of six, with four pairs. The greater the number of interchanges, the larger the circles

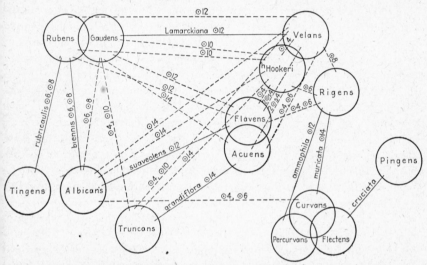

Fig. 130.—Diagram showing the cytological configurations of various complex combinations in Oenothera. For example, *O. Lamarckiana* is *gaudens · velans*. In each case the number of rings and of chromosomes in each ring is given, the remainder of the fourteen chromosomes being in pairs. Thus, "⊙4, ⊙6" means that there is one ring of four, one ring of six, and two pairs of chromosomes. (*From Cleland.*)

until some hybrids produce a ring of 14 chromosomes. The two haploid sets in each ring are held intact by balanced lethals.

By studying the number and size of chromosome rings in combinations between known gene complexes (Fig. 130), Cleland has been able to determine the number and arbitrary location of such interchanges, and by this means to predict the chromosome configuration in yet untried combinations between known complexes.

The genetic analysis combined with the hypothesis of reciprocal translocation and of balanced lethals thus makes it possible to understand the complexities of inheritance in Oenothera. Chromosome rings, of greater or less size, have now been reported as occurring naturally in a considerable number of species, and the hypothesis advanced to explain the genetic behavior in Oenothera will doubtless apply to them as well.

Inversions in Drosophila pseudoobscura.—Examination of the salivary chromosomes (p. 164) has led to the discovery of a great deal of variation in gene arrangement in the different local strains of the same species. In the *D. pseudoobscura* strains inhabiting separate parts of the species range in the Western United States, this variability takes the form of numerous inversions as shown by Dobzhansky and Sturtevant. Different orders of the bands are characteristic of different local strains. Such variations are detected by crossing members of different local strains and examining the pairing of the salivary chromosomes in the hybrid larvae. Where the parents have very different band orders, large inversion loops (Fig. 87, p. 234) are formed in the hybrids since the homologous parts of the chromosomes tend to pair. When these pairs are not opposite to each other, different levels pair and the chromosome becomes contorted. When the parents differ by only a small inversion, this is marked by failure of pairing over a short region without contortion. Since the bands in every chromosome form a characteristic sequence, the length of the inverted sections and point of breakage can often be specified in detail. In some cases two parent chromosomes differ by a single inversion and this variation could obviously have arisen by a single step; in others, the chromosomes differ by two nonoverlapping inversions, while in others two or more inversions in one chromosome may overlap.

The latter type of change is most frequent in *D. pseudoobscura*, indicating that strains differ by multiple inversions and that such variations are therefore of relatively frequent occurrence in this species. By estimating the number of steps (independent occurrence of inversions) required to derive the band order of one strain from that characteristic of another, it has been possible to estimate the width or closeness of relationship of the two strains, and this is of great importance for studying phylogenetic relationships (p. 350). Here we are concerned chiefly with the fact that inversions reduce or prevent crossing over between homologous chromosomes and that variations of this type, while not necessarily accompanied by direct changes in the phenotype, lead to the isolation of genetic systems (chromosomes) from each other; may tend to preserve heterozygosity and by rearrangement of genes may lead to translocations, deficiencies and other changes. In this respect inversions as found in Drosophila and translocations as found in Oenothera, Datura, and other organisms have similar significance for the origin of variations. Moreover, the fact that position effects due to several of these types of chromosome changes simulate gene mutations indicates that the distinction between these two main categories of new genetic variations is not as sharp as it formerly seemed to be.

The relation of chromosome changes to evolution will be discussed in the next chapter.

REFERENCES

BELLING, J., and A. F. BLAKESLEE. 1924. The configurations and sizes of the chromosomes in the trivalents of 25-chromosome Daturas. Proc. Nat. Acad. Sci. **10.**

BLAKESLEE, A. F. 1937. Studies in the behavior of chromosomes. U.S. Dept. Agr. Yearbook Separate **1605.**

CLELAND, R. E., and A. F. BLAKESLEE. 1931. Segmental interchange, the basis of chromosomal attachments in Oenothera. Cytologia **2.**

DARLINGTON, C. D. 1936. Recent advances in cytology. 2d ed. Philadelphia.

DOBZHANSKY, T. 1937. Genetics and the origin of species. New York.

———— and A. H. STURTEVANT. 1938. Inversions in the chromosomes of *Drosophila pseudoobscura.* Genetics **23.**

KARPECHENKO, G. D. 1928. Polypoid hybrids of *Raphanus sativus* × *Brassica oleracea.* Zeitschr. Ind. Abst. Vererb. **48.**

MORGAN, T. H. 1928. The theory of the gene. New Haven.

MÜNTZING, A. 1936. The evolutionary significance of autopolyploidy. Hereditas **21.**

RENNER, O. 1925. Untersuchungen über die faktorielle Konstitution einiger komplexheterozygotischen Oenotheren. Bibliotheca Genetica **9.**

RHOADES, M. M., and B. McCLINTOCK. 1935. The cytogenetics of maize. Bot. Rev. **1.**

VON WETTSTEIN, F. 1937. Zellgrössenregulation und Fertilwerden einer polyploiden Bryum-Sippe. Zeitschr. Ind. Abst. Vererb. **74.**

PROBLEMS

371. How might an allopolyploid arise other than by doubling the chromosome number of a hybrid?

372. Name at least one important practical result which may be expected to follow from our ability to double the number of chromosomes in a plant.

373. In polyploid series of species in nature (such as the wheats, barleys, and many others), the differences between members of the series in body size and in cell size are often very much less than in polyploid series which have been developed experimentally. Explain.

374. What reason can you suggest for the fact that it is apparently impossible to increase chromosome number experimentally beyond a certain point?

375. Why is a haploid individual usually sterile? Name some important exceptions to this rule.

376. What factor affecting size might be operative in allopolyploids but not in autopolyploids?

377. What relationship can you suggest between the occurrence of polyploid series and the occurrence of duplicate factors?

378. Why does polyploidy tend to prevent the appearance of gene mutations?

379. What similarities and what differences are there between the effects of doubling a section of chromosome, as in the case of repeats, and doubling it through polyploidy?

380. Why do you think it is that an extra chromosome is much more readily transmitted, in plants, through female gametes than through male gametes.

381. How would you account for the great diversity of chromosome numbers in related species of a single genus, as in the case of Crepis (p. 351)?

382. Sometimes a primary mutant is *not* intermediate between its two secondaries. Explain.

Note.—In Datura Blakeslee has found 12 mutants, each of which is due to the presence of three chromosomes instead of two, in one of the 12 sets. The mutant "Poinsettia" he finds to be due to the presence of three chromosomes in the set which carries the genes for purple and white flower color. Letting A stand for purple and a for white, there may thus be four kinds of Poinsettia plants: AAA, AAa Aaa (purple), and aaa (white); and three kinds of normals, AA, Aa (purple), and aa (white). The formation of female gametes here takes place much as it did in the nondisjunctional females of Drosophila. In the pollen, however, *none of the grains with the extra chromosome are able to function*, apparently on account of the upset balance between the chromosome sets. All pollen grains formed by purple Poinsettia plants are A and a, while the eggs may be A, AA, Aa, a, or aa. The female gametes formed by an individual with the genotype AAa, for example, are two A, two Aa, one AA, and one a. This may perhaps be worked out most readily by writing the genotype thus: $\dfrac{A\diagdown\!\!A}{a\diagup}$ and making the three possible reduction divisions, AA and a, Aa and A, and Aa and A. If these were male gametes, the AA and Aa types would not develop, and the survivors would be two-thirds A and one-third a.

383. What will be the ratio of purple-flowered to white-flowered plants in the normal ($2n$) offspring and in the Poinsettia ($2n + 1$) offspring from the following crosses?

Female parent × male parent		Female parent × male parent	
AAa	AAA	Aaa	AAA
AAa	AAa	Aaa	AAa
AAa	Aaa	Aaa	Aaa
AAa	aaa	Aaa	aaa
AAa	AA	Aaa	AA
AAa	Aa	Aaa	Aa
AAa	aa	Aaa	aa

384. Explain how it is possible, by means of trisomic ratios, to determine the pair of chromosomes associated with a given linkage group.

385. If the F_1 of a cross between purple-flowered tetraploid and white-flowered tetraploid Datura ($PPpp$) is crossed back to its white-flowered parent, what will be the appearance of the offspring?

386. If a tetraploid with the genotype $Pppp$ is selfed, what will be the appearance of its offspring as to flower color?

387. The offspring of haplo-IV, normal-eyed Drosophila crossed to diplo-IV, eyeless ones are half normal diplo-IV and half eyeless haplo-IV. If these two F_1 types are crossed, what will their offspring look like as to eyes and number of IV chromosomes?

388. Assume that a triplo-IV, normal-eyed Drosophila is crossed with a diplo-IV, eyeless. If the F_1 triplo-IV flies are crossed with the F_1 diplo-IV ones, what will be the eye character and IV chromosome constitution of their offspring?

389. Construct two hypothetical prime types in Datura which, when crossed, will show a ring of eight chromosomes in the F_1.

390. Assume that in Datura two lines differ by one segmental interchange, one line being $1 \cdot 2, 3 \cdot 4$ and the other $1 \cdot 3, 2 \cdot 4$, but that in the second line chromosome segment 3 has suffered a complete inversion. What would you expect to be the configuration of these two pairs of chromosomes in the F_1 from a cross between these two lines?

391. What will be the configuration as to rings and pairs of chromosomes, in the types AB, BC, and AC, the end arrangement of complexes A, B, and C being as follows:

$$A: 1 \cdot 4, \quad 2 \cdot 5, \quad 3 \cdot 7, \quad 6 \cdot 10, \quad 8 \cdot 11, \quad 9 \cdot 13, \quad 12 \cdot 14$$
$$B: 1 \cdot 3, \quad 2 \cdot 6, \quad 5 \cdot 7, \quad 8 \cdot \ 9, \quad 10 \cdot 11, \quad 13 \cdot 14, \quad 12 \cdot \ 4$$
$$C: 1 \cdot 3, \quad 2 \cdot 5, \quad 4 \cdot 6, \quad 8 \cdot 14, \quad 10 \cdot 11, \quad 9 \cdot 13, \quad 7 \cdot 12$$

392. Using the arbitrary formulas for the complex combinations given in problem 391, what would be the linkage relations in each of them of a gene located in chromosome-end 1?

393. Using the known cytological configurations for the Oenothera species shown in Fig. 130, draw up an arbitrary end-arrangement formula which will explain the cytological facts for each of the complexes involved.

394. From the data in Fig. 130, what configuration should be found in *albicans · truncans?*

395. In maize assume that Race 1, which is homozygous for the recessive endosperm characters a, b, c, d, e, f, g, and h is pollinated by pollen from Race 2, which is homozygous for the dominant alleles A, B, C, D, E, F, G, and H; but that the pollen has been subjected to irradiation before being placed on the styles of Race 1. If some of the resulting kernels are phenotypically $AbcdEFGH$, how would you explain this result?

396. Race 1 with genes A, B, C, D, and E, in the same chromosome and known to be arranged in that order, is crossed with Race 2, homozygous for the recessive alleles of all these genes. The F_1 crossed back on $a\ b\ c\ d\ e$ is found to produce only four types of gametes: *A B C D E, A B C De, a b c d E,* and *a b c d e*. Explain these facts.

397. Race 1 with genes *A, B, C, D, E, F, G, H,* and *I* in the same chromosome and known to be arranged in that order is crossed with Race 2 which is known to possess all the recessive alleles of these genes. Back crosses show that in the F_1 there is crossing over between *A-B, G-H,* and *H-I* but never between *B-C, C-D, D-E, E-F,* or *F-G*. Explain these facts and map the chromosome, for these genes, as it occurs in Races 1 and 2.

398. In a case in *Drosophila melanogaster,* yellow-bodied females bred to gray-bodied (wild-type) males always produced yellow daughters and wild type sons. How can this reversal of the ordinary course of sex-linked inheritance be explained?

399. In the case of semisterile maize (see Fig. 127) all the genes in each complete set of chromosomes (1 · 2 and 3 · 4, for example) are, of course, linked, just as though they were in one chromosome. Rhoades studied cases of double crossing over in such a system where one crossover was in one arm and the other in the opposite one (as in arms 2 and 3 in Fig. 127) and found that there was no interference, coincidence being 1.0. Explain this difference from the usual behavior of double crossovers.

400. In maize, Race I and Race II differ by a single segmental interchange. I is genetically *aa* and II is *AA*. The F_1 from a cross between them is semisterile and *Aa*. When this is crossed back on Race I, the following offspring are produced: 35 per cent normal *a*, 35 per cent semisterile *A*, 15 per cent normal *A*, and 15 per cent semisterile *a*. Where, with reference to locus *a*, is the translocation point?

401. Race I, above, is also homozygous for gene *bb* and II for *BB*, so that the semisterile hybrid is *Bb*. When this, as before, is crossed back to Race I, the following offspring are produced: 45 per cent normal *b*, 45 per cent semisterile *B*, 5 per cent normal *B*, and 5 per cent semisterile *b*. It is known that in Race I, *a* and *b* are in the same chromosome and between 25 and 30 units apart. For Race I, map the chromosome in which *a* and *b* occur, showing the position of these genes and of the translocation point.

402. In Race I, genes *c* and *d* are in the chromosome which later undergoes segmental interchange with that containing *a* and *b*, thus forming Race II. In Race II *d* is now found to be linked with *b*, and *c* with *a*. By use of data similar to that presented in the two preceding problems, it can be shown that *c* gives 10 per cent crossing over with the translocation point and *d* gives 5 per cent. Make a diagram of the four chromosomes involved in the translocation between Races I and II as they appear at synapsis in the semisterile hybrid between these races, showing the location of the four genes and the two translocation points.

CHAPTER XV

GENETICS AND EVOLUTION

We have now an adequate working outline of the physical basis and of the mechanism of inheritance. Before the entire phenomenon of inheritance can be understood, however, there are still two major problems that must be solved. One is concerned with the genetic basis of organic evolution, the other with the mechanism by which genes control development. These problems are discussed in the present chapter and the concluding one.

The importance of a knowledge of inheritance for the development of evolutionary theory was recognized when the young science of genetics (sometimes termed "experimental evolution") was established. It was hoped that the new knowledge would prove of service in interpreting evolution. This hope was not immediately fulfilled. In recent years, however, a more complete understanding of their own problems has made it possible for geneticists to make substantial contributions to a knowledge of the mechanism of evolution, especially as to two of its problems. These are, first, the origin and nature of inherited variations and, second, the processes by which these variations give rise to segregated groups of individuals, the new races, species, and higher taxonomic categories. An extensive survey of the bearing of genetics or these problems has recently been made by Dobzhansky (1937a).

THE ORIGIN OF EVOLUTIONARY DIFFERENCES

In previous chapters the various types of inherited differences have been described, chiefly from the results of breeding experiments and cytological observations. The question now arises as to whether differences like these are actually responsible for evolutionary change. The answer is definitely an affirmative one. The difficulty or impossibility of obtaining offspring from crosses between individuals of different species, and especially of higher groups, makes it hard to obtain very much direct information here, but all the evidence at hand indicates clearly that gene mutations and chromosome changes, essentially the same as those observed in the laboratory and under cultivation, occur in nature and are responsible for the diversity of organisms.

Gene Mutations in Evolution.—Many of the genic differences that have been employed in genetic experiments have arisen in nature and distinguish varieties and races of plants and animals. The single-gene differences between spiny and smooth capsule and between purple and white flower color in Datura occur in nature and are examples of many such differences in plants which are the basis of recognized varietal or specific characters. Among animals the dextral and sinistral coiling of the shells of fresh-water snails, known to be due to a single gene (p. 251), distinguish local races of Partula (Crampton). Races of man are characterized by marked differences in the percentage among them of the various blood groups, now known to be due to a series of three multiple alleles. More complex hereditary differences have been shown to characterize many geographical and ecological races of plants and animals. Perhaps even more convincing are the now numerous cases in which gene mutations have been collected by sampling wild populations. Dubinin and his coworkers, by trapping wild individuals of *Drosophila melanogaster* in various localities in the Soviet Union, have shown many of them to be carrying gene mutations of various sorts, similar to, or in many cases identical with, those that have appeared in this species in the laboratory.

Genic differences between groups generally regarded as "good species" are not so easy to demonstrate because of the difficulty of obtaining fertile crosses between them. The distinctions between *Antirrhinum majus* and *A. molle* as studied by Baur, however, seem clearly to be due to different gene combinations, and those between *Canna indica* and *C. glauca* have been reduced to a series of genes by Honing. A similar analysis has been made of the differences between *Lycopersicum esculentum* and *L. pimpinellifolium* by Lindstrom, and there are many others among plants. Evidence from animal species crosses is not so detailed but much of it exists, of which Sumner's studies of species crosses in Peromyscus may be cited as an example.

Chromosome Changes in Evolution.—Differences due to chromosome changes are also very abundant in nature. Notable among these are the cases of polyploidy. Many instances of what seem clearly to be autotetraploids (p. 320), derived from diploid races or species, have been reported from nature. Thus *Tradescantia occidentalis* is represented by diploid individuals in Texas and by tetraploid ones over a much wider range. In Europe *Biscutella laevigata* also exists in both diploid and tetraploid phases, the former chiefly in Germany and the latter ranging over central Europe and Italy. In all such cases the same structural features characterize the tetraploid forms (large cells, stocky habit) as when these arise under cultivation, but it is significant that the tetraploids seem physiologically rather distinct. They usually have wider ranges than their diploid ancestors and seem to be more successful types. Polyploidy here may give rise to new types in nature without involving any genic changes.

Probably more common in nature are allotetraploids (p. 322). *Galeopsis Tetrahit* is a good species with a haploid chromosome number of 16. Müntzing has succeeded in synthesizing it by crossing *G. pubescens* and *G. speciosa* (both with 8 chromosomes) and obtaining among their descendants an allotetraploid plant (with 16 chromosomes) which seemed to be essentially like *G. Tetrahit*. *Spartina Townsendii*, which seems to have appeared in England about a hundred years ago, has a chromosome number of 126, and there is good taxonomic and cytological evidence that it arose as an allotetraploid from a cross of *S. stricta* (2n = 56) with *S. alterniflora* (2n = 70).

Other similar cases have been reported. These are true-breeding types, distinct from their parents and sterile in crosses with them. Here

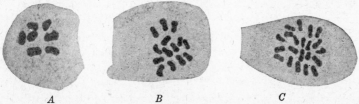

A   B   C

Fig. 131.—Chromosome differences in species of wheat. Reduction division in pollen mother cells of A, *Triticum monococcum*, 7 chromosomes; B, *T. durum*, 14 chromosomes; C, *T. vulgare*, 21 chromosomes. (*From Sax.*)

what is essentially a new species seems to have arisen at one step without the occurrence of any gene mutations. In allotetraploids, which owe their origin to two species rather than one, the doubling of the chromosome complement makes it possible for an interspecific or even an intergeneric hybrid, usually sterile, to form viable gametes and perpetuate itself. By this means two lines, which have become considerably diversified during the course of evolution, such as species of two genera, may recombine their genic complements and serve as the basis for further evolutionary change.

As a result of crosses between polyploid types the various polyploid series of species occurring in so many plant genera seem to have arisen. Thus in Triticum there are species with 14, 28, and 42 chromosomes (2n) (Fig. 131); in Viola with 12, 18, 24, 30, 36, 42, 48, 54, and 96; and in Prunus with 16, 24, 32, 40, 48, and 72.

Polyploidy in animals is much less common, doubtless because of the separation of the sexes, and seems not to have been an important evolutionary factor.

The various differences in chromosomal structure observed in culture—translocations, inversions, duplications, and deficiencies—are also found in wild populations and frequently distinguish races and species.

The various "prime types" in *Datura Stramonium* described by Blakeslee, which may be recognized by the occurrence of chromosome rings in the offspring of crosses between two types (p. 331), owe their origin to a series of reciprocal translocations between the various chromosomes. Each of the prime types has a definite geographical distribution as shown in Table XXVIII and probably arose from a single translocation in nature. Thus some 540 races of *Datura Stramonium* found in nature

TABLE XXVIII.—DISTRIBUTION OF PRIME TYPES IN NATURE OF 530
RACES OF DATURA
(*After Blakeslee, Bergner, and Avery, 1937*)

Cryptic prime types		P.T. 1	P.T. 2	P.T. 3	P.T. 4	P.T. 7
Modified chromosomes		Standard	$\dfrac{1.18}{2.17}$	$\dfrac{11.21}{12.22}$	$\dfrac{3.21}{4.22}$	$\dfrac{9.10}{19.20}$
Condition in F_1's with line 1		12 bivalents	10 BV.$\langle\!\rangle$ $+\odot 4$	10 BV.$\langle\!\rangle$ $+\odot 4$	10 BV.$\langle\!\rangle$ $+\odot 4$	10 BV.$\langle\!\rangle$ $+\lambda 4$
No. races	Origin					
82	Virginia and North Carolina..........	47	17		29	4
134	Other U.S.A........	115	7		3	11
16	West Indies........	6	5		4	5
10	Central America....		10	3		
5	Columbia and Venezuela.............		5			
15	Brazil.............	15				
32	Peru (purple).......		32	32		
19	Chile (purple).......		19	19		
9	Chile (white).......		9			
33	Spain and Portugal.	2	24	1	19	7
36	Italy..............	1	35		3	1
19	Russia.............	1	18			
52	Other European.....	4	48		1	
7	Japan and Korea....	7				
26	Other Asiatic.......		26			
26	Africa.............	3	12		12	12
5	Australia..........	1	2		2	2
4	Hawaii............				1	4

could be classified into five prime types: prime type 1 (the "standard" race) and four other types differing from it by segmental interchanges. Practically all the races of Eastern Europe and Asia (except Japan) are prime type 2; in South America (Fig. 132) the races of Brazil are prime type 1 and have white flowers; the races of Peru are a combination of type 3 with type 2, and have purple flowers; in Chile the same combination (2 and 3) occurs in purple-flowered types while the white-flowered ones

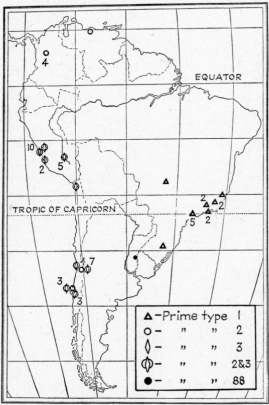

EQUATOR

TROPIC OF CAPRICORN

△	– Prime type		1
○	–	,, ,,	2
◊	–	,, ,,	3
Φ	–	,, ,,	2&3
●	–	,, ,,	88

Fig. 132.—Distribution of prime types of *Datura Stramonium* in South America. (*From Blakeslee, Bergner, and Avery.*)

are prime type 2, which occurs also in Colombia and Venezuela. This sharp separation of the different chromosome arrangements within the same species indicates one of the steps through which differentiation within the species is occurring. Blakeslee has shown how through heteroploidy these may give rise to visibly distinct new true-breeding types.

The specific chromosome complements in Oenothera, which are the bases of the gene complexes analyzed by Renner, have evidently arisen by translocation. Cleland has traced the evolution of some of these types from simple species like *O. Hookeri*, in which all the chromosomes are paired, to complex ring formations and has studied their geographical distribution. The frequently reported cases of chromosome rings in other genera indicates that translocation may be of relatively common occurrence in nature.

It should be remembered that whatever differences in the effects of genes may be due to their position (assuming that this is a different phenomenon from gene mutation) will appear in these translocation types and may serve as an added cause of evolutionary diversity.

The inversion of chromosomal segments is evidently another common source of racial and specific differences in nature. The best analyzed of these cases is that of the two Races A and B of *Drosophila pseudoobscura*, studied by Dobzhansky and others. By use of the salivary gland technique, it has been possible to show that these two races differ by four inverted sections, two in the X chromosome and one each in chromosomes II and III. These races are indistinguishable morphologically but show certain definite physiological differences, and occupy different though somewhat overlapping geographical ranges. When crossed, they produce sterile male offspring, and they seem always to be distinct. Within each race there are several distinct gene arrangements, and the extent and character of these may be determined by the number and distribution of the loops in the salivary chromosomes of individuals heterozygous for two types. One arrangement occurs in both races and is probably the ancestral one. By comparing the various arrangements with each other, it is possible to set up a tentative phylogenetic series from this ancestral type and thus to trace the progressive changes in arrangement which have accompanied the evolution of these two races.

The degree of divergence to which such progressive chromosome rearrangements may lead is perhaps shown by a comparison of the salivary chromosomes of two distinct species. *Drosophila pseudoobscura* crossed with *D. miranda* produces a sterile hybrid. Although the chromosomes of the parent species are the same in number and general appearance at metaphase, the salivary chromosomes of the hybrid are so different in gene order that the homologues either fail to pair or show complex inversion loops (Fig. 87, p. 234). Salivary band sequences show different arrangements of genes within the same chromosome of the two species, as well as the same genes in different chromosomes. These differences have probably arisen by inversions and translocations.

Most deficiencies, at least of any appreciable size, are lethal, but they may occur in the Y chromosome of Drosophila, which seems to contain few genes, and may thus serve to distinguish various races. In *D. pseudoobscura* Dobzhansky has found seven different types of Y chromosome, distinguished chiefly by length (at metaphase) and position of spindle attachment. Each type is found in a definite area as shown for the three types of Race B in Fig. 133.

Bridges has shown that in Drosophila duplications of series of genes occur in two parts of the same chromosome ("repeats"). This, too, may ultimately result in evolutionary change.

Heteroploid forms, such as those described in Datura and now known in many other plants, are apparently not common in nature; but they

may give rise, as Blakeslee has shown, to various homozygous types with one or more extra chromosomes. Perhaps by such a process as this there have arisen some of these series of species the chromosome numbers in which form an almost continuous series and are not multiples of a basic number. Thus related species of Crepis have 3, 4, 5, 6, 8, 9, and 11 chromosomes, and in Carex the series is even more extensive.

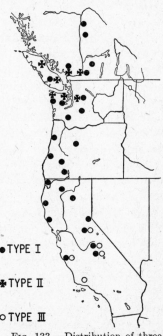

The various types of inheritable differences, both genic and chromosomal, which have here been discussed and which are evidently appearing constantly in wild populations, will in themselves provide material for a considerable amount of evolutionary change. It should not be forgotten that by the mechanism of inheritance these new types may be recombined in an almost limitless number of ways, so that probably the most prolific source of actual variation is the genic recombination resulting from crosses between different types.

●TYPE I

✳TYPE II

○TYPE III

FIG. 133.—Distribution of three different types of Y chromosome in *Drosophila pseudoobscura*, Race B. (*From Dobzhansky.*)

This source of variability has been stressed by many, notably Lotsy, as of primary importance in evolution, and it is undoubtedly of great significance; but it cannot be the only source, for there must arise in some way a series of actual gene differences before these can be recombined in hybridization.

THE ORIGIN OF EVOLUTIONARY SEGREGATION

The second main evolutionary problem, toward a solution of which genetics may contribute, is why this extensive series of constantly appearing inheritable variations, which in the aggregate must be enormous in actual number, does not result in a chaos of intergrading and interfertile types, a situation suggested by conditions actually existing in certain taxonomically "difficult" groups such as parts of the genus Rubus (the blackberries). In most of the organic world this is far from being the case, for there tends to be a definite sorting out of variants into races, species, and higher taxonomic categories, all but the lowest of which have become so completely isolated from each other that they readily maintain their individual existence. The problem of the origin of *species* is a very definite one and is by no means synonymous with that of evolution in general. In this field, too, genetics has now been able to make substantial contributions.

The Effect of Inbreeding.—First, it has become evident that something more than isolation and natural selection, long regarded as the primary factors in speciation, are here involved. An understanding of the particulate mechanism of inheritance makes it clear that the very process of Mendelian segregation necessarily tends to result in a sorting out of various genetically different types. This is most obviously true if a species is self-fertilized, as are many plants. If such an individual through a chance cross becomes heterozygous for a gene Aa, its offspring in a few generations will evidently become about half AA and half aa, the number of heterozygotes steadily diminishing, as was first shown by Mendel himself (p. 284). In the same way if it is heterozygous for two genes, $Aa\,Bb$, its offspring will soon become sorted out into four equal and homozygous genotypes: $AABB$, $AAbb$, $aaBB$ and $aabb$. The number of different combinations ultimately appearing will be much greater than the number of pairs of segregating genes (2^n). It is clear that in such types there will soon appear (if occasional mutations and cross-fertilizations occur) a host of genetically distinct and homozygous races, among which recessive genes are as numerous as dominant ones.

Genetic Equilibrium in Cross-fertilized Types.—In most plants, however, and in practically all animals, self-fertilization is either impossible because of the separation of the sexes or is prevented by self-sterility or some other mechanism. Even here, segregation results in the establishment of distinct types. If two individuals Aa and Aa are crossed and their offspring interbreed freely in large populations and if all offspring are equally viable, then one-fourth of the resulting population will tend to be AA, one-half Aa, and one-fourth aa in all later generations (Hardy's Law). The recessive gene is just as abundant in the population as the dominant one, and the recessive trait, far from being swamped out, maintains itself in a definite fraction of the population so that an equilibrium between the two types is established. It can readily be shown that if the original proportions of the two genes are unequal, this proportion is constantly maintained among them. If the proportion of A in the original population is represented by q and that of a by $1 - q$, then the population in the second and all later generations will reach an equilibrium according to the following formula (Hardy's Law):

$$q^2 \, AA : 2q \, (1 - q) \, Aa : (1 - q)^2 \, aa$$

This equilibrium may evidently be disturbed (quite apart from factors affecting the survival of one group in preference to the other) if mutations or chromosome changes appear. If these are all in one direction, the population will gradually become completely changed; but if, as seems more common, those in one direction are opposed by others in the reverse direction (*A* to *a* and *a* to *A*), equilibrium will again be established if the mutation rates are constant. Thus in a population pure for *A*, if the mutation from *A* to *a* is twice as frequent as from *a* to *A*, equilibrium will be attained when gene *a* is twice as abundant in the population as gene *A* or when two-thirds of the chromosomes carry *a* and one-third *A*.

Genetic equilibrium thus results from the mechanism of segregation and the mutation rate. They tend to produce a constant proportion between genes and thus between visibly different groups, but without altering the variability of the population as a whole.

Reduction in Variability in Limited Populations.—Since, in nature, many genes are mutating and individuals of many types crossing freely, it would seem probable (disregarding the effects of selection) that all possible genic combinations would result and that the population, highly variable, would attain genetic equilibrium. This would be the case only if the population were unlimited in size. Most populations, however, remain approximately fixed as to the number of their individuals which can survive, owing to limitations in the amount of food or space or for other reasons. It is a noteworthy fact, largely unrecognized until the recent mathematical studies of populations, especially by Wright, that under these conditions the very mechanism of inheritance itself tends to reduce the diversity of the population by eliminating certain genes entirely and fixing others in a homozygous condition. To take a very simple example, let us assume that a population is limited to only two individuals and that these are originally both heterozygous, *Aa* and *Aa*. Their offspring will obviously fall into the four equal classes *AA*, *Aa*, *Aa*, and *aa*, the absolute size of which will depend on the number of the offspring produced. If only two individuals can survive to maturity, however, it is evident that in less than half of the cases will the two genes be equally represented among them (*Aa* and *Aa*, or *AA* and *aa*) but that much oftener the two survivors will be *AA* and *AA*, *AA* and *Aa*, *Aa* and *aa*, or *aa* and *aa*. The population should ultimately, under this limitation, be composed entirely of *A* or entirely of *a*, and the other gene will have been irretrievably lost. Of course, such a small population is unknown in nature, but in any limited one the same tendency operates, and the smaller the population is, the more rapid will be the loss of genes. In very large groups this is least effective.

It should be emphasized that the size of a population, in this sense, is the total number of sexually mature and freely interbreeding individuals within it, so that actually most populations in nature are much smaller than at first they seem to be. Whenever a large group of individuals (a race, variety, or species) is broken up into smaller local ones by barriers of any sort, the reduction in diversity within these small populations will evidently proceed much more rapidly than in the original larger group; and since the loss and fixation of genes is a purely random process, each group is likely to have a different combination of genes from every other one, and a diverse series of local, relatively pure, races will result. This differentiation into local races will occur quite independently of natural selection. The mechanism which brings it about thus accounts for the very numerous cases where isolation produces local races (as of land snails in separate valleys in Hawaii) but where the differences between these seem not to be related to any factors which determine survival. Even where no physical barriers between groups exist, individuals usually tend to breed with those that are near them and thus constitute, in effect, a small population.

Thus as a result of the mechanism of genetic segregation itself, and of the necessary limitation of population size, the great variety of new types produced by gene mutations and chromosome changes tends first to become thoroughly shuffled and then to become sorted out into distinct groups or races of increasing genetic purity and of lessened variability.

There are other and more obvious factors that tend to produce the same result. Chief among these are differential viability and natural selection. Evidence from genetics has proved useful in a study of both.

The Effect of Differences in Viability.—It is obvious that many genetic changes result in a reduction of vigor and viability. Many of these are actually lethal and lead to the death of the zygote at some stage of its development. It is perhaps to be expected that any random alteration of the normal or "wild" type of a species would result in a less efficient organic mechanism, and such seems usually to be the case. Even where there is no obvious reason why the abnormal type should be less successful, it often is so. Thus Harris found that bean seedlings with three or four cotyledons and primary leaves, instead of the normal two, were less efficient in food production and had a higher mortality than normal seedlings grown under identical conditions.

The viability of various gene mutations in *Drosophila funebris* has been found by Timofeeff-Ressovsky to vary greatly, a few of them exceeding the wild type but most being definitely below it. Furthermore, their viability as compared with wild type varied with temperature and with the presence of other mutations. Thus the gene miniature had a viability of 69 per cent of wild type and bobbed one of 85.1 per cent, whereas the combination *miniature-bobbed* went up to 96.6 per cent. The reasons for such differences are not evident. Occasionally there are obvious developmental disharmonies due to differences in relative sizes of parts, such as tall stem with weak supporting tissue, the disadvantages of which are obvious. Undoubtedly there are more subtle disharmonies between genic combinations, but our knowledge of these must wait for a fuller understanding of the genic control of development. At all events, it is obvious that the various mutations that appear in nature are not equally likely to survive, even under identical and optimum conditions, so that some combinations will tend to drop out of the population regardless of the operation of other factors.

The Effect of Natural Selection.—The elimination of certain variants is also doubtless brought about by the action of natural selection in eliminating individuals that are less well adapted to their environment than are others. The efficacy of this process has been actively debated since Darwin's day, but the amount of actual experimental information here is not very great. Evidence is at hand, however, which indicates that between races differences do exist which act to favor or to prevent survival under conditions of competition. Timofeeff-Ressovsky collected local strains of *Drosophila funebris* from widely separated regions in Europe and compared the ability of each to survive, under very unfavorable conditions of crowding and food, with that of a single standard strain. The differences were very considerable and were also found to vary with the temperature under which the test was made. In general, strains from warmer regions showed a higher survival at higher temperatures, and vice versa. There is a good deal of evidence of this sort, indicating that local races have become adapted to their environment, presumably through selection.

As to how effective this selection has been and how much of evolutionary change is the result of it, genetic evidence is not conclusive. An analysis of population changes that may be expected to result from the mechanism of inheritance, however (as discussed earlier in this chapter), makes it clear that local races, genetically pure and quite distinct from one another, may become established by this means alone without the operation of selection. It seems altogether likely that both processes are at work.

Mathematical analysis of theoretical population changes further shows that in small populations the random sorting out of genetically different races is likely to be the chief factor, with selection playing a relatively small part. In large ones, however, where the loss of genes and the random establishment of types is much slower, the same amount of selective advantage should play a dominant part in determining which genetic types will survive and which will not.

Obviously the rates of mutation of various genes are also very important here. If the more rapid mutation rate is in the direction favored by selection, change will evidently be rapid. If it is in the opposite direction, a definite equilibrium may be established.

It can also be shown that where the frequency of a given gene in the population is very low or very high, a selective advantage in its favor, unless marked, will take a very long time to change the population over to the new type, but that the rate of change is much higher with intermediate frequencies. In other words, with a new advantageous mutation, its increase in the population at first is slow, then much faster, then very slow again to the time when it is completely established. These facts are all of importance in evaluating the role of selection in evolutionary change.

Thus the separation of a population into distinct groups seems to depend upon a number of factors working in various directions, and the ultimate result is due to their interaction. Mutational and other changes, differing in frequency, direction, and viability, tend to increase the variability of the population. With inbreeding, a separation into homozygous combinations will rapidly occur. Under cross-fertilization, a definite genetic equilibrium tends to become established but is actually attained only where populations are very large. In limited and rather small populations, variability tends to decrease rapidly, and a series of rather fixed types results. Selection eliminates the clearly unfit at once and favors the survival of some types over others. Selection can operate, however, only where there is variability for it to act upon, and therefore factors that modify population size (and thus variability) modify the effectiveness and rapidity of selection therein. Selection operates not on the effect of a single gene but on that of the combination of all of them; and among the almost infinite number of these combinations which result from crossing, some are better adapted than others to a given environment and will survive. These become separated from one another by the extinction of intermediate and less well-adapted forms and constitute a series of distinct but related groups. As the environment changes, each group must change with it or perish. Those that have become fixed genetically will disappear, while those that have succeeded in maintaining or acquiring a certain degree of variability will be able, through selection, to change in type to meet the new conditions. Mutation, isolation, selection, and segregation are thus all concerned in the process of the formation of distinct groups of individuals, the germs of new races and species.

The Effect of Self-sterility.—Opposed to these tendencies toward the isolation of groups and races, there is among many plants an extensive series of mechanisms, both morphological and physiological, which operate in precisely the other direction. Where both types of gametes are produced in the same individual, self-fertilization, the closest form of inbreeding, will tend to occur and to produce complete homozygosity in the shortest possible time. The dangers of this process for many plants (and animals) and the advantages of at least some degree of heterozygosity for the maintenance of physiological vigor have been discussed in a preceding chapter (p. 285). The various mechanisms that operate to prevent this result are important not only for the individual plant but for the species as a whole, for they prevent the rapid loss of variability that would otherwise ensue and which must be maintained if selection is to operate most efficiently in establishing successful types. When these mechanisms in bisexual plants are fully effective, the individuals become essentially unisexual.

With many of the devices to insure cross-fertilization, genetics has little direct concern. One of the most important of these, however—the phenomenon of self-sterility or self-incompatibility—has in recent years been subjected to genetic analysis with fruitful results. It has long been known that, in many plants which produce normal, functional gametes of both sexes, these gametes are apparently unable to unite in fertilization, so that the individual fails to produce offspring by self-fertilization. Such sterility is termed *self-sterility* or *self-incompatibility* to distinguish it from the many other types of sterility which may be due to various causes. Incompatibility is most common in self-fertilization, although cross-incompatibility, in which gametes from two different individuals fail to unite under certain conditions, is not unusual. In over 100 species among about fifty families of plants self-fertilization has been found to be impossible, although cross-fertilization is readily accomplished. The same phenomenon is sometimes found among hermaphroditic animals, such as the ascidians Styela and Ciona. The degree of incompatibility often varies with external or internal conditions, as Stout has shown, and plants which are at one time self-incompatible may later become compatible. In other plants, however, which are less subject to environmental influences of this sort, a definite genetic basis for incompatibility has been determined. In general, self-compatible (self-fertile) and self-incompatible individuals, when crossed, produce self-compatible offspring; and in the F_2, compatibility and incompatibility seem to segregate in simple Mendelian fashion. The genetic relations between various incompatible types in these same species, however, are more complex. A detailed genetic analysis of such forms in Nicotiana, which provides excellent material for this purpose, has been carried out by East and his students and has thrown much light on both the genetics and the physiology of incompatibility.

Individuals of *Nicotiana forgetiana* and *N. alata* are self-sterile but normally produce abundant seed in crosses. Hybrids between the two species are self-sterile but are fertile in crosses. In the F_2 from such a cross 20 plants were self-pollinated and were also interpollinated in most of the possible combinations and by enough tests to establish fertility or sterility with certainty. All the self-pollinations were sterile, and three of the interpollinations as well. Fertile seed from a number of fruits were planted, and five successive generations grown, the members of which were tested. It was found that sterility persisted unchanged but that the frequency of cross-sterility gradually increased, a fact attributed to the progressively increasing homozygosity of the material. Thorough testing indicated that it was possible to divide the individuals of the last generation into five classes, the members of each of which were all self-sterile and infertile with all other plants of the same class but entirely fertile with all the other classes. By inbreeding, made possible through pollination two days before normal opening of the flower, these classes were further purified. The clue to the cause of their difference was found in the behavior of certain families consisting of only two such classes. Here class A crossed with class B produced two types of plants in equal numbers: those like B and plants different from either A or B, a new class C. Similarly, B $\times$ A gave half A plants and half C plants. In every case half of the offspring were like the class of the pollen parent and half unlike either parent. *The female parent class never appeared among her own offspring.* This result is interpreted as due to the interaction of a series of three multiple allelic genes S_1, S_2, and S_3. Class A is arbitrarily designated S_1S_3, class B, S_1S_2, and class C, S_2S_3. Each class, being heterozygous, will produce two types of pollen at reduction. The assumption is that in any given plant the ovules can be fertilized only by pollen which contains a gene *different* from either of the plant's own genes. Thus a plant of class A (S_1S_3) pollinated by class B (S_1S_2) will allow only the S_2 pollen to function and thus will produce S_1S_2 offspring (class B) and S_2S_3 (class C). This hypothesis, which is shown graphically in Table XXIX, has been tested in various ways and seems to explain the results satisfactorily.

The genes controlling self-sterility apparently produce their effect by controlling the rate of pollen-tube growth. In compatible matings the tubes grow rapidly, but in incompatible ones they grow so slowly that before the gametes reach an ovule the flower has withered. In the case of the three allelic genes just described the rate of pollen-tube growth is apparently determined by the interaction between the diploid sporophytic tissue of the style and the haploid gametophytic tissue of the pollen tube. The maximum of rapidity, which is essential to fertilization, occurs only when all three genes involved are different. Later investigations by East and Yarnel have shown that there are at least 15 alleles of this series which act in the same way and an additional one which *stimulates* pollen tube growth in all crosses.

TABLE XXIX.—PROGENY OBTAINED FROM INTERCROSSING THREE STERILITY CLASSES IN NICOTIANA

		Male parent		
		A S_1S_3	B S_1S_2	C S_2S_3
Female Parent	A S_1S_3	Sterile	S_1S_2 S_2S_3	S_1S_2 S_2S_3
	B S_1S_2	S_1S_3 S_2S_3	Sterile	S_1S_3 S_2S_3
	C S_2S_3	S_1S_2 S_1S_3	S_1S_2 S_1S_3	Sterile

Stout has recently reviewed the genetics of similar and of more complex cases of incompatibility.

THE ORIGIN OF NEW SPECIES

The development of separate and distinct races is only one step in the evolution of species. The continued isolation of these groups is essential if their success, so far as it is acquired by selection, is to be preserved; for if they meet and mingle a host of new combinations will again appear, most of which will be less well adapted than the original types, and the good effects of selection will be lost.

Isolating Factors.—This isolation may be maintained in a variety of ways. It may be strictly geographical; but groups thus separated, unless there is some more fundamental cause for separation, are hardly more than geographic races. More important are those factors that normally prevent the crossing of two groups even if their ranges overlap. Habitats or seasonal distribution may be so diverse that individuals of two races do not meet. More fundamental are morphological or physiological mechanisms that operate to prevent crossing of dissimilar groups. Thus the conformation of the sex organs may be such that mating is difficult or impossible, or more subtle differences may prevent mutual attraction between members of different groups. Gametes of one race may be less effective in another than the latter's own gametes, resulting in a selective fertilization. Thus by a study of the behavior of pollen mixtures, Jones has found that in maize a plant's own pollen grows much

Fig. 134.—Ears of maize from a plant pure for white, starchy endosperm (left) and yellow, sugary endosperm (right) each of which has been pollinated by a mixture of pollen from the two plants. The plant's own pollen has effected fertilization in the great majority of cases. (*From Jones.*)

more rapidly on its own stigmas, and is thus more likely to effect fertilization than is pollen from another source, a result precisely opposite to the effect of self-sterility.

By using individuals differing in an endosperm character, it was possible to determine directly the type of pollen effecting fertilization (Fig. 134). Thus a plant bearing factors for white endosperm (recessive) was pollinated with a mixture of its own pollen and that from a plant otherwise similar except that it was homozygous for yellow endosperm. Pollination by the "white" (self) pollen produces white seeds and by the "yellow" pollen, yellow seeds. An extensive study by this method of the frequency of pollination by a plant's own pollen as compared with foreign pollen showed clearly that there was a distinct preponderance in favor of the former, even though the seed produced by the latter was somewhat heavier and thus presumably more vigorous. Essentially similar results have been obtained in tomato, cotton, and Oenothera. There is thus evidently a rather widespread tendency favorable to a plant's own pollen in fertilization.

The means by which this is brought about are not well understood. In maize, and probably in the other cases, it results from the more rapid

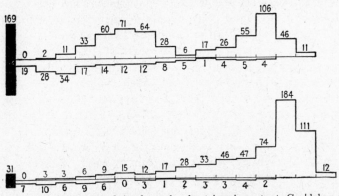

FIG. 135.—Pollen-tube growth in the style of a trisomic mutant, Cocklebur (above), and of a normal diploid plant (below) in Datura. The stigma is at the left, and toward the right are given and plotted the numbers of pollen tubes at successive millimeter intervals down the style. Number of ungerminated pollen grains shown by black bar at left. Normal pollen tubes above the datum line; swollen or burst ones below. (*From Buchholz and Blakeslee.*)

growth of pollen tubes of one type as compared with the other. These differences in rate of pollen tube growth seem to be due to genetic factors. In maize, a gene markedly increasing rate of such growth has been isolated, and from the distortion that it produces in segregating ratios, its linkage with two other genes has been determined. In Datura, pollen from plants heterozygous for the gene "tricarpel" produces many swollen and abnormal pollen tubes which do not effect fertilization and which presumably carry the recessive gene. Buchholz and Blakeslee have shown that the pollen from a trisomic mutant of Datura, half of which is normal and half of which carries the extra chromosome, produces two types of pollen tubes, one type of which is normal, grows rapidly, and effects fertilization, and the other type of which grows much more slowly and rarely reaches the ovary (Fig. 135). Since the extra chromosome is rarely transmitted through the pollen, these shorter tubes are presumably from the grains carrying this chromosome, and their defective growth is probably due to the lack of balance thus produced.

In certain closely related animal species sperm from one may occasionally fertilize eggs from the other but never as frequently as will sperm from its own species.

Even if hybrids are formed, they may not live to maturity, owing to some developmental disharmony. Sometimes the cause of this may be determined. Thus in certain cherry hybrids the embryos develop to a certain stage and then die. Tukey was able to carry them to normal development by removing them from the ovary when partly grown and cultivating them outside. Here evidently the nutritional balance between parent and embryo has been upset by hybridization.

As a result of these various factors most species have become entirely infertile with others and thus maintain their type unchanged. The genetic origin of this infertility is not easy to understand. Dobzhansky has given some evidence that genic interaction is a factor here. Should one gene mutate in one locally isolated race and another gene in another, when these genes later come together, their complementary action may be such as to prevent development of the hybrid. Some such physiological mechanism as occurs in the cases of gene-controlled self- and cross-sterility is probably involved; but in all these cases a preliminary isolation would seem to be necessary to develop the genic changes required.

Sterility of Hybrids.—In a great many cases, perfectly vigorous interspecific hybrid offspring can be produced; but here another important factor in preserving specific isolation appears, for most of such hybrids are sterile. The cause of this sterility is often not far to seek, for where the chromosomes of the two parents are unlike, normal pairing at meiosis evidently will not take place and gametes consequently fail to be produced. This may result from differences in the number or size of the chromosomes, in the character of the genes that they contain, or in the arrangement of these genes. Translocation is a common cause for defective gametes since many of them, in an individual heterozygous for a translocation, will lack certain genes. The extensive rearrangements of genic material resulting from a long period of specific isolation thus often result in failure to pair. That such failure is actually a cause of sterility may be seen from a comparison between certain hybrids and the allotetraploids derived from them (p. 323). Thus the F_1 hybrid between Raphanus and Brassica is sterile, but when each chromosome is doubled, pairing becomes possible again and fertility is restored.

There are also apparently many cases of genic as opposed to chromosomal sterility. The process of meiosis itself may be disturbed by gene action, as in the case of the "sticky" gene described by Beadle in maize, which, when homozygous, results in partial or complete sterility. To gene action may probably be ascribed the malformation of the sex organs and the general disturbance of the reproductive process found in many sterile hybrids.   Dobzhansky has analyzed crosses between Races A and B of *Drosophila pseudoobscura*, where the resulting males are always sterile, and he concludes that in almost all the chromosomes of both races there are genes which by complementary action in the hybrid are concerned with the production of this sterility.

As a result of these various isolating factors, the groups or races established by mutation, segregation, and isolation become set into more permanent form as species.   The genetic mechanisms by which this result is brought about are still by no means well understood, but at least a substantial beginning has been made toward their analysis. The development of genetics, especially as it concerns the genetics of populations, will doubtless continue to make important contributions to evolutionary theory and especially to that most important problem, long ago propounded by Darwin, the origin of species.

REFERENCES

BLAKESLEE, A. F. 1930. Extra chromosomes as a source of variations in the Jimson weed. Smithsonian Rept.

———. 1928. The genetics of Datura. Zeitschr. Ind. Abst. Vererb. Suppl. Bd. **1.**

———, A. DOROTHY BERGNER and A. G. AVERY. 1937. The geographical distribution of chromosomal prime types in *Datura Stramonium.* Cytologia, Fujii Jubliee Volume.

BUCHHOLZ, J. T., and A. F. BLAKESLEE. 1927. Abnormalities in pollen tube growth in Datura due to the gene "tricarpel." Proc. Nat. Acad. Sci. **13.**

——— and ———. 1930. Pollen-tube growth and control of gametophytic selection in Cocklebur, a 25-chromosome Datura. Bot. Gaz. **90.**

CLELAND, R. E. 1934. Cyto-taxonomic studies on certain Oenotheras from California. Proc. Amer. Phil. Soc. **75.**

CRAMPTON, H. E. 1932. Studies on the variation, distribution, and evolution of the genus Partula. The species inhabiting Moorea. Carnegie Inst. Washington Publ. **410.**

DARWIN, C. 1859. The origin of species. London.

———. 1868. Variation in animals and plants under domestication. New York.

DE VRIES, H. 1909. The mutation theory. (Translated by Farmer and Darbishire.) Chicago.

DOBZHANSKY, T. 1937(*a*). Genetics and the origin of species. New York. (Contains extensive bibliography.)

———. 1937(*b*). Further data on the variation of the Y chromosome in *Drosophila pseudoobscura.* Genetics **22.**

EAST, E. M., and D. F. JONES. 1919. Inbreeding and outbreeding. Philadelphia.

——— and S. H. YARNEL. 1929. Studies on self-sterility VIII. Self-sterility allelomorphs. Genetics **14.**

——— and ———. 1932. The behavior of crosses between self-sterile and self-fertile plants. Genetics **17.**

FISHER, R. A. 1931. The evolution of dominance. Biol. Rev. **6.**

———. 1930. The genetical theory of natural selection. 2d ed. Oxford.

HALDANE, J. B. S. 1924–1927. A mathematical theory of natural and artificial selection. Trans. and Proc. Cambridge Phil. Soc.

HARDY, G. H. 1908. Mendelian proportions in a mixed population. Science **28**: 49–50.

HARRIS, J. A. 1918. Further studies on the interrelationship of morphological and physiological characters in seedlings of Phaseolus. Memoirs Brooklyn Bot. Garden **1**.

HONING, J. A. 1923 and 1928. Canna crosses I and II. Med. Landbousch. Wageningen **26, 32**.

JONES, D. F. 1928. Selective fertilization. Chicago.

LINDSTROM, E. W. 1932. A fertile tetraploid tomato. Jour. Hered. **23**.

LOTSY, J. P. 1916. Evolution by means of hybridization. The Hague.

MÜNTZING, A. 1936. The evolutionary significance of autopolyploidy. Hereditas **21**.

RENNER, O. 1925. Untersuchungen über die faktorielle Konstitution einiger komplex-heterozygotischen Oenotheren. Bibliographia Genetica **9**.

STOUT, A. B. 1938. The genetics of incompatibilities in homomorphic flowering plants. Bot. Rev. **4**.

TIMOFEEFF-RESSOVSKY, N. W. 1934. Über die Vitalität einiger Genmutationen und ihrer Kombinationen bei *Drosophila funebris*, etc. Zeitschr. Ind. Abst. Vererb. **66**.

TUKEY, H. B. 1933. Embryo abortion in early-ripening varieties of *Prunus ovium*. Bot. Gaz. **94**.

WRIGHT, S. 1932. The roles of mutation, inbreeding, crossbreeding and selection in evolution. Proc. VI Int. Cong. Genetics **1**.

———. 1935. Evolution in populations in approximate equilibrium. Jour. Genetics **30**.

PROBLEMS

403. In order to decide whether a new type of plant or animal which arises under observation is a new species or not, what criteria would you employ?

404. Darwin observed that species belonging to large genera tended to be more variable than species of small genera. What genetic explanation can you offer for this difference in variability?

405. What genetic interpretation can you suggest for the fact that species have apparently evolved much more rapidly among flowering plants than among gymnosperms (coniferous trees and their allies)?

406. What genetic explanation can you offer for the fact that certain genera (such as the blackberries and hawthorns among plants) are highly variable and difficult to group into species, whereas in most genera the species are comparatively easy to separate?

407. Certain species, or genera, are *endemic*, occupying a range restricted to a certain region. What two explanations can you offer for such restricted distributions?

408. Give two reasons why animals and plants under domestication are more variable than corresponding wild species?

409. Assume that an animal population is made up of the following individuals, which interbreed and multiply in large numbers: AA, Aa, AA, AA, and

Aa. Assuming that there is no selective factor in operation, what will be the proportion of *AA*, *Aa*, and *aa* individuals in the third generation?

410. Make the same assumptions as in the preceding problem, except that the population has the following composition: *Aa, AA, aa, AA, AA, Aa, aa,* and *AA.* What will be the genetic constitution of the second generation?

411. If a self-fertilized plant has the genetic constitution *Aa Bb,* what will be the genetic constitution of the third generation of its offspring, assuming that *A* and *B* are inherited independently?

412. If the organism in the preceding question is a mammal, how different would be the result?

413. If the following animal population interbreeds freely and multiplies in large numbers and if *A* and *B* are inherited independently, what will be the genetic constitution of the first generation of its offspring? *AaBb AAbb AaBB AABB aaBb aabb AABb Aabb AABb AaBb.*

414. If a population originally has equal numbers of two genes *A* and *a* but is limited in size to two individuals in each generation, what will be the chance that the genes are still equally abundant in the third generation? What will be this chance if the population is limited to three individuals a generation? to four individuals?

415. Other things being equal, would you expect to find a larger number of recessive lethals in a large or a small population (breeding unit)?

416. Why are overlapping inversions most useful in deducing the width of relationship between two interfertile races (p. 350)?

417. What evidence can you present that selective fertilization is not very common?

418. How do you reconcile the phenomena of selective fertilization and self-sterility?

419. Would you expect selective fertilization to be found as frequently in animals as in plants? Why?

420. Enumerate as many causes for sterility as you know.

421. What evidence would be required to show that two races (such as *Drosophila pseudoobscura* A and B) differ by complementary fertility factors?

422. Selection is usually more effective with cross-fertilized than with self-fertilized plants. Explain.

423. Will selection for dominant characters be more or less effective than for recessive ones? Why?

424. If selection in one sex proves to be more successful in improving a stock of animals than does selection in the other sex, what conclusion can you draw as to the method of inheritance of the character in question?

425. In maize, if a gene increases rate of pollen-tube growth, how would you determine the linkage group to which it belongs?

CHAPTER XVI

GENETICS AND DEVELOPMENT

The principles of genetics, as set forth in the earlier chapters of this book, have been derived chiefly from a study of the behavior of genes and chromosomes at the time of maturation of the gametes and of fertilization. Since, however, genes are known only through their effects, the principles governing their transmission are in fact inferences from the known behavior in heredity of the differentiating characters of the developed organism. Between these two ends of the life cycle there occurs in all multicellular plants and animals a long chain of developmental changes. Our study of heredity cannot be complete until we have inquired how the genetic constitution, as determined by the genes and chromosomes in the gametes, is related, causally, to the developed characters.

Gene and Character.—While attention was confined chiefly to the beginning and the end of the developmental process, the idea arose that a single gene determined a single "unit character." The inadequacy of such a conception becomes apparent as soon as the general character of development is recalled. The organism reaches its final form through a series of changes in which each more complex condition arises out of an earlier and simpler one which preceded it, in a manner that embryologists describe as epigenesis. The cells in general divide equationally so that each, apart from rare cases of somatic mutation or somatic segregation, receives the same nuclear content and the same genes.

The question is immediately raised, How can the same genetic constitution produce different characters in the different parts? Moreover, development is coordinated so that the parts are at some stage interdependent, and modifications induced at such a time by mutant genes or by environment are likely to affect many characters. In fact careful study of the effects of gene mutations shows that in general they do produce widespread changes. The first mutant in Drosophila was called "white" from its effect on the eye, although later study has shown that it is accompanied by changes in testis color, spermatheca shape, fertility, and viability. Although most genes studied have some major effect by which they can be recognized, they are often found to produce many other less conspicuous ones. Conversely, it has already been pointed out that such an apparently simple character as the agouti coat of the wild rodent depends upon the simultaneous presence of at least a dozen interacting genes since, when any one of these mutates, the coat color is changed. Characters in general depend upon the interaction of many genes, perhaps upon the genotype as a whole; and genes in general affect not one but many characters.

There is as yet relatively little direct evidence on the actual changes in development brought about by changes in the genotype, but it is already evident that the relations between genes and characters are usually indirect ones involving several steps related as members of a chain of reactions.

The first reactions are probably those that occur within the cells and result in the production of active materials, such as enzymes or hormones. That the genes act within the cells is evident from cases in which neighboring cells contain different genes, as in somatic mutation (p. 300) and each exhibits the phenotype characteristic of its own genetic constitution. In some mosaics, however, the genes in one patch of tissue exert an influence on the characters of other cells of different genetic constitution, as Sturtevant showed in studies of mosaic eyes in Drosophila. Such action at a distance is now known to be due in some cases to the production of diffusible substances like hormones (p. 377). Such secondary reactions may be growth processes (cell multiplication, cell enlargement, etc.) general metabolic processes, or the production of other substances with effects on growth, form, and color. Modification of one stage of one of these processes may set in train a series of modifications in later ones. The actual modifications in development, both direct and indirect, which are controlled by genes can in many cases be interpreted most simply as the result of changes in the rates of various developmental processes, as discussed later. Goldschmidt (1938) has recently published an extensive review of many such cases, and his work should be consulted for a more detailed account.

Methods of Attack.—At present it is a hopeless task to try to determine, through direct study of the genes themselves, how they operate to control development. Far more refined methods than we now possess must be available before this can be attempted. Perhaps when our knowledge is more complete as to the kinds of changes that the gene undergoes as it mutates, knowledge now being gained more rapidly than ever before through the study of mutations induced by radiation, we shall be in a position to analyze the mechanism of gene action more directly.

A more promising method of attack for the present is to observe and describe, in morphological, chemical, and physical terms, the differences that exist between individuals differing by one or more genes and thus to make an analysis of the effects produced by these genes. It is often possible in this way to determine the particular processes affected and to gain an idea as to how the effect may have been produced. The farther back in development this analysis can be carried, the closer will it approach the primary action of the gene itself; but observation of more than the last few steps has thus far been impossible. Such a descriptive method is sometimes called that of *phenogenetics*, the study of the development of phenotypes.

Description may be supplemented by experiment in some cases, notably through an application of the methods employed in experimental embryology. By this means genetically diverse tissues may be brought together during development and their effect upon one another observed. This has proved especially successful in analyzing various chemical changes produced by gene action.

It is sometimes possible by modifying the environment in a specific fashion to produce a developmental effect—a phenocopy—very similar to that of a genic difference, and thus to gain a clue as to the means by which the genic difference itself is determined.

At best, the problems in this field are exceedingly difficult, and only tentative beginnings toward their solution have yet been made. In the following pages there are described a few of the developmental differences which have been studied by the methods here described.

The Development of Size Differences.—The genetic basis of size differences, in body or organ, is usually difficult to analyze, since many genes, similar in activity, seem to be involved. Developmentally, however, such differences are among the easiest to study for they can be accurately described by measurement and their progressive changes thus quantitatively determined.

Differences in size are evidently only differences in amount of growth, and the whole problem of the genetic control of size involves the genetic control of growth in general. The size to which an organ or organism grows may depend upon (1) the initial size of the egg, primordium, or "embryonic capital" from which its growth begins; (2) the rate at which it grows; or (3) the length of time during which growth continues. Each of these may be controlled by gene action.

1. *Embryo Size.*—In the discussion of heterosis (p. 285) attention has been called to the part that embryo-size differences may play in causing final size. With the same rate and duration of growth, one primordium twice as large as another will grow into an organ twice as large. The significance of initial size can well be seen in the growth of fruits. Miss Houghtaling found that in the earliest distinguishable flower primordia in tomatoes, the ovary was markedly larger in races

where it develops into a large fruit 10 cm. or more wide (as in most commercial varieties) than in the currant type, where the mature fruit is only about 1.2 cm. wide (Fig. 136). In the various races of *Cucurbita pepo* (the squashes and certain gourds) which differ so greatly in fruit size that the large races may have fruits more than 500 times the volume of the smallest ones, the very young ovary primordia at the same relative stage of development also show marked size differences. In maize and other plants differences in the size of the embryo in the seed have been shown to affect plant size at maturity, at least to some degree.

The variation in early size must be due to earlier differences in growth rate, and there is evidence that such differences sometimes persist for only a limited time. Certainly what happens in these very earliest stages is of critical importance in the development of many traits. That differences in growth rate actually do appear almost at the beginning of

Fig. 136.—Flower primordia of a small-fruited (left) and of a large-fruited (right) race of tomato, showing comparative organ sizes at the same stage of development. × 90. (*From Houghtaling.*)

development is well shown by the results of Gregory and Castle, who found that only 40 hours after fertilization the embryos of a race of large rabbits were bigger than those of a smaller race. In general, however, little is known as to the establishment of these important initial differences.

2. *Rate of Growth.*—The most obvious mechanism by which genes might affect size is through a control of the rates of growth, and such control has been shown in a number of cases. The male of Drosophila, for example, develops more slowly and emerges from the pupal state somewhat later than the larger female; the legs of Ancon sheep grow more slowly than those of normal ones so that the adults have the characteristic short legs, this difference from normal depending mainly on a single factor; "creeper" fowls, also with very short limbs, owe their difference from normal to a reduction in general growth rate at the time the limbs are growing most rapidly. Doubtless many inherited size differences are due to such genic effects on growth rates. In many cases, however, where the growth rates of large and of small organs have been measured, they have been found to be remarkably similar. Thus a large pumpkin and a small gourd may have essentially the same growth

rate, their differences in size being due to differences in initial size, or in duration of growth.

3. *Duration of Growth.*—In general, larger animals and plants tend to have a longer growing period than smaller ones. Dwarfness is often the result of a relatively early stoppage of growth. The effect of a gene producing dwarfism in mice has already been described. Here the gene affects primarily the amount and rate of production of a growth-regulating hormone in the anterior pituitary gland (p. 116). Animals pure for this gene stop growing at two or three weeks of age, while their normal litter mates continue to grow for several months longer.

Variations in size among plants may be due to a similar cause. Tall races (among annuals) in general are those that continue growing for a relatively long period before being checked by the development of flowers or by some other physiological factor. Genes that affect time of flowering or the position of the inflorescence may thus markedly influence size. In beans, a single gene affecting the differentiation of organs at the growing point determines whether the flowers are axillary or terminal. In the former case the vine keeps on growing until checked by external conditions and produces the tall, climbing type of plant. In the latter, the flower cluster stops terminal growth and a short, bushy plant is the result.

Cellular Basis of Size Differences.—Differences in size of an organ or organism may also be analyzed into differences in the size of its constituent cells. Thus Painter found no differences in cell size between large and small races of rabbits but a profound one in cell number. Large leaves, fruits, and other plant organs usually contain many more cells than do smaller ones. Differences in cell number are evidently due either to differences in rate of cell division or (probably more commonly) to differences in duration of mitotic activity.

Cell size, however, is by no means without importance in determining organ and body size. Tetraploid plants, especially autotetraploids, tend to be noticeably stouter and to have larger leaves and flowers, than diploids. These differences are clearly associated with a cell volume averaging about twice as great as in the diploid (Fig. 137) and this, in turn, results from a doubled chromosome number and larger nuclei. Haploid plants, in the same way, are smaller in all their parts than diploid, and are composed of cells of about half the diploid volume. Such differences have been reported in Datura, maize, tomato, and many other seed plants and are also conspicuous in the extensive polyploid series in mosses studied by von Wettstein.

Cell size and body size may be affected by differences in chromosome mass aside from polyploidy. In Drosophila, Dobzhansky found that each small bristle on the wing corresponds to one cell, so that by counting the number of bristles in a measured area it is possible to calculate the average size of the individual cells. By this means he found that the reduced size of wings in the mutant "miniature" is due chiefly to decrease in cell size. He also showed, by comparing cell sizes in males, females, triploids, supermales, superfemales, and intersexes (among which there are marked differences in chromosome number and volume) that cell size in general increases with increase in amount of chromatin. Such a result does not hold for all organisms, apparently, for Goldschmidt found that in races of Lymantria differing considerably in chromatin mass there were no significant differences in cell or body size.

Aside from these instances where cell size is related to chromosome number or volume there are many others, especially in plants, in which

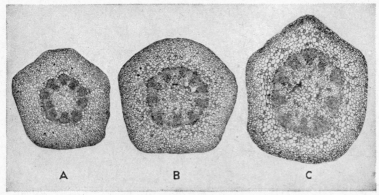

Fig. 137.—Cross sections of flower stalks of haploid (*A*), diploid (*B*), and tetraploid (*C*) plants of Datura.

it seems to depend on ordinary genic differences. Thus among the many races of *Cucurbita pepo*, which differ greatly in fruit size, there are very considerable differences in cell volume, the cells of the fruit wall at maturity ranging from 300,000 cubic microns in some races to about twenty times that volume. Cucurbit fruits well illustrate the importance of cell size in plant development for there is often an increase of about 10,000 times in cell volume between the tissues of the tiny ovary primordium and the tissues of the mature fruit. In extreme cases this difference may even reach 100,000 times. In the early stages of development, until about the time of flowering, cell multiplication occurs, and the number of cells is determined. Division now ceases and cell expansion takes place. The extent of both cell division and cell expansion is important in determining fruit size. Both are clearly inherited, and they seem to be independent of one another genetically. The effects of single genes have as yet been shown in only a few such traits, since most of them seem to be governed by multiple genes.

The Development of Shape Differences.—The possession of a specific form, both of the body as a whole and of its component parts, is one of the most distinctive features of organisms. These forms are clearly under the control of genes, and they provide some of the most familiar examples of Mendelian heredity. The single gene difference between spherical and disk fruits in squash; between spherical and pear-shaped fruits in tomato; between lobed and entire leaves in Japanese morning-glory; between single, rose, and pea combs in poultry; and between the many wing forms in Drosophila may be cited. The mechanism by which

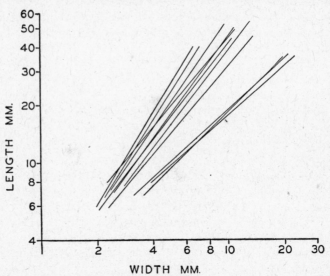

WIDTH MM.

FIG. 138.—Segregation of a single-gene difference in relative rate of growth of fruit length and width. An F_2 from a cross between two pure lines of Lagenaria, in one of which length grows relatively fast and in the other relatively slowly, in comparison to width. The eight plants at the left show the dominant growth ratio, the three at the right, the recessive. Both are plotted logarithmically.

form differences are determined involves the development of form in general, and this in turn is closely related to the whole problem of organization and organic correlation, as to the control of which very little is known.

In the simplest cases, where the dimensional relationships of a single organ are involved, a developmental analysis is not difficult. Cucurbit fruits differing in shape have been measured from their earliest visible primordia to maturity and the origin of these shape differences thus observed. The *relative* rates of growth of the various dimensions are often unequal and are found to be constant over long periods and therefore to produce a constantly changing form. Thus in the "Club" gourd, length constantly grows faster than width for most of its development, so that the shape changes from almost isodiametric in the smallest primordium to one that is about fifteen times as long as wide in the mature fruit. In other races, on the contrary, growth in width exceeds that in length by a constant amount. The ratio between the two dimensional growth rates does not change and may be expressed by a constant, α, the ratio of the two logarithmic growth rates to each other.[1] Experiment indicates that it is this ratio, rather than any particular ratio between dimensions, that is genically controlled (Fig. 138). The duration of the period of unequal growth rates may be brief, establishing a shape for the young ovary which then persists through later development when growth is uniform in all dimensions; or it may continue much longer. Such differences in dimensional growth rates occur primarily during the period of cell division and are related to constant differences in the plane in which the cells divide. This, in turn, is evidently one manifestation of cell polarity. The genic control of shape in such cases therefore seems to be exercised through a control of cell polarity. Less commonly, dimensional changes are associated with modification of cell shape during the period of cell expansion.

These relatively simple form changes arising from constant differences in relative dimensional growth rates are common throughout animals and plants. The genic mechanisms by which they are controlled are far from clear. Hormone action, differences in electric potential, and various other means for producing inequalities on growth have been suggested, but our ignorance in this field is still almost complete.

More complex form differences involve changes, not in a single organ, but in the relative growth rates of two organs or parts, by which the general bodily pattern is altered. Here again it is commonly found that although two such parts are growing at different rates, the ratio between these rates is constant, so that a constant and predictable change in form occurs during growth. This is the general phenomenon of allometry to which attention has been particularly directed by Huxley, Teissier, and others. A well-known example is that of the crab, *Uca pugnax*, where the large claw grows faster than the rest of the body so that the ratio of claw to body changes as the animal grows. Here again the ratio of the two growth rates is constant. Many similar examples could be cited from animal and plant development. Allometric growth is merely the old problem of organic correlation expressed in more precise terms. These constant growth relationships are clearly inherited, but here, too, we have little information as to how genes control them except that the control is exercised over the whole system or body.

---

[1] In the formula of simple allometry as stated by Huxley and Teissier, where $y = bx^\alpha$. In the present case, x and y are dimensions, b is the value of y when $x = 1$, and α is the growth ratio.

A third type of form determination is still more complex. Many genetically controlled differences are sharply localized and involve differences in the size of specific parts. Changes in the size of wing, eye, and bristles in Drosophila and in the length of legs in Ancon sheep, of the tail in mice, and of the ears in rabbits are familiar examples from animals. Differences in the size of leaf, flower, and fruit are similar examples from plants. Here the specific part is altered but the whole is little changed, so that, unlike the types of form change previously discussed, the genes seem to have a local rather than a general effect.

Careful developmental studies, however, show that such a conclusion may be too hasty and that even here the genic influence is not a purely

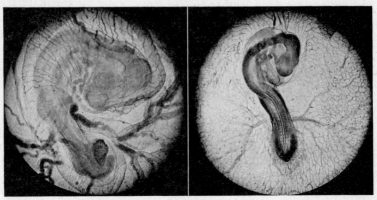

Fig. 139.—Photographs at same magnification of embryos of normal chicken (left) and homozygous Creeper (right) at 72 hours of incubation to show delayed growth of the Creeper, which is about to die. (*From Landauer.*)

local one. In the case of the "Creeper" fowl, for example, the legs (and to a less extent the wings) are much shortened in comparison with the normal, apparently a localized effect of the single dominant mutation which differentiates creeper from normal.

The embryological studies of Landauer however have shown that this mutation has not one but many effects in all parts of the body and that the several effects are consequences of a retardation of growth which occurs in the early embryo. Embryos homozygous for the creeper mutation usually die at the end of the third day of incubation (Fig. 139). As early as at 36 hours they fall behind the normal in growth, and the hind limbs which, in the normal are growing rapidly at this time, fail to grow in the homozygotes. Rarely a homozygote lives until a later embryonic period; such animals are smaller than normal, have only rudiments of the hind limbs, and show abnormalities of head, eyes, and other parts (Fig. 140). A study of the various parts shows that they deviate from normal in the order of their normal growth potencies during the earlier period of retardation. The parts which in the normal are growing most rapidly at that time are most abnormal in the homozygote.

In the heterozygotes the differences in limb length and proportion are established in the early embryo, at least before the seventh day, and thereafter the different bones grow at about the same relative rates so that the altered growth pattern appears to be a result of the retardation suffered in the earlier period.

That this effect of the Creeper mutation is of a general nonspecific character is indicated by the experiments of Fell and Landauer who induced Creeper characters in early normal limb rudiments by growing them in culture media with abnormally low nutritive content. The apparently localized character changes are thus due to a general effect of the mutation on growth and metabolism.

In some cases a mutation disturbs some organic correlation or form dependence, as in the case of the Brachyury or short-tailed mutant type in the mouse. Here the shortness of the tail in the heterozygote is due to the absence of the posterior part of the notochord. In the absence of notochord the neural tube does not develop normally and the somites, which first differentiate independently, fail to persist; so that the tail distal to the end of the notochord degenerates before birth (Fig. 141). Embryos homozygous for this mutation lack normal notochord and somites and the neural tube is markedly abnormal. Such

Fig. 140.—A homozygous Creeper embryo which has lived beyond the lethal period, showing marked changes in legs (only toes showing), wings (less reduced), head and eyes. (*From Landauer.*)

embryos always die at the end of the tenth day of development. Chesley has shown that this mutation affects fundamental form relations of a more general nature than the apparently local effect of the mutant would indicate.

In such cases as these, the genes evidently control what are sometimes called "organizers" or "morphogenetic fields," those general developmental patterns or schedules that are specifically associated with a given genotype. As our knowledge of the operation of these relationships increases, we shall be in a better position than now to determine just how they are affected by genic differences.

The Development of Color Differences in Animals.—The mechanisms through which genes produce their effects must obviously involve, at some stage in the chain, chemical precursors which differ in different genotypes. Some differences of this sort have been demonstrated by recent work on mutant genes affecting the development of color in insects.

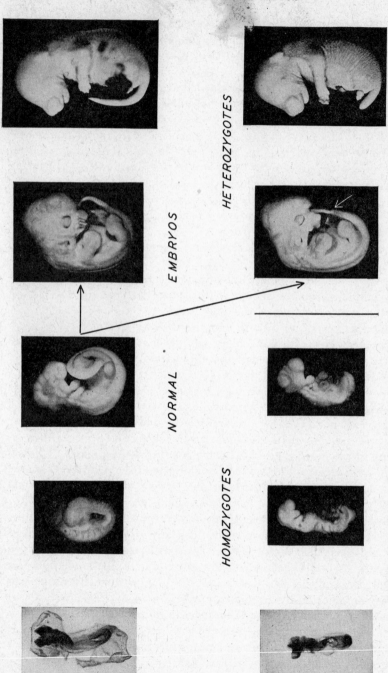

Fig. 141.—The effects on development of a mutation in the house mouse. Above, from left, normal embryos of 9, 9½, 10½, 11, and 16½ days of development; below, litter mates of above, showing homozygotes at 9, 9½ and 10½ days and heterozygotes at 11 and 16½ days. The homozygote at 10½ days is shown just before death and lacks tail bud and hind limb buds. In the heterozygote at 11 days the constriction in the tail marks the end of the notochord; by 16½ days the end of the tail has been resorbed. (*After Chesley.*)

Eye Color in the Flour Moth.—In the European flour moth, *Ephestia Kühniella,* Kühn and his coworkers have found mutant genes which affect the colors of various parts of both the larva and the adult. The differences brought about by one such gene substitution are shown below:

Character affected	Color in wild type AA or Aa	Color in mutant aa
Adult eyes	Black	Red
Adult brain	Dark brown	Pale red
Adult testes	Brown-violet	Colorless
Larval skin	Reddish	White
Larval eyes	Much pigment	Little pigment

Caspari transplanted the testes from AA or Aa larvae to those of the mutant type aa. The grafts retained their dark color and caused certain of the characters of the aa host to develop the A phenotype, that is, aa imagoes with A testes implants had black instead of red eyes; the testes and brain of the host resembled those of the wild type to a greater or lesser degree, and if the transplantation was made into early aa larvae, the larval skin and larval eyes in later molts assumed the A characters. Similar results were obtained by implanting ovaries or brains from A to aa larvae. In the reciprocal type of transplantation, aa brain and testes implanted into A larvae assumed A characters. Homotransplantation of A tissue to other A larvae or aa tissues to other aa larvae showed that the changes described above were not due to the operation or injury to tissues.

Kühn and his associates assumed that a substance contained in certain implanted tissues of genotype AA or Aa could produce their characteristic effects in host tissues which did not contain this gene. Since the substance was diffusible and separable from A tissues by extraction with alcohol and with acetone they called it A hormone. An interesting proof of the dependence of the A characters on a circulating substance which a animals lack was obtained by implanting A tissue into aa females which were then bred to aa males. This cross would normally produce larvae with the a characters—colorless skin, little pigment in eyes, etc. But larvae from the a mothers with implanted A tissues produced larvae with the A characters. One route by which the gene A produced its effects on many tissues was thereby disclosed. The actual chemical nature of the effective substance has not yet been discovered.

Eye Color in Drosophila.—A chain of reactions involving at least two different substances concerned in producing the wild-type eye color in Drosophila has been demonstrated by Beadle and Ephrussi. In dipterous insects many of the structures of the adult or imago, such as the compound eyes, legs, and wings, develop from anlage which are formed within the late embryo or early larval stages. These anlage are known as imaginal disks. In Drosophila the imaginal disk of the compound eye can be transplanted from one larva to another and then can continue its development in the body cavity of the host. When the host has undergone metamorphosis and has emerged as an imago, the implanted eyes can

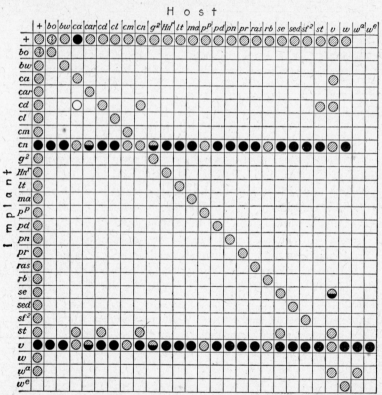

FIG. 142.—Diagrammatic representation of the results of eye transplantation in Drosophila. Shaded circles indicate autonomous development; for example, brown (*bw*) disks transplanted into wild-type (+) larvae, develop brown color. Black circles indicate nonautonomous development of pigmentation. Circles half black and half shaded indicate that the resulting implant is intermediate in color. (*From Beadle and Ephrussi.*)

be dissected out from the body cavity and their color characteristics observed. The colors of intact eyes are apparently not altered by the operation itself or by development within the body cavity.

When eye disks are taken from larvae of races with mutant eye colors (white, peach, pink, carmine, etc.) and implanted into wild-type larvae, or the reverse, the disks usually develop autonomously (Fig. 142), that is, they produce eyes with the color of their own genotype and are not affected by the genotype of the host. There are, however, two important exceptions. Eye disks from larvae with the mutant gene vermilion implanted into wild-type larvae develop not vermilion but wild-type color. Similarly, eye disks from larvae with the mutant eye-color gene cinnabar (an eye color like vermilion) implanted into wild-type larvae develop wild-type pigmentation. In both cases something from the host has caused the implant to develop a phenotype corresponding not to its own genotype but to that of its host. Beadle and Ephrussi have assumed that the vermilion and cinnabar mutant flies each lack some substance which is an essential link in the chain of reactions leading to the formation of the wild-type eye pigment, that the eye anlage remain sensitive to such substances and that, in the cases just quoted, the essential substance has been supplied to the anlage from the body fluids of the host.

It has been shown that the substance that is lacking in the vermilion eye is not the same as the substance that is lacking in the cinnabar eye. When eye disks from vermilion larvae are transplanted into cinnabar larvae, the implants develop wild-type pigmentation, showing that the cinnabar host supplies what is lacking in vermilion. However, when eye disks from cinnabar larvae are transplanted into vermilion larvae, the implants develop cinnabar pigmentation; vermilion does not supply what is lacking in cinnabar. It appears then that two substances are lacking in vermilion, that one is lacking in cinnabar, and that both are present in the wild type. Other observations show that the second of the substances (the one that cinnabar lacks) is produced only when the first is present, that is, one substance acts as a precursor of the other. Thus have been demonstrated two related links in a chain of reactions leading to the development of wild-type eye color, and this chain has apparently been broken at an earlier point by the mutation to vermilion, at a later point by the mutation to cinnabar.

As in the case of Ephestia, these substances affected by gene mutation in Drosophila are of the nature of hormones; they are heat stable, diffusible, and dialyzable.

Interestingly enough, the substances assumed as members of the normal eye-color reaction chain are not species specific. The Drosophila substances are found in several other invertebrates and extracts of Ephestia A hormone cause the development of wild-type eye color in the Drosophila cinnabar eye (Becker and Plagge). Extracts from *aa* Ephestia, however, are without effect on cinnabar, and it is assumed that the mutation from *A* to *a* in Ephestia has broken the eye pigment reaction chain at or before the same point as the mutation from wild type to vermilion in Drosophila, that is, at a stage previous to the formation of the precursor of the substance which is lacking in cinnabar.

These two cases reveal one of the mechanisms through which genes exert their effects on the adult characters. Diffusible substances like hormones have been shown to play a large part in the control of development in vertebrates; the same type of evidence is now available for certain insects, and the effects of auxins on determination of growth, size, and form in plants are now becoming known. The production and specific character of such hormone-like substances have been shown in other cases, for example the dwarf mutant in the mouse, to depend upon particular genes.

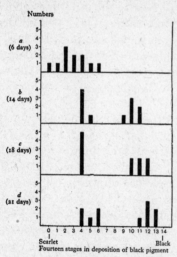

Numbers

a (6 days)

b (14 days)

c (18 days)

d (21 days)

0 1 2 3 4 5 6 7 8 9 10 11 12 13 14
Scarlet   Black
Fourteen stages in deposition of black pigment

Fig. 143.—Frequency polygons of a red-eyed family of Gammarus segregating for rapid and slow darkening of eyes classified at intervals from 6 to 14 days of age. Individuals on the right are those whose eyes darken rapidly; those on left darken slowly. (*From Ford and Huxley.*)

In other cases differences in eye color seem to be due to differences in the rate of chemical change. In the brine shrimp, *Gammarus chevreuxi*, the wild-type animals have black eyes. A mutant race with red eyes differs from wild type by a recessive gene. The red gene appears to act, as Ford and Huxley have shown, chiefly by slowing down the rate at which the black pigment melanin is formed in the eye. The wild-type eye, which is black at hatching, is itself red before hatching but darkens very rapidly; the red-eyed variety darkens much more slowly; while several other genes affecting the darkness of the eye do so by changing the rate of melanin deposition (Fig. 143). Similar retardations in rate may be brought about by low temperature. The action of certain genes in Drosophila may possibly be interpreted in the same way, and it is well known that in man, for instance, the eyes of brown-eyed children are blue at birth and darken with age, reaching the final state at different ages. In these cases the genes may be considered as affecting primarily the rates of developmental processes and secondarily the times at which various reactions are set in motion.

Effects of Genes on Chemical Components in Plants.—Genic control over various characters in plants is often more direct, that is, the reaction chain connecting the gene and its visible effect seems often to be shorter and simpler, than in the more complex animal organism. This is well illustrated by the effects of genes on specific chemical constituents in plants. One of the most direct relationships has been shown by Brink's study of the effects of the recessive waxy gene in maize which controls the character of the carbohydrate in pollen, embryo sac, and endosperm.

Ordinarily, maize pollen stains blue with iodine, but pollen from waxy plants stains reddish brown. A normal plant heterozygous for waxy produces two kinds of pollen grains: half with the normal gene, which stain blue; half with the waxy gene, which stain red-brown with iodine, showing that the waxy gene affects directly the kind of carbohydrate in the pollen. The biochemical studies of Brink have made it very probable that a primary effect of the waxy gene is on the production of an enzyme (amylase) slightly different from that produced by the nonwaxy gene. The sugars from which the starch is built are the same in both waxy and nonwaxy pollen, but the two enzymes catalyze slightly different reactions, so that the same components become organized into slightly different compounds, one of which (waxy starch) gives the red-brown reaction; the other (normal starch), the usual blue with iodine. The waxy starch also is broken down more slowly under the action of its enzymes, and the waxy pollen tubes probably grow more slowly for this reason. The direct effect of this gene is thus upon the character of an enzyme which may secondarily change the speed of specific reactions.

An apparently direct effect of a gene on a chemical component of plant cells has been brought to light by Mangelsdorf and Fraps. The difference between yellow, Y, and white endosperm, y, in maize is known to be determined by a single pair of genes. Yellow corn is also known to be much richer in vitamin A than white corn and this difference is determined by the yellow-white pair of genes. Because of the triploid nature of the endosperm in maize, it is possible to obtain by proper crosses maize seeds with endosperm of composition yyy, yyY, yYY, and YYY or with 0, 1, 2, and 3 yellow genes, respectively. Seeds of these four sorts, fed to rats according to a standard technique for estimating vitamin A units, proved to contain approximately, 0, 2.25, 5.00, and 7.50 units of vitamin A per gram. The amount of vitamin A was thus directly proportional to the number of Y genes, which shows that Y is directly responsible for the formation of vitamin A and makes it unlikely that Y itself acts as an enzyme, since such direct proportionality is not a usual feature of enzyme action.

Plant Colors.—The most extensive chemical studies of the effects of genes on colors have been carried out by Wheldale (Mrs. Onslow), Scott-Moncrieff, and others. The colors of flowers, fruits, autumn leaves, and some generally distributed colors are due chiefly to soluble pigments in the epidermal cells. Those which are responsible for the various shades or mixtures of red and blue (pinks, purples, magentas, lavenders) belong to the group of pigments known as anthocyanins. These are compounds of carbon, hydrogen, and oxygen, all containing a pyrene ring differing in the number of hydroxyl groups in the molecule. Many pure anthocyanins have been isolated in crystalline form. All give blue salts with

alkalies and red salts with acids.   The yellow and ivory colors are due
to anthoxanthins which belong to a related group of pigments known as
flavones and flavonols, also derived from sugars with different molecular
structure.   It is probable that in the plant the anthocyanins arise from
flavonols by loss of oxygen (reduction).   The genes affecting flower color
apparently do so by altering the chemical constitution, distribution,
relative amounts, and degrees of oxidation of these pigments, and the
relative acidity of the medium.   Interactions between genes affecting
these basic chemical conditions have been shown to produce a wide
variety of colors in Antirrhinum, Primula, Pelargonium, and other plants.
Occasionally a mutant change in flower color can be shown to be due to a
relatively simple change in the anthocyanin nucleus as in the difference
between rose-pink and salmon-pink in *Pelargonium zonale* which Scott-
Moncrieff has shown to be due to the substitution of hydroxyl for hydrogen
at the same position in the molecule.   Since many of the changes in such
chemical components are catalyzed by specific enzymes, it is possible that
genes affecting flower color do so by controlling the character of enzymes.

Effects of the Genotype on Viability.—Most mutative changes are
accompanied by changes in viability, and this may be taken as evidence
that the genes directly affect vital processes.   This has already been
emphasized for new gene mutations (p. 296) for deficiencies (p. 335) which
are nearly always lethal when homozygous, and for various chromosomal
changes such as translocations which are often accompanied by lethal
effects.   The recognition of lethals as of frequent occurrence among
both natural and induced mutations indicates that normal or "wild-type"
viability depends on the presence of most, or all, of the genes in normal
condition.   Yet the appearance of all intergrading conditions between
complete lethality in the earliest stages of the zygote and reduced viability
or life length of the developed animal or plant shows that lethals constitute no sharp or absolute category but that most changes of the genotype
share in this effect.

There is some evidence that the stage at which development is termin-
ated depends in a rough way on the degree of modification of the genotype.   Poulson compared the effects of several deficiencies in Drosophila
varying in extent from complete absence of the X chromosome (nullo-X)
through absence of half of the X to absence of a short section of this
chromosome (Notch deficiency).   In the first case development stopped
before the formation of the blastoderm, in the last case after complete
formation of the embryo, and in the second at an intermediate condition.
Demerec, however, has shown that not all loci in the chromosome are
of equal importance; deficiencies for most X chromosome loci act both
as zygote lethals and as cell lethals, that is, cells lacking one of these loci
die.   But some deficiencies do not act as cell lethals, showing either that

such loci do not have such important effects on vital processes or that their contributions to such processes are carried out as well by other (duplicated or repeated) loci. Although it may be in general true that the larger the change the earlier and more severe may be its lethal effect, it is probable that different loci contribute unequally to the processes controlling viability.

We learn relatively little from the mere occurrence of viability effects, however, concerning how the genes actually produce these effects. Descriptive and experimental studies on developing mutant forms show that in some cases a form dependence or organizer relation is changed (as in the short-tailed or tailless mouse). Here Ephrussi (1933) has shown that some of the tissues of the lethal embryo (homozygous for the short-tailed mutation, *TT*, p. 375) can survive and grow in tissue culture, while Baltzer and Hadorn's studies of hybrid merogones in Triton show that certain parts of a lethal embryo will live and differentiate if transplanted to a normal embryo, while the head mesenchyme, a tissue of local importance in development, fails to do so. Death of the whole is thus due to a disturbed growth correlation, but since the correlation of the whole depends upon the important role played by one part, it becomes very difficult to distinguish between disturbed correlation and a deficiency of a specific part.

In a few cases it has been shown that, even after a part has been developed, its viability and future differentiation depend upon a specific genotype which may be altered by mutation. Thus in the short-tailed mouse (p. 376) the tail develops in the embryo, but the part posterior to a constriction which appears early in embryonic life degenerates and is resorbed. Similarly Goldschmidt has shown that certain of the mutant forms in Drosophila which as adults show scalloping or absence of parts of the wing, actually develop fully formed wings in the pupae; thereafter parts of the wing undergo degeneration. Similar phenotypes are produced by heat treatment of the larvae, and Goldschmidt believes that dedifferentiation or reverse processes of a pathological nature are set in train by the mutant gene in one case and the temperature shock in the other and that the earlier these begin in development the greater is the effect.

In these and other instances it is possible to suppose that the mutant gene fails to carry some essential process to completion. Wright has given reasons for supposing that recessives in general show some loss or inactivation of function as compared with dominant or wild-type genes and characterizes such mutants, which include the majority of natural mutations, as less efficient than their wild-type alleles. They thus produce little effect when heterozygous, that is, they are recessive, and lead to decreased viability when homozygous.

Genic Balance.—That a given trait is due not to a single gene alone but to the interaction of many or all of them is shown by the fact of genic balance, well illustrated by the relationship between heteroploidy and plant characters in Datura (p. 327). In this plant many mutant types are known which depart from normal in various ways affecting all parts of the individual. These types have been found to be associated with characteristic changes in the ratios between the different kinds of

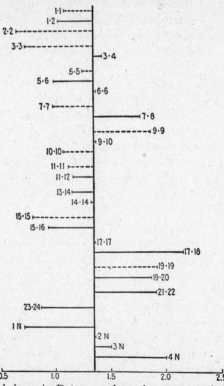

Fig. 144.—Genic balance in Datura as shown by an anatomical character, the area of the pith (in square millimeters) in the flower stalk. Vertical line, mean area of diploid. Areas of primary (solid) and secondary (dotted) mutants (and of polyploid series) shown by ends of horizontal lines.

chromosomes. The wild type has 12 pairs of chromosomes. When the members of any one pair are in excess, certain characters in all plant parts regularly differ from this normal type. The differences produced are characteristic of the particular chromosome which is in excess and which thus modifies, in one direction or another, the normal genic balance exhibited by the diploid. The latter is essentially the average of the effects of all the chromosomes. Thus, for a given trait, the condition of the diploid is the average of the conditions of the 12 primary mutants, each of which has one extra member of one of the chromosome sets (Fig. 144).

In the haploid, diploid, triploid, and tetraploid types, however, there are, respectively, 12 single chromosomes, 12 sets of two, 12 sets of three, and 12 sets of four. Here the proportional representation of each kind of chromosome is the same, and the plants have the same general set of

Fig. 145.—Chromosome mutants and chromosome balance in Datura, as shown by differences in capsule form. Above, at left, the normal diploid type, from plant with twelve pairs of chromosomes. Below (left) the mutant "Globe," in which one set of chromosomes has three members, thus upsetting the normal balance. The effect of this particular chromosome set is evidently to flatten the capsule, for the addition of an extra chromosome to it results in a flatter capsule than the normal. The addition of *two* extra chromosomes (as shown to the right of this) flattens the capsule still further.

Above, at right, a capsule from a tetraploid plant, which has four chromosomes in each set, instead of the normal two. The balance between the twelve sets is thus maintained and there is little difference from the normal in capsule form. The results of the addition of one, two, and three chromosomes to the globe set are shown below. It is evident that the change produced by each additional chromosome is less than it is in a corresponding diploid plant, presumably because the number of chromosomes is greater, the contribution of a single chromosome is less in proportion to the whole, and the balance is therefore less upset. (*From Blakeslee.*)

characters as the diploid or wild type. The balance has not been disturbed.

The effect of balance is further shown where the proportional relations are changed in the more complex heteroploids. When a particular one of the chromosome sets has 3 members, the other sets still having only 2 each (a $2n + 1$ or trisomic plant), the group of characters constituting the type "Globe" appears. If there are 4 of these Globe chromosomes and 2 members in each of the other sets ($2n + 2$), all the Globe characters are enhanced, that is, they depart from the normal in the same direction but to a greater degree, than in the $2n + 1$ Globe. If in a tetraploid an extra Globe chromosome is present, the departure from the wild type is not so marked as in the $2n + 1$ Globe, for now there are 5 Globe chromosomes to 4 of each of the others. A tetraploid with 2 extra Globe chromosomes, however, shows an accentuation of the Globe characters equivalent to that in the $2n + 1$ type; and a tetraploid with 3 extra Globe chromosomes shows nearly as extreme a departure in the Globe direction as in the $2n + 2$ type. The effects of such extra chromosomes on one character—capsule shape—are shown in Fig. 145. The ratios between the numbers of Globe chromosomes and all others are shown in Table XXX.

TABLE XXX

Type	Number of Globe chromosomes	Total number of other chromosomes	Ratio	Appearance of Globe character + = exaggeration − = decrease
Diploid $2n$	2	22	1:11	Wild type
Triploid $3n$	3	33	1:11	Wild type
Tetraploid $4n$	4	44	1:11	Wild type
Globe $2n + 1$	3	22	1: 7.3	Globe
Globe $2n + 2$	4	22	1: 5.5	Globe ++
Globe $3n + 1$	4	33	1: 8.2	Globe −
Globe $4n + 1$	5	44	1: 8.8	Globe −
Globe $4n + 2$	6	44	1: 7.3	Globe
Globe $4n + 3$	7	44	1: 6.3	Globe +

The degree of departure from the wild type in all these cases is thus correlated with the ratio which this chromosome bears to the other chromosomes. A similar dependence of the sexual characters of Drosophila upon genic balance has been illustrated in another connection (p. 261).

Parallelism between Environmental and Genic Effects.—In the investigations thus far discussed attempts have been made to discover something of the nature of gene action by comparing development in individuals of unlike genic constitution. This method is useful in making clear just what developmental processes and resulting characters are affected by gene action and how great this effect is, but it has yielded less information as to *how* the effects are produced.

Another method of studying this perplexing problem is through an attempt to imitate the effect of genic action by changing the environment in a specific way. Where this can be accomplished, it provides at least a suggestion as to the mechanism of the genic control of development. Some success has attended such efforts with a number of organisms, but the results of Goldschmidt and others on the effect of temperature shocks during development in Drosophila are especially noteworthy. By subjecting larvae to a relatively high temperature (35–37°C.) for from 6 to 24 hours at ages of from four to seven days, Goldschmidt was able to produce a high percentage (sometimes up to 100 per cent) of adults which resembled very closely certain known mutants. The genetic constitution of these flies was unchanged, as later breeding experiments showed, but their developmental history seemed to be identical with one or another of the forms known to result from gene mutations. The action of the environment here is specific, for with a given racial stock, larval age, duration of exposure, and intensity of heat, a specific type tends to be produced in a high proportion of individuals. These environmentally produced imitations of gene mutants Goldschmidt has termed *phenocopies*. Some of the more important, together with conditions leading to their production, are shown in Table XXXI.

TABLE XXXI.—PRODUCTION OF DEFINITE PHENOCOPIES UNDER TYPICAL CONDITIONS

Phenotype	Age days	$t°$	Exposure, hours	Optimum per cent of phenocopies
Scalloped	4½–5½	35	12–24	70
Curly	6–7	35–37	18–24	76
Ski	6–6½	36–37	12	43
Spread	5½	35	18–24	91
Curved	5–7	36	18	23
Dumpy	5	36	12	34
Lancet	7	36–37	18	22
Miniature	5½–7	36–37	12–18	40
Blistered	5–6	36	18	10
Rolled	7	35–37	18–24	40
Trident	7	35–37	6–24	82
Eye size	5½–6	37	18	100
Horns	7	35	24	4
Benign	4½	35	18–24	75

Not only are single mutants copied, but series of grades resembling all types of known multiple alleles. Modification of given gene mutants may be made in the same way. Thus by exposing vestigial-winged stock to a wide temperature range (14–30.9°C.) a series of progeny was produced with varying wing sizes from almost wingless to almost normal, closely resembling a quantitative allelic series. Similarly, increased temperature reduces eye size, for flies with Bar eyes grown at high temperatures have an eye size as small as those with Ultrabar eyes grown at a lower temperature, the temperature effect clearly paralleling the genic one (Fig. 146).

One important result of these experiments has been to show that for many effects there is a very limited sensitive or critical period—sometimes only a few hours long—during which the effect is determined. A change in temperature applied before or after this period is without effect. This

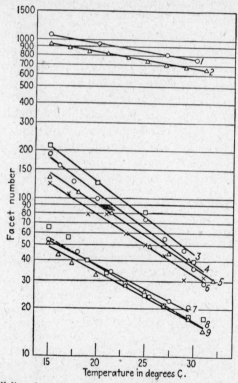

FIG. 146.—Parallelism between effect of increased temperature and of Bar genes in reducing eye size in Drosophila. 1 and 2, wild type; 3, 4, 5, and 6, Bar; 7, 8, and 9, Ultrabar. (*From Hersh.*)

suggests that during such critical stages in development there exist alternative paths of growth and differentiation which lead to different character effects. Gene differences, like environmental ones, may determine which path is to be followed.

Thus in the case of some of the mutants at the vestigial locus in Drosophila, the wing bud develops normally up to a certain point, but after this time parts of the wing degenerate and produce the shortening and scalloping which characterize the vestigial series (Fig. 147). In the more extreme modifications the degenerative process appears to set in earlier; in less extreme ones, later. This parallels the action of environmental factors whose effects depend upon the time when they are applied.

Genes and Rates.—The fact that temperature changes during development may imitate in their results the effects of specific genes lends support to the idea, already mentioned, that one of the chief results of a gene difference is a change in the rate of one or more physiological processes. In the production of phenocopies rate changes are brought about by temperature differences. In genetically different races they

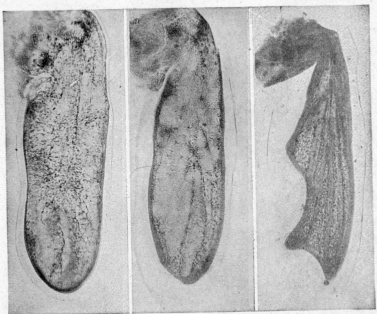

FIG. 147.—The effects of the vestigial-notch (vg/vg^{no}) genotype on the development of the wings in Drosophila pupae. Left, a wing shortly after pupation, still normal. Center, a later stage showing beginning of degeneration. Right, a still later stage, degeneration of outer parts completed. (*From Goldschmidt.*)

are probably induced by differing concentrations of enzymes, hormones, organizers, or other catalyzing substances, arising in some way from changes in the gene itself.

The hypothesis that gene effects in development are determined primarily through altered rates of various metabolic processes is one of the important ideas that has emerged from the study of developmental genetics. It can be applied in so many cases and presents such a relatively simple picture of the mechanism of gene action that many students of the problem, following Goldschmidt, regard rate changes as the chief means by which genes work. We should be cautious as yet in applying the rate hypothesis universally, however, for there are certain types of characters, notably the important ones of form or pattern, which are hard to interpret on this basis. The possible relationship between genes and rates has already done much to bring genetics and the physical sciences closer together, and it provides a most useful hypothesis for an attack upon the problems of developmental genetics.

These ideas on gene action derived from genetically analyzed material take on added significance when one notices their general resemblance to the leading ideas which are emerging from the modern work in experimental morphology. Thus Stockard observed that changes in rate of development often cause profound differences on the adult. He found that fish eggs placed, during early development, in solutions of substances which tended to retard the rate of development produced embryos and adults with a single median eye (Cyclopean monsters) and other evidences of deficient development in the head region. Treatment before or after a short critical period does not produce these changes. The new characters are nonspecific; they can be called forth by a wide variety of conditions whose chief effect is to increase or decrease the rate of development. The localization of the effect is due to the rapidity with which certain parts are developing at the time when the change occurs. Those parts which are moving most rapidly at the time when the general slowing down occurs are most affected.

The general theory of axial gradients as developed by Child is couched in somewhat similar terms. It is assumed that those regions of the early embryo which show the highest activity, as judged by their rate of metabolism, exercise a dominant influence over the development of the regions nearest to them. When, as is frequent, the dominant region is the head, the other regions along the line from head to tail show the effects of the activity of the head region according to their position relative to it. Through the establishment of such a gradient, one region is able to determine a pattern and to induce a specific type of differentiation chiefly by virtue of its greater metabolic rate.

Spemann's theory of organization centers is fundamentally similar. Here influences are shown to emanate from certain centers of high growth activity and to control the differentiation of tissues near them. The classic experiment is the transplantation of a tiny bit of tissue, near the dorsal lip of the blastopore, from an early amphibian embryo to another location in another embryo. Here the piece induces the formation of a new neural tube and other fundamental structures of a new embryo out of tissues which would otherwise have formed quite different organs.

The significant features in all these cases are variations (1) in rates of development at critical times and (2) in the relationships of parts. It is probably through such channels that reconciliation may be brought about, insofar as this may eventually be possible, between theories of gene action and general theories of dev~' ~r ~nt.

Prospects.—These few facts and ideas about the relations between genes and characters have been obtained chiefly through a study of the development of phenotypes, by an extension of the traditional methods of genetics to which Haecker gave the name phenogenetics, but which fall within the field more usually called Developmental Genetics or Physiological Genetics. Such questions are at present under active investigation, and considerable progress may be expected, chiefly through the application of the methods of descriptive embryology and of developmental mechanics and physiology, such as transplantation, explantation, and controlled modification of the environment. The results so far have been to extend our knowledge of developmental effects back toward the gene without actually reaching its first or intracellular effects. Many facts point to the likelihood that genes produce or secondarily influence catalytic processes; and one of the most remarkable facts regarding the gene, that it reproduces itself so faithfully, has been taken to indicate that it acts as an autocatalyst, producing another gene in its own image at each cell division. The great gap in our knowledge, that between the gene and its first recognizable effect, will probably remain until other techniques and ideas, chiefly those from physics and chemistry, are developed and applied.

In the meantime other hypotheses are emerging from studies of mutation that are directed toward elucidating the structure of the gene. Some of the channels through which a gene produces its effects may eventually be inferred from knowledge of the kinds of changes it undergoes when it mutates. Although the study of mutations induced by radiations has provided new and important information about this process, it has not yet progressed far enough to permit final conclusions concerning the structure of the gene or the nature of the cell processes which are altered by mutation. Most investigators agree that the chromosomes consist of a discontinuous series of loci each with characteristic properties probably dependent in part upon the molecular structure of the material at each locus. This local structure is frequently pictured as a large protein molecule to which are attached various side chains which may change in position or in quantity.

The recent discovery that the effects of certain genes are in part determined by their positions in the chromosome and by their relations to the neighboring genes calls into question many of the older ideas. If it is found to be generally true that the phenotypic effects of a gene are functions of its position, these effects may be due to interactions between local and immediate products of gene activity rather than to the more distant and secondary reactions which have usually been assumed from studies of development. Several investigators, notably Goldschmidt, have recently suggested that the chromosome and not the gene is the essential molecular unit and that genic changes (point mutations) derive their properties from changes in the pattern of this long molecular structure. Although it holds promise for the future, the position-effect hypothesis, because of its radical nature and the few cases in which conclusive proof for it has been offered, cannot as yet be directly related to developmental genetics.

REFERENCES

BEADLE, G. W., and B. EPHRUSSI. 1936. The differentiation of eye pigments in Drosophila as studied by transplantation. Genetics **21**.

BECKER, E., and E. PLAGGE. 1937. Vergleich der Augenausfärbung bedingende Genwirkstoffe von Ephestia und Drosophila. Naturwiss. **25**.

BLAKESLEE, Å. F. 1928. The genetics of Datura. Zeitschr. Ind. Abst. Vererb. Suppl. Bd. **1**.

BRINK, R. A. 1927. Genetics and the problems of development. Amer. Nat. **61**.

———. 1929. Studies on the physiology of a gene. Quart. Rev. Biol. **4**.

CHESLEY, P. 1925. Development of the short-tailed mutant in the housemouse. Jour. Exp. Zool. **70**.

DOBZHANSKY, T. 1929. The influence of the quantity and quality of chromosome material on the size of the cells in Drosophila melanogaster. Arch. Entw.-Mech. **115**.

———. 1927. The manifold effects of the genes. Zeitschr. Ind. Abst. Vererb.

EPHRUSSI, B. 1933. Sur le facteur léthal des souris brachyures. C. R. Acad. Sci. Paris **197**.

FELL, H. B., and W. LANDAUER. 1935. Experiments on skeletal growth and development in vitro in relation to the problem of avian phokomelia. Proc. Roy. Soc. London B **118**.

FORD, E. B., and J. S. HUXLEY. 1927. Mendelian genes and rates of development in Gammarus chevreuxi. British Jour. Exp. Biol. **5**.

GOLDSCHMIDT, R. 1938. Physiological Genetics. New York. (Contains an extensive bibliography of this field.)

GREGORY, P. W., and W. E. CASTLE. 1931. Further studies on the embryological basis of size inheritance in the rabbit. Jour. Exp. Zool. **59**.

HADORN, E. 1937. Die Entwicklungsphysiologische Auswirkung der disharmonischen Kern-Plasmakombination beim Bastardmerogon Triton palmatus (♀) × Triton cristatus ♂. Arch. Entw.-Mech. **136**.

HAECKER, V. 1925. Aufgaben und Ergebnisse der Phänogenetik. Bibliographia Genetica **5**.

HUXLEY, J. S. 1932. Problems of relative growth. New York.

KÜHN, A., E. CASPARI, and E. PLAGGE. 1935. Über hormonale Genwirkungen bei Ephestia Kühniella. Nachr. Ges. Wiss. Göttingen. Biol. **2**.

LANDAUER, W. 1932. III. The early development and lethal expression of homozygous creeper embryos. Jour. Genetics **25**.

———. 1933. IV. Die Missbildungen homozygoter Krüperembryonen auf späteren Entwicklungsstadien. Zeitschr. Mikr.-Anat. Forsch. **32**.

——— and L. C. DUNN. 1930. Studies on the creeper fowl I: Genetics. Jour. Genetics **23**.

MANGELSDORF, P. C., and G. S. FRAPS. 1931. A direct quantitative relationship between vitamin A in corn and the number of genes for yellow pigmentation. Science **73**.

MORGAN, T. H. 1927. Experimental embryology. New York.

———. 1934. Embryology and genetics. New York.

PAINTER, T. S. 1928. Cell size and body size in rabbits. Jour. Exp. Zool. **50**.

POULSON, D. F. 1937. Chromosomal deficiencies and the embryonic development of *Drosophila melanogaster*. Proc. Nat. Acad. Sci. **23**.

SCOTT-MONCRIEFF, R. 1931. The chemical effect of a Mendelian factor. Nature **129**.

SINNOTT, E. W. 1936. A developmental analysis of inherited shape differences in cucurbit fruits. Amer. Nat. **70**.

——— and L. C. DUNN. 1935. The effect of genes on the development of size and form. Biol. Rev. **10**.

WRIGHT, S. 1934. Physiological and evolutionary theories of dominance. Amer Nat. **68**.

PROBLEMS

426. How would you decide by experimental methods whether changes in many characters were manifold effects of the same gene or were due to closely linked genes?

427. In poultry a bit of tissue from an early homozygous creeper embryo, when grafted into a normal egg, may live beyond the time when the creeper embryo usually dies. What conclusions can you draw from this fact?

428. What are the chief reasons for supposing that genes exert their effects through intermediate products in the cytoplasm?

429. At what period in the life of a cell do you think that the genes would be most likely to affect the cytoplasm?

430. In what ways do you think that a gene might affect the rate of development?

431. With what other conditions in the cell do you think the plane of the mitotic spindle would be correlated?

432. How can a gene affecting egg characters be detected in a male?

433. In what ways might a gene which causes retardation in development (as in the case of creeper fowl embryos) cause the death of the individuals homozygous for it?

434. It has been shown in primroses that genes which result in deeply cut and lobed leaves tend to affect the petals of the flower in somewhat the same way. Explain.

435. The dominant gene for Brachyury (p. 375) causes a considerable shortening of the tail in the European house mouse. When such mice are crossed with Oriental house mice (*Mus bactrianus*), hybrids with the Brachyury gene have tails of normal or nearly normal length. Suggest an explanation.

436. In house mice two true-breeding tailless lines, A and B, have been derived from the Brachyury stock (p. 375). The litter size in each line is about half that of normal mice. Line A tailless crossed with line B tailless produces about two-thirds tailless and one-third normal and litter size is about three-fourths that of normal mice. Suggest an explanation.

437. Below are given the mean wing lengths of female vestigial-winged Drosophila which were hatched and began their larval life in an incubator at 27°C. and were then transferred after various periods (given in column at left) to 17°C., at which temperature they completed their development (data from Stanley).

Hours at 27°C.	Mean Wing Length, Millimeters
0	0.556 ± 0.009
8	0.574 ± 0.010
16	0.550 ± 0.007
24	0.584 ± 0.004
32	0.598 ± 0.006
40	0.621 ± 0.012
48	0.641 ± 0.005
56	0.664 ± 0.005
64	0.716 ± 0.004
72	0.721 ± 0.007
88	0.710 ± 0.009
112	0.691 ± 0.011
136	0.669 ± 0.012
184	0.678 ± 0.013

From these data what is the effect of temperature on the development of vestigial wings? Define the "critical period" for this effect?

438. In *Gammarus chevreuxi* crosses of wild type with dark red eyes (rapidly darkening type) by certain red-eyed mutant stocks (slowly darkening type) give rapid darkening F_1 and 3 rapid: 1 slow in F_2 (Fig. 143, p. 380). Certain other red-eyed (slow) stocks crossed with dark red (rapid) stocks give rapid darkening in F_1 and in F_2 a range of variation from extremely rapid to extremely slow without clear segregation. Extreme types from this F_2 breed true; F_2 intermediate types bred together again produce the F_2 range of variability. How would you interpret these data in terms of rate factors and how would you test your interpretation experimentally?

439. In Gammarus assume that a gene d retards the development of black pigment (darkening) until sexual maturity. If RR is rapid darkening (black) type and $rrDD$ is normal slowly darkening (red) type, what results would you expect from the following crosses (describe eye color of progeny (1) before and (2) after sexual maturity):

F_2 from $rrDD \times rr\ dd$
F_1 from $rr\ Dd \times rr\ dd$
F_1 from $rr\ Dd \times Rr\ DD$
F_1 from $Rr\ dd \times rr\ Dd$

Note.—In four-o'clocks there are two factors, Y and R, which affect flower color. Neither is completely dominant, and the two interact on each other to produce seven different flower colors, as follows:

$YY\,RR$ = crimson	$Yy\,RR$ = magenta
$YY\,Rr$ = orange-red	$Yy\,Rr$ = magenta-rose
$YY\,rr$ = yellow	$Yy\,rr$ = pale yellow
$yy\,RR$ and $yy\,rr$ = white	

440. In Four-o'clocks, cross a crimson-flowered plant with a white one, $yy\,rr$. What will be the appearance of the F_1? Of the F_2? Of the offspring of the F_1 crossed back on its crimson parent? On its white parent?

441. What will be the flower color in the offspring of the following four-o'clock crosses?

$$YY\,Rr \times yy\,Rr \qquad\qquad Yy\,rr \times yy\,Rr$$

442. What assumptions can you make regarding the chief chemical effects of the genes Y and R in the preceding problems. How would you test the assumptions?

APPENDIX

CULTURE METHODS FOR DROSOPHILA MELANOGASTER

The carrying out of actual breeding experiments in the laboratory is a valuable aid to an understanding and critical appreciation of the principles set forth in this book. The best animal material for such experiments is *Drosophila melanogaster* of which wild-type and mutant stocks may now be obtained from biological supply companies. As an aid in breeding Drosophila we have added a brief summary of some methods that have been found satisfactory by investigators and laboratory classes. It is based chiefly on the recent paper of Bridges.[1] A more detailed account of technical methods will be found in the paper of Lebedeff.[2]

The chief requirements of this insect are (1) living yeast cells, which form the chief food of the larvae; (2) an optimum temperature of about 25°C., although for ordinary segregation experiments this may vary from 22 to 27°, that is, about the usual room temperature; (3) adequate, but not too much, moisture.

The food conditions are met by several culture media which provide a good physical substrate and a sufficient supply of sugars for good growth of yeast. Recipes for three such media are given below:

TABLE XXXII
(Parts per 100, grams or cubic centimeters)

	1. Banana	2. Corn-meal	3. Banana molasses
Water.....................................	47.8	74.3	60.0
Agar-agar.................................	1.5	1.5	1.5
Banana pulp...............................	50.0	....	24.0
Molasses..................................	....	13.5	12.0
Corn meal.................................	....	10.0	
Brewers' yeast (dried)....................	....	(1.5)*	1.8
"Moldex" 10 per cent solution	0.7	0.7	0.7

* This formula may be enriched and the quality and yield of flies increased by addition of dried brewers' yeast to the cooked food mixture. If yeast is used, reduce molasses to 12 parts.

Mixture 1 is easily prepared and best for weak stocks. Mixture 2 is cheaper and prepared from materials that can be kept on hand; it is adequate for all except weak stocks and is recommended for general laboratory use; may be improved by

[1] BRIDGES, C. B. 1937. Revised data on culture media and mutant loci in *Drosophila melanogaster*. Tabulae Biologicae **14**: 343–353.

[2] LEBEDEFF, G. A. 1937. Methoden zur Züchtung von Drosophila. Handbuch der Biologischen Arbeitsmethoden. Abt. **9**: 1115–1182.

397

added yeast. Mixture 3 is more costly but an excellent medium for experiments where large yield and optimum growing conditions are essential.

Concerning the ingredients the following specifications are given by Bridges.

Agar—the cheapest grade (No. 3) is satisfactory.

Bananas—peeled pulp of fresh, fully ripened fruit, strained or put through potato ricer.

Molasses—the best is sorghum molasses; sugar-cane molasses, free from sulphur dioxide, is satisfactory. "Karo" corn syrup is about as good.

Corn meal—ground yellow maize meal; may be replaced by boiled potato or wheat flour.

Moldex—very important since it eliminates molds, but in concentrations above 0.1 reduces growth of yeast and flies. Use Moldex-A dissolved in 95 per cent alcohol. Same concentration of Nipagin-T or Nipagin-M (more expensive) may be substituted. Moldex-A may be obtained from Glyco Products Co., 148 Lafayette St., New York City.

The method of preparation of Mixture 2, as employed at the Genetics Laboratory, Columbia University, is given to illustrate application of such a formula to the small quantities usually prepared by individual students. The ratio of the ingredients is slightly modified for convenience in weighing and measuring.

Materials for 12 half-pint (wide-mouthed or milk) bottles: water, 750 cc.; agar, 15 grams; molasses, 125 cc.; corn meal, 110 grams; Moldex, 1.0 gram; 95 per cent alcohol, 5 cc.

1. Dissolve Moldex in alcohol.
2. Cut agar into small pieces and soak in 500 cc. of water for ten minutes.
3. Soak corn meal (and brewers' yeast, if used) in remaining 250 cc. of water.
4. Add Moldex solution to agar solution.
5. Boil agar mixture slowly until agar is dissolved.
6. Add molasses to agar solution with constant stirring; bring to boil.
7. Add corn-meal suspension to agar solution, stirring constantly; keep mixture at a boil for a few minutes.
8. Uncap 12 sterilized bottles and pour about 1 to 1½ inches of medium into each; avoid spilling food on tops or sides of bottles.
9. In each bottle place a strip of filter paper or paper towel with its end in the food. This is to provide additional surface on which larvae may crawl up to pupate.
10. Plug bottles with unwaxed milk bottle caps or with cotton batting wrapped in cheesecloth, and allow to cool to room temperature.
11. When cool, cut out from each culture a small portion of the food mass at its side to make a channel for the escape of carbon dioxide generated under the food mass. If this is not done, the whole food cake may rise in the bottle.
12. If bottles are to be used immediately (the best procedure), seed the surface of the food mass with yeast as follows: Shake ¼ cake of moist yeast (Fleischmann's or similar cake) in a 1- by 4-inch vial of water and add two drops of the suspension to the food surface in each culture bottle.
13. If culture bottles must be stored (in refrigerator), do not sow yeast until they are to be used. Allow cultures to reach room temperature before yeasting.
14. Add flies to be mated (two or three females and two or three males).

Virgin females may be secured from stock cultures from which all imagoes had been removed twelve hours previously. When virgin females are needed from an experimental culture, two counts should be made within eighteen hours; females from the second count will be virgin. If flies to be mated are under ether, they should be brushed into small cone of paper and the cone so placed in culture bottle that the flies will not fall out until they have recovered from etherization. Kill all cultures by heating in an oven as soon as counts are completed. Parasites, especially mites, increase in old cultures and spread to new ones.

For methods of securing virgin females, anesthetizing flies for observation, and other technical points the student is referred to the paper by Lebedeff cited above. A detailed description of the mutants of Drosophila and their inheritance, as known up to 1925, is given by Morgan, Bridges, and Sturtevant.[1] The list of most useful mutants in Fig. 82 will suggest crosses for segregation, assortment, linkage, mapping, and other experiments.

For original experiments the effects of various mutants in combination or of multiple alleles in compounds; the effects of temperature on dominance, on crossing over, and on nondisjunction; the determination of the time of death of lethals; and the effects of inversions on crossing over are suggested as providing, not only interesting experiments for the student, but new information concerning heredity and development in Drosophila.

[1] MORGAN, T. H., C. B. BRIDGES, and A. H. STURTEVANT. 1925. The genetics of Drosophila. Bibliographia Genetica **2**.

INDEX

401